Environmental Science: Teacher's Edition

Contents in Brief

P9-DBL-979

Teacher's Edition

See Program Component List on page ii

Student Edition

Prentice Hall Science Explorer

Series Tables of Contents

Teacher's Edition

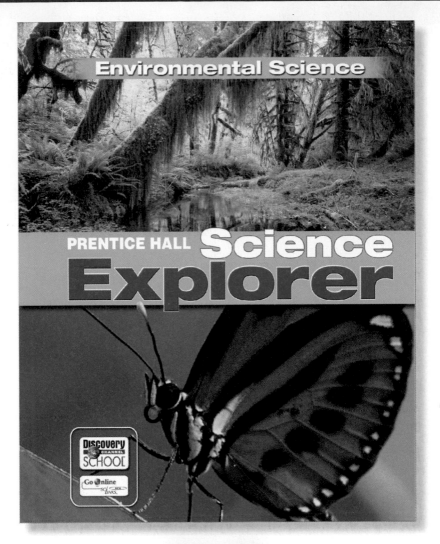

Environmental Science

PRENTICE HALL Science Explorer

PEARSON

Prentice Hall

Needham, Massachusetts
Upper Saddle River, New Jersey

Pearson Prentice Hall™ is a trademark of Pearson Education, Inc.
Pearson® is a registered trademark of Pearson plc.
Prentice Hall® is a registered trademark of Pearson Education, Inc.
Lab zone™ is a trademark of Pearson Education, Inc.

Planet Diary® is a registered trademark of Addison Wesley Longman, Inc.

Discovery Channel School® is a registered trademark of Discovery Communications, Inc., used under license.
The Discovery Channel logo is a trademark of Discovery Communications, Inc.

SciLinks® is a trademark of the National Science Teachers Association. The SciLinks® service includes copyrighted materials and is owned and provided by the National Science Teachers Association. All rights reserved.

Science News® is a registered trademark of Science Services, Inc.

ISBN 0-13-181123-1   1 2 3 4 5 6 7 8 9 10   08 07 06 05 04

Pacing Options

SCIENCE EXPLORER offers many aids to help you plan your instruction time, whether regular class periods or block scheduling. Section-by-section lesson plans for each chapter include suggested times for Student Edition activities. TeacherExpress™ and the Lab zone™ Easy Planner CD-ROM will help you manage your time electronically.

PRENTICE HALL
TeacherEXPRESS™
Plan · Teach · Assess

Lab zone™

Pacing Chart

	PERIODS	BLOCKS		PERIODS	BLOCKS
Careers: Treetop Scientist	1	—	**Chapter 4 Land, Water, and Air Resources**		
Chapter 1 Populations and Communities			Chapter 4 Project: Design and Build a Product Package	Ongoing	Ongoing
Chapter 1 Project: What's a Crowd?	Ongoing	Ongoing	1 Conserving Land and Soil	2–3	1–1$\frac{1}{2}$
1 Living Things and the Environment	2–3	1–1$\frac{1}{2}$	2 Waste Disposal and Recycling	2–3	1–1$\frac{1}{2}$
2 Integrating Mathematics: Studying Populations	2–3	1–1$\frac{1}{2}$	3 Water Pollution and Solutions	1–2	$\frac{1}{2}$–1
3 Interactions Among Living Things	1–2	$\frac{1}{2}$–1	4 Air Pollution and Solutions	2–3	1–1$\frac{1}{2}$
4 Changes in Communities	2–3	1–1$\frac{1}{2}$	5 Integrating Earth Science: Global Changes in the Atmosphere	2–3	1–1$\frac{1}{2}$
Chapter 1 Review and Assessment	1	$\frac{1}{2}$	Chapter 1 Review and Assessment	1	$\frac{1}{2}$
Chapter 2 Ecosystems and Biomes			**Chapter 5 Energy Resources**		
Chapter 2 Project: Breaking It Down	Ongoing	Ongoing	Chapter 5 Project: Energy Audit	Ongoing	Ongoing
1 Energy Flow in Ecosystems	1–2	$\frac{1}{2}$–1	1 Fossil Fuels	1–2	$\frac{1}{2}$–1
2 Integrating Chemistry: Cycles of Matter	1–2	$\frac{1}{2}$–1	2 Tech & Design: Renewable Sources of Energy	2–3	1–1$\frac{1}{2}$
3 Biogeography	1–2	$\frac{1}{2}$–1	3 Nuclear energy	1–2	$\frac{1}{2}$–1
4 Biomes	2–3	1–1$\frac{1}{2}$	4 Energy Conservation	1–2	$\frac{1}{2}$–1
5 Aquatic Ecosystems	2–3	1–1$\frac{1}{2}$	Chapter 1 Review and Assessment	1	$\frac{1}{2}$
Chapter 2 Review and Assessment	1	$\frac{1}{2}$	Interdisciplinary Exploration: African Rain Forests	2–3	1–1$\frac{1}{2}$
Chapter 3 Living Resources					
Chapter 3 Project: Variety Show	Ongoing	Ongoing			
1 Environmental Issues	2–3	1$\frac{1}{2}$–2			
2 Forests and Fisheries	1–2	$\frac{1}{2}$–1			
3 Biodiversity	2–3	1–1$\frac{1}{2}$			
4 Integrating Health: The Search for New Medicines	1–2	$\frac{1}{2}$–1			
Chapter 3 Review and Assessment	1	$\frac{1}{2}$			

Research-Based and Proven to Work

As the originator of the small book concept in middle school science, and as the nation's number one science publisher, Prentice Hall takes pride in the fact that we've always listened closely to teachers. In doing so, we've developed programs that effectively meet the needs of your classroom.

As we continue to listen, we realize that raising the achievement level of all students is the number one challenge facing teachers today. To assist you in meeting this latest challenge, Prentice Hall has combined the very best author team with solid research to create a program that meets your high standards and will assure that no child is left behind.

With Prentice Hall, you can be confident not only that your students will be motivated, inspired, and excited to learn science, but that they will also achieve the success needed in today's environment of the No Child Left Behind (NCLB) legislation and testing reform.

On the following pages, you will read about the key elements found throughout *Science Explorer* that truly set this program apart and assure success for you and your students.

As we continue to listen, we realize that raising the achievement level of all students is the number one challenge facing teachers today.

A Science Program Backed by Research

In developing Prentice Hall *Science Explorer*, we used research studies as a central, guiding element. Research on *Science Explorer* indicated key elements of a textbook program that ensure students' success: support for reading and mathematics in science, consistent opportunities for inquiry, and an ongoing assessment strand. This research was conducted in phases and continues today.

1. Exploratory: Needs Assessment

Along with periodic surveys concerning state and national standards as well as curriculum issues and challenges, we conducted specific product development research, which included discussions with teachers and advisory panels, focus groups, and quantitative surveys. We explored the specific needs of teachers, students, and other educators regarding each book we developed in Prentice Hall *Science Explorer*.

2. Formative: Prototype Development and Field-Testing

During this phase of research, we worked to develop prototype materials. Then we tested the materials by field-testing with students and teachers and by performing qualitative and quantitative surveys. In our early prototype testing, we received feedback about our lesson structure. Results were channeled back into the program development for improvement.

3. Summative: Validation Research

Finally, we conducted and continue to conduct long-term research based on scientific, experimental designs under actual classroom conditions. This research identifies what works and what can be improved in the next revision of Prentice Hall *Science Explorer*. We also continue to monitor the program in the market. We talk to our users about what works, and then we begin the cycle over again. The next section contains highlights of this research.

A Science Program With Proven Results

In a year-long study in 2000–2001, students in six states using Prentice Hall *Science Explorer* outscored students using other science programs on a nationally normed standardized test.

The study investigated the effects of science textbook programs at the eighth-grade level. Twelve eighth-grade science classes with a total of 223 students participated in the study. The selected classes were of similar student ability levels.

Each class was tested at the beginning of the school year using the TerraNova CTBS Basic Battery Plus, and then retested at the end of the school year. The final results, shown in the graph, show a significant improvement in test scores from the pre-test to the post-test evaluation.

• All tests were scored by CTB/McGraw-Hill, the publisher of the TerraNova exam. Statistical analyses and conclusions were performed by an independent firm, Pulse Analytics, Inc.

In Japan, Lesson Study Research has been employed for a number of years as a tool for teachers to improve their curriculum. In April 2003, Prentice Hall adapted this methodology to focus on a lesson from this edition. Our goal was to test the effectiveness of lesson pedagogy and improve it while in the program development stage. In all three classrooms tested, student learning increased an average of 10 points from the pre- to the post-assessment.

• Detailed results of these studies can be obtained at **www.PHSchool.com/research.**

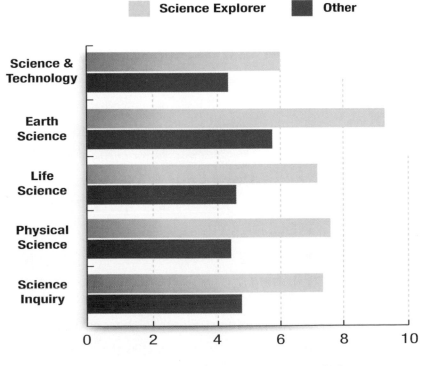

Mean Point Gain (Test Results)

Foundational Research: Inquiry in the Science Classroom

"How do I know if my students are inquiring?" "If students are busy doing lots of hands-on activities, are they using inquiry?" "What is inquiry, anyway?" If you're confused, you are not alone. Inquiry is the heart and soul of science education, with most of us in continuous pursuit of achieving it with our students!

Defining Science Inquiry

What is it? Simply put, inquiry is the intellectual side of science. It is thinking like a scientist—being inquisitive, asking why, and searching for answers. The National Science Education Content Standards define inquiry as the process in which students begin with a question, design an investigation, gather evidence, formulate an answer to the original question, and communicate the investigative process and results. Since it is often difficult to accomplish all this in one class period, the standards also acknowledge that at times students need to practice only one or two inquiry components.

Understanding Inquiry

The National Research Council in Inquiry and the National Science Education Standards (2000) identified several "essential features" of classroom inquiry. We have modified these essential features into questions to guide you in your quest for enhanced and more thoughtful student inquiry.

1. **Who asks the question?** In most curricula, these focusing questions are an element given in the materials. As a teacher you can look for labs that, at least on a periodic basis, allow students to pursue their own questions.

2. **Who designs the procedures?** To gain experience with the logic underlying experimentation, students need continuous practice with designing procedures. Some labs in which the primary target is content acquisition designate procedures. But others should ask students to do so.

3. **Who decides what data to collect?** Students need practice in determining the data to collect.

4. **Who formulates explanations based upon the data?** Students should be challenged to think—to analyze and draw conclusions based on their data, not just copy answers from the text materials.

5. **Who communicates and justifies the results?** Activities should push students to not only communicate but justify their answers. Activities also should be thoughtfully designed and interesting so that students want to share their results and argue about conclusions.

Making Time for Inquiry

One last question—Must each and every activity have students do all of this? The answer is an obvious and emphatic No. You will find a great variety of activities in *Science Explorer*. Some activities focus on content acquisition, and thus they specify the question and most of the procedures. But many others stress in-depth inquiry from start to finish. Because inquiry is an intellectual pursuit, it cannot merely be characterized by keeping students busy and active. Too many students have a knack for being physically but not intellectually engaged in science. It is our job to help them engage intellectually.

Michael J. Padilla, Ph.D.
Program Author of *Science Explorer*
Professor of Science Education
University of Georgia
Athens, Georgia

"Because inquiry is an intellectual pursuit, it cannot merely be characterized by keeping students busy and active."

Evaluator's Checklist

Does your science program promote inquiry by—

✔ Enabling students to pursue their own questions

✔ Allowing students to design their own procedures

✔ Letting students determine what data are best to collect

✔ Challenging students to think critically

✔ Pushing students to justify their answers

Inquiry in *Science Explorer*

Science Explorer offers the most opportunities to get students to think like a scientist. By providing inquiry opportunities throughout the program, *Science Explorer* enables students to enhance their understanding by participating in the discovery.

Student Edition Inquiry

Six lab and activity options are included in every chapter, structured from directed to open-ended—providing you the flexibility to address all types of learners and accommodate your class time and equipment requirements. As Michael Padilla notes, some focus on content acquisition, and thus the question and most of the procedures are specified. But many others stress in-depth inquiry from start to finish. The graph below shows how, in general, inquiry levels are addressed in the Student Edition.

Science Explorer encourages students to develop inquiry skills across the spectrum from teacher-guided to open-ended. Even more opportunities for real-life applications of inquiry are included in Science & Society, Science & Technology, Careers in Science, and Interdisciplinary Exploration features.

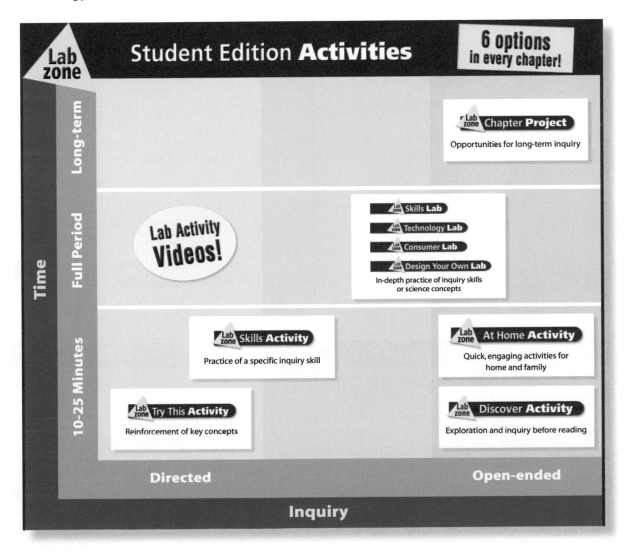

Inquiry Skills Chart

SCIENCE EXPLORER provides comprehensive teaching, practice, and assessment of science skills, with an emphasis on the process skills necessary for inquiry. This chart lists the skills covered in the program and cites the page numbers where each skill is covered.

	Student Text: Projects and Labs	Student Text: Activities	Student Text: Caption and Review Questions	Teacher's Edition: Extensions
Basic Process SKILLS				
Observing	12, 40–41, 68–69, 74–75, 80–81, 88, 94, 130–131, 144–145, 156–157	31, 61, 70, 106, 132, 134, 158	25, 49, 141, 148	8, 26, 28, 33, 45, 70, 119, 135, 140, 162, 163, 167
Inferring	12, 69, 74–75, 80–81, 88, 94, 114–115	6, 27, 48, 50, 64, 89, 95, 99, 103, 138, 149, 174, 179	20, 28, 56, 67, 78, 102, 109, 140, 142, 143, 166	18, 64, 72
Predicting	12, 21, 88, 131	24, 27, 54, 67, 103, 116, 143, 163	10, 53, 57, 73, 78, 93, 104, 107, 109, 112, 121, 125, 137, 143, 151, 171, 178, 182, 188	27, 33, 45, 51, 58, 102, 169
Classifying	69, 74–75, 80–81, 115	30, 35, 42, 126	10, 31, 35, 38, 43, 47, 66, 78, 87, 143, 171, 178, 188	71, 161
Making Models	12, 40–41, 68–69, 114–115, 130–131	19, 44, 136, 168, 178		19, 61, 63, 91, 96, 120, 124, 135, 148, 175
Communicating	4–5, 12, 21, 40–41, 69, 75, 80–81, 88, 94, 114–115, 131, 144–145, 156–157, 172–173, 183	35, 73, 105	38	52, 56, 58, 59, 66, 127, 135, 141
Measuring	4–5, 40–41, 183	140		
Calculating	21, 94	14, 15, 16, 92, 129, 147, 151, 175	18, 20, 46, 137, 154, 188	14, 15, 17, 126, 163
Creating Data Tables	21, 69, 80–81, 144, 156–157	42, 47	38	47
Graphing		125, 160	38, 112	67, 84
Advanced Process SKILLS				
Posing Questions		32, 122, 132, 164, 165		
Developing Hypotheses	4–5, 40–41, 75	49, 58, 146, 165	31, 38, 53, 93, 105, 108, 112, 121, 129, 154	47, 142, 150
Designing Experiments	12, 41, 69, 75, 94, 131, 144–145, 183	143		145

Advanced Process SKILLS (continued)

	Student Text: Projects and Labs	Student Text: Activities	Student Text: Caption and Review Questions	Teacher's Edition: Extensions
Controlling Variables	4–5, 41, 144–145, 183			47
Forming Operational Definitions		13, 82		
Interpreting Data	21, 40–41, 78, 94, 144–145, 156–157	27, 67, 103, 122, 149, 163	38, 112, 154, 188	
Drawing Conclusions	12, 78, 94, 131, 144–145, 156–157, 172–173, 183	9, 27, 49, 67, 149, 163	20	45, 48, 52, 96, 108, 141

Critical Thinking SKILLS

Comparing and Contrasting	78, 80–81	58, 73, 143	26, 31, 35, 47, 53, 63, 67, 78, 90, 93, 109, 112, 121, 129, 143, 164, 169, 187, 188	7, 32, 34, 58, 72, 86, 99, 111, 166, 174
Applying Concepts			8, 20, 31, 33, 57, 67, 93, 105, 143, 150, 154, 171, 182	52, 56, 96, 102, 180
Interpreting Diagrams, Graphs, Photographs, and Maps		27, 67, 73, 103, 149, 163	10, 17, 45, 51, 55, 59, 71, 95, 118, 120, 123, 135, 139, 147, 154, 159, 161, 177, 178	9, 10, 25, 28, 34, 56, 62, 65, 98, 106, 177
Relating Cause and Effect		138	10, 38, 47, 52, 54, 57, 67, 87, 97, 105, 112, 121, 137, 151, 161, 178, 188	138, 176
Making Generalizations			10, 38, 53, 61, 83, 98, 112, 154, 170	40, 151, 162
Making Judgments			87, 105, 129, 137, 164, 188	
Problem Solving			38, 105, 129, 136, 151, 154, 164	

Informational Organizational SKILLS

Concept Maps			111	76
Compare/Contrast Tables		32, 58		
Venn Diagrams		174		
Flowcharts				
Cycle Diagrams		48	49, 51, 52	49

The *Science Explorer* program provides additional teaching, reinforcement, and assessment of skills in the *Inquiry Skills Activities Book* and the *Integrated Science Laboratory Manual*.

A National Look at Science Education

Project 2061 was established by the American Association for the Advancement of Science (AAAS) as a long-term project to improve science education nationwide. A primary goal of Project 2061 is to define a "common core of learning"—the knowledge and skills we want all students to achieve. Project 2061 published *Science for All Americans* in 1989 and followed this with Benchmarks for Science Literacy in 1993. Benchmarks recommends what students should know and be able to do by the end of grades 2, 5, 8, and 12. Project 2061 clearly states that *Benchmarks* is not a curriculum but a tool for designing successful curricula.

The National Research Council (NRC) used *Science for All Americans* and *Benchmarks* to develop the National Science Education Standards (NSES), which were published in 1996. The NSES are organized into six categories (Content, Teaching, Assessment, Professional Development, Program, and System) to help schools establish the conditions necessary to achieve scientific literacy for all students.

Michael Padilla, the program author of *Science Explorer,* guided one of six teams of teachers whose work led to the publication of *Benchmarks.* He also was a contributing writer of the National Science Education Standards. Under his guidance, *Science Explorer* has implemented these standards through its inquiry approach, a focus on student learning of important concepts and skills, and teacher support aligned with the NSES teaching standards.

Neither *Benchmarks* nor the NSES requires a single, uniform national curriculum, and in fact there is a great diversity nationwide in science curricula. The correlations that follow are designed to help you use the *Science Explorer* program to meet your particular curriculum needs.

Meeting the National Science Education Standards

POPULATIONS AND COMMUNITIES

Science as Inquiry (Content Standard A)
- **Design and conduct a scientific investigation** Students design an experiment to determine the effect of crowding on plant growth. *(Chapter Project)*
- **Use appropriate tools and techniques to gather, analyze, and interpret data** Students model using the mark-and-recapture method to estimate the size of a population. *(Skillsd Lab)*
- **Develop descriptions, explanations, predictions, and models using evidence** Students study the interactions between biotic and abiotic factors in a model ecosystem. *(Skills Lab)*
- **Communicate scientific procedures and explanations** Students present a report and graph of their project results. *(Chapter Project)*

Life Science (Content Standard C)
- **Populations and ecosystems** The levels of organization in the environment include organism, population, community, and ecosystem. *(Section 1)*

Science in Personal and Social Perspectives (Content Standard F)
- **Science and technology in society** Students analyze the issue of animal overpopulation. *(Science and Society)*

ECOSYSTEMS AND BIOMES

Science as Inquiry (Content Standard A)
- **Design and conduct a scientific experiment** Students investigate the effects of variables on decomposition. *(Chapter Project)*
- **Develop descriptions, explanations, predictions, and models using evidence** Students investigate how abiotic factors create different biomes. Students observe how a community changes over time. *(Skills Lab)*

Life Science (Content Standard C)
- **Populations and ecosystems** Students observe the role of soil organisms on decomposition. An organism's energy role in an ecosystem may be that of producer, consumer, or decomposer. Biogeography is the study of where organisms live. Students observe how climate affects biomes. Students observe succession in a pond community. *(Chapter Project; Sections 1, 2, 3, 4, 5; Skills Labs)*

A National Look at Science Education (continued)

ECOSYSTEMS AND BIOMES

Earth and Space Science (Content Standard D)
● **Structure of the Earth system** The water cycle is the continuous process by which water moves from Earth's surface to the atmosphere and back. Primary succession is the series of changes that occur in an area where no ecosystem previously existed. *(Sections 2, 5)*

LIVING RESOURCES

Science as Inquiry (Content Standard A)
● **Design and conduct an investigation** Students observe diversity of organisms. *(Chapter Project)*
● **Develop descriptions, explanations, predictions, and models using evidence** Students model paper recycling. Students observe a tree cross section to draw conclusions about how the tree grew. *(Skills Labs)*

Life Science (Content Standard C)
● **Diversity and adaptions of organisms** The number of different species in an area is called biodiversity. Plants in many ecosystems produce chemicals that protect them. *(Chapter Project; Sections 3, 4)*

Science in Personal and Social Perspectives (Content Standard F)
● **Populations, resources, and environments** Human activities can threaten biodiversity. *(Section 3)*
● **Science and technology in society** Environmental issues include resource management, population growth, and pollution. *(Section 1)*

History and Nature of Science (Content Standard G)
● **History of Science** Certain individuals have influenced the viewpoints of others toward the environment. *(Science & History)*

LAND, WATER, AND AIR RESOURCES

Science as Inquiry (Content Standard A)
● **Design and conduct a scientific investigation** Students investigate how rainfall can cause erosion. *(Skills Labs)*
● **Develop descriptions, explanations, predictions, and models using evidence** Students model landfills to see how they work. *(Skills Lab)*

Earth and Space Science (Content Standard D)
● **Structure of the Earth system** Soil is a complex system made up of living and nonliving things. *(Section 1)*
● **Structure of the Earth system** Air is a mixture of nitrogen, oxygen, carbon dioxide, water vapor, and other gases. Earth has a limited supply of fresh water. *(Sections 3,4)*

Science and Technology (Content Standard E)
● **Evaluate completed technological designs or products** Students analyze and create a model of product packaging. *(Chapter Project)*
● **Understandings about science and technology** Technology can help control pollution. *(Chapter Project; Sections 1, 2, 3)*

Science in Personal and Social Perspectives (Content Standard F)
● **Personal health** Pollution can affect the health of humans. Exposure to hazardous wastes can affect health. *(Sections 2, 3, 4)*
● **Natural hazards** Poor soil management can result in erosion, nutrient depletion, and desertification. *(Section 1; Skills Lab*
● **Risks and benefits** Small changes in people's behavior can help reduce pollution. *(Sections 2, 3, 4)*

ENERGY RESOURCES

Science as Inquiry (Content Standard A)
● **Design and conduct a scientific investigation** Students investigate how solar energy can be used to cook food and compare how well different materials stop heat transfer. *(Technology Lab; Consumer Lab)*
● **Use appropriate tools and techniques to gather, analyze, and interpret data** Students evaluate energy use in their school. *(Chapter Project)*

Physical Science (Content Standard B)
● **Transfer of energy** Fuel provides energy as the result of a chemical change. Nuclear reactions convert matter into energy. *(Sections 1, 3)*

Science and Technology (Content Standard C)
● **Understandings about science and technology** The energy stored in fuels can be used to generate electricity. Technologies to capture and use solar energy, wind and water power, and alternative fuels help meet energy needs. Nuclear fission can be used to generate electricity. *(Sections 1, 2, 3)*

Science in Personal and Social Perspectives *(Content Standard D)*
● **Science and technology in society** Students evaluate the benefits and costs of hybrid cars. *(Science and Society)*

Note: To see how the benchmarks are supported by *SCIENCE EXPLORER,* go to **PHSchool.com.**

Reading

Reading Comprehension in the Science Classroom

Q&A

Q: Why are science texts often difficult for students to read and comprehend?

A: In general, science texts make complex literacy and knowledge demands on learners. They have a more technical vocabulary, a more demanding syntax, and place a greater emphasis on inferential reasoning.

Q: What does research say about facilitating comprehension?

A: Studies comparing novices and experts show that the conceptual organization of experts' knowledge is very different from that of novices. For example, experts emphasize core concepts when organizing knowledge, while novices focus on superficial details. To facilitate comprehension, effective teaching strategies should support and scaffold students as they build an understanding of the key concepts and concept relationships within a text unit.

Q: What strategies can teachers use to facilitate comprehension?

A: Three complementary strategies are very important in facilitating student comprehension of science texts. First, guide student interaction with the text using the built-in strategies. Second, organize the curriculum in terms of core concepts (e.g., the **Key Concepts** in each section). Third, develop visual representations of the relationships among the key concepts and vocabulary that can be referred to during instruction.

Nancy Romance, Ph.D.
Professor of Science Education
Florida Atlantic University
Fort Lauderdale, Florida

"Effective teaching strategies should support and scaffold students as they build an understanding of the key concepts and concept relationships within a text unit."

Reading Support in *Science Explorer*

The latest research emphasizes the importance of activating learners' prior knowledge and teaching them to distinguish core concepts from less important information. These skills are now more important than ever, because success in science requires students to read, understand, and connect complex terms and concepts.

Before students read—

Reading Preview introduces students to the key concepts and key terms they'll find in each section. The **Target Reading Skill** is identified and applied with a graphic organizer.

During the section—

Boldface Sentences identify each key concept and encourage students to focus on the big ideas of science.

Reading Checkpoints reinforce students' understanding by slowing them down to review after every concept is discussed.

Caption Questions draw students into the art and photos, helping them connect the content to the images.

After students read—

Section Assessment revisits the **Target Reading Skill** and encourages students to use the graphic organizer.

Each review question is scaffolded and models the way students think, by first easing them into a review and then challenging them with increasingly more difficult questions.

Evaluator's Checklist

Does your science program promote reading comprehension with—

- ✔ Text structured in an outline format and key concepts highlighted in boldface type
- ✔ Real-world applications to activate prior knowledge
- ✔ Key concepts, critical vocabulary, and a reading skill for every section
- ✔ Sample graphic organizers for each section
- ✔ Relevant photos and carefully constructed graphics with questions
- ✔ Reading checkpoints that appear in each section
- ✔ Scaffolded questions in section assessments

Math in the Science Classroom

Why should students concern themselves with mathematics in your science class?

Good science requires good data from which to draw conclusions. Technology enhances the ability to measure in a variety of ways. Often the scientist must measure large amounts of data, and thus an aim of analysis is to reduce the data to a summary that makes sense and is consistent with established norms of communication—i.e., mathematics.

Calculating measures of central tendency (e.g., mean, median, or mode), variability (e.g., range), and shape (graphic representations) can effectively reduce 500 data points to 3 without losing the essential characteristics of the data. Scientists understand that a trade-off exists between precision and richness as data are folded into categories, and so margins of error can be quantified in mathematical terms and factored into all scientific findings.

Mathematics is the language used by scientists to model change in the world. Understanding change is a vital part of the inquiry process. Mathematics serves as a common language to communicate across the sciences. Fields of scientific research that originated as separate disciplines are now integrated, such as happened with bioengineering. What do the sciences have in common? Each uses the language of mathematics to communicate about data and the process of data analysis. Recognizing this need, *Science Explorer* integrates mathematics practice throughout the program and gives students ample opportunity to hone their math skills.

Clearly, mathematics plays an important role in your science classroom!

William Tate, Ph.D.
Professor of Education and
American Culture Studies
Washington University
St. Louis, Missouri

> "Mathematics is the language used by scientists to model change in the world."

Integrated Math Support

In the Student Edition

The math instruction is based on principles derived from Prentice Hall's research-based mathematics program.

Sample Problems, Math Practice, Analyzing Data, and a Math Skills Handbook all help to provide practice at point of use, encouraging students to Read and Understand, Plan and Solve, and then Look Back and Check.

Color-coded variables aid student navigation and help reinforce their comprehension.

In the Teacher's Edition

Math teaching notes enable the science teacher to support math instruction and math objectives on high-stakes tests.

In the Guided Reading and Study Workbook

These unique worksheets help students master reading and enhance their study and math skills. Students can create a record of their work for study and review.

Evaluator's Checklist

Does your science program promote math skills by—

✔ Giving students opportunities to collect data
✔ Providing students opportunities to analyze data
✔ Enabling students to practice math skills
✔ Helping students solve equations by using color-coded variables
✔ Using sample problems to apply science concepts

Technology and Design

Technology and Design in the Science Classroom

Much of the world we live in is designed and made by humans. The buildings in which we live, the cars we drive, the medicines we take, and often the food we eat are products of technology. The knowledge and skills needed to understand the processes used to create these products should be a component of every student's basic literacy.

Some schools offer hands-on instruction on how technology development works through industrial arts curricula. Even then, there is a disconnect among science (understanding how nature works), mathematics (understanding data-driven models), and technology (understanding the human-made world). The link among these fields of study is the engineering design process—that process by which one identifies a human need and uses science knowledge and human ingenuity to create a technology to satisfy the need. Engineering gives students the problem-solving and design skills they will need to succeed in our sophisticated, three-dimensional, technological world.

As a complement to "science as inquiry," the National Science Education Standards (NRC, 1996) call for students at all age levels to develop the abilities related to "technology as design," including the ability to identify and frame a problem and then to design, implement, and evaluate a solution. At the 5–8 grade level, the standards call for students to be engaged in complex problem-solving and to learn more about how science and technology complement each other. It's also important for students to understand that there are often constraints involved in design as well as trade-offs and unintended consequences of technological solutions to problems.

As the *Standards for Technological Literacy* (ITEA, 2000) state, "Science and technology are like conjoined twins. While they have separate identities they must remain inextricably connected." Both sets of standards emphasize how progress in science leads to new developments in technology, while technological innovation in turn drives advances in science.

Ioannis Miaoulis, Ph.D.
President
Museum of Science
Boston, Massachusetts

"Engineering gives students the problem-solving and design skills they will need to succeed in our sophisticated, three-dimensional, technological world."

Evaluator's Checklist

Does your science program promote technology and design by—

✔ Incorporating technology and design concepts and skills into the science curriculum

✔ Giving students opportunities to identify and solve technological design problems

✔ Providing students opportunities to analyze the impact of technology on society

✔ Enabling students to practice technology and design skills

Technology and Design

Technology and Design in *Science Explorer*

How often do you hear your students ask: "Why do I need to learn this?" Connecting them to the world of technology and design in their everyday life is one way to help answer this question. It is also why so many state science curricula are now emphasizing technology and design concepts and skills.

Science Explorer makes a special effort to include a technology and design strand that encourages students to not only identify a need but to take what they learned in science and apply it to design a possible solution, build a prototype, test and evaluate the design, and/or troubleshoot the design. This strand also provides definitions of technology and engineering and discusses the similarities and differences between these endeavors and science. Students will learn to analyze the risks and benefits of a new technology and to consider the tradeoffs, such as safety, costs, efficiency, and appearance.

In the Student Edition

Integrated Technology & Design Sections

Sections throughout *Science Explorer* specifically integrate technology and design with the content of the text. For example, students not only learn how seismographs work but also learn what role seismographs play in society and how people use the data that are gathered.

Technology Labs

These labs help students gain experience in designing and building a device or product that meets a particular need or solves a problem. Students follow a design process of Research and Investigate, Design and Build, and Evaluate and Redesign.

Chapter Projects

Chapter Projects work hand-in-hand with the chapter content. Students design, build, and test based on real-world situations. They have the opportunity to apply the knowledge and skills learned to building a product.

Special Features

This technology and design strand is also reflected in Technology & Society and Science & Society features as well as Technology & History timelines. These highly visual features introduce a technology and its impact on society. For example, students learn how a hybrid car differs from a traditional car.

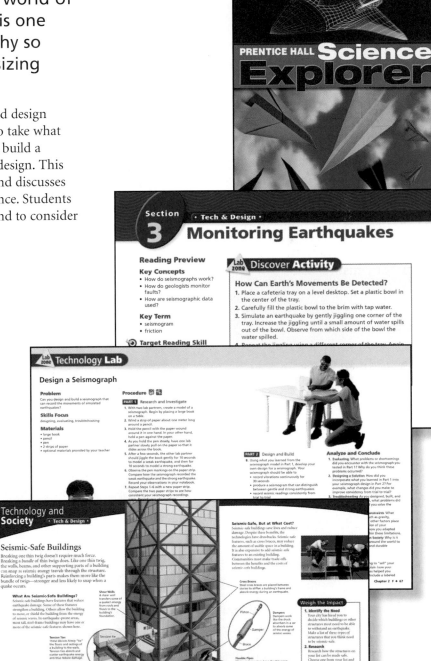

Assessment in the Science Curriculum

No Child Left Behind clearly challenges school districts across the nation to raise expectations for all students with testing of student achievement in science beginning in 2007–2008.

A primary goal of NCLB is to provide classroom teachers with better data from scientifically valid assessments in order to inform instructional planning and to identify students who are at risk and require intervention. It has been a common practice to teach a science lesson, administer a test, grade it, and move on. This practice is a thing of the past. With the spotlight now on improving student performance, it is essential to use assessment results as a way to identify student strengths and challenges. Providing student feedback and obtaining student input is a valuable, essential part of the assessment process.

Assessment is a never-ending cycle, as is shown in the following diagram. Although you may begin at any point in the assessment cycle, the basic process is the same.

An important assessment strategy is to ensure that students have ample opportunities to check their understanding of skills and concepts before moving on to the next topic. Checking for understanding also includes asking appropriate, probing questions with each example presented. This enables students and teachers to know whether the skills or concepts being introduced are actually understood.

Eileen Depka
Supervisor of Standards
and Assessment
Waukesha, Wisconsin

"Meeting the NCLB challenge will necessitate an integrated approach to assessment with a variety of assessment tools."

Use a variety of assessment tools to gain information and strengthen student understanding.

Implement the plan with a focus on gathering and using assessment information throughout.

Analyze assessment results to create a picture of student strengths and challenges.

IMPLEMENT · **ASSESS** · **ANALYZE** · **TARGET** · **STRATEGIZE**

Identify strategies to achieve the target, create a plan for implementation, and choose assessments tools.

Choose a target to create a focused path on which to proceed.

Evaluator's Checklist

Does your science program include assessments that—

✔ Are embedded before, during, and after lesson instruction

✔ Align to standards and to the instructional program

✔ Assess both skill acquisition and understanding

✔ Include meaningful rubrics to guide students

✔ Mirror the various formats of standardized tests

Assessment in *Science Explorer*

Science Explorer's remarkable range of strategies for checking progress will help teachers find the right opportunity for reaching all their students.

The assessment strategies in *Science Explorer* will help both students and teachers alike ensure student success in content mastery as well as high-stakes test performance. A wealth of opportunities built into the Student Edition help students monitor their own progress. Teachers are supported with ongoing assessment opportunities in the Teacher's Edition and an easy-to-use, editable test generator linked to content objectives. These integrated, ongoing assessment tools assure success.

Especially to support state and national testing objectives, Prentice Hall has developed test preparation materials that model the NCLB approach.

- **Diagnostic Assessment** tools provide in-depth analysis of strengths and weaknesses, areas of difficulty, and probable underlying causes that can help teachers make instructional decisions and plan intervention strategies.

- **Progress Monitoring** tools aligned with content objectives and state tests provide ongoing, longitudinal records of student achievement detailing individual student progress toward meeting end-of-year and end-of-schooling grade level, district, or state standards.

- **Outcomes** tools that mimic state and national tests show whether individual students have met the expected standards and can help a school system judge whether it has made adequate progress in improving its performance year by year.

Caption Questions enhance critical thinking skills

Reading Checkpoints reinforce students' understanding

Scaffolded Section Assessment Questions model the way students think

Comprehensive Chapter Reviews and Assessment provide opportunities for students to check their own understanding and practice valuable high-stakes test-taking skills

Exam*View*®, Computer Test Bank CD-ROM provides teachers access to thousands of modifiable test questions in English and Spanish

Test Preparation Blackline Masters and Student Workbook include diagnostic and prescription tools, progress-monitoring aids, and practice tests that help teachers focus on improving test scores.

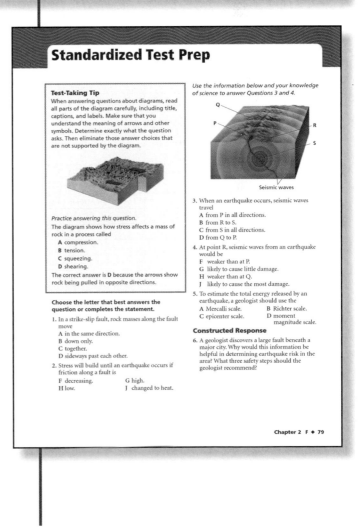

Master Materials List

SCIENCE EXPLORER offers an abundance of activity options in the Student Edition so you can pick and choose those that suit your needs. Prentice Hall has worked with Neo/SCI Corporation to develop Consumable Kits and Nonconsumable Kits that precisely match the needs of the SCIENCE EXPLORER labs. Use this Master Materials List or the Materials Ordering CD-ROM to help order your supplies. For more information on materials kits for this program, contact your local Prentice Hall sales representative or Neo/SCI Corporation at 1-800-526-6689 or www.neosci.com.

Consumable Materials

Description	Textbook Section(s)	Quantity per class	Description	Textbook Section(s)	Quantity per class
* Aluminum foil, roll	5-2 (Lab)	1	* Orange peels	2-1 (CP)	1
Beans, dried, box	1-2 (TT)	1	Paper, oaktag, sheet	5-2 (Lab)	1
* Bottle, plastic, 2 L	1-1 (Lab), 2-1 (CP)	15	Paper squares	1-1 (TT), 1-2 (Lab)	30
Bottle caps	2-1 (CP)		* Paper, white sheet	1-1 (DIS)	20
Brine shrimp eggs, 1g	1-1 (TT)	1	Paper, unlined sheets	1-4 (DIS)	5
Bromthymol blue solution, 0.1%, 250 mL	2-2 (TT)		Paper plate	3-3 (DIS)	5
		1	Paper towel	4-1 (DIS)	5
* Bulb, 15-watt, compact fluorescent	5-4 (DIS)	5	* Pen	1-1 (DIS)	
Bulb, 60-watt, incandescent	5-4 (DIS)	5	* Pencil	3-1 (DIS), 3-4 (DIS), 4-1 (DIS)	
* Cactus, live	2-4 (TT)	1	Pencils, colored, pkg/4	2(Lab)	5
Cards, index, pkg/100	2-4 (Lab)	1	Perfume	4-4 (DIS)	5
* Carton, milk or juice	2-4 (Lab)	5	Petri dish, pkg/20, with lids	4-4 (Lab)	
Charcoal, bag, 1 lb	1-1 (Lab), 4-3 (TT), 5-6 (Lab)	2	pH chart	4-4 (TT)	1
Cheesecloth, 2 M piece	4-2 (Lab)	1	pH paper strips, pkg/50	4-4 (TT)	
* Compost materials	2-1 (CP),	5	Pipe cleaners, pkg/10	4-5 (DIS)	1
Containers and matching lids made of paper, glass, plastic, plastic foam, and metal	2-3 (DIS), 3-4 (Lab)		* Plants, vascular	1-1 (Lab)	1
			* Plants, woodland moss	1-1 (Lab)	10
Corn kernels	2-3 (DIS)		Plastic bag, resealable	5-2 (DIS)	1
Coverslips, pkg/100	2-5 (Lab)	1	Plastic bag, small	4-2 (Lab)	5
Cups, plastic	2-2 (TT), 3-4 (DIS), 4-3 (DIS), 4-3 (TT), 4-4 (TT)	35	Platic wrap roll, 50 sq ft	1-1 (Lab), 2-2 (TT) 2-4 (Lab), 3-2 (Lab), 4-2 (Lab)	5
* Detergent, 100 mL	4-4 (Lab)		* Pond water, 1 L	2-5 (Lab)	1
Dropper, plastic, 1 mL pkg/10	2-5 (Lab), 4-3 (DIS)	1	Rainwater	4-4 (TT)	1
* Eggshells	2-1 (CP)	2	Rubber band, larger	1-1 (Lab)	5
Elodea, sprigs	2-2 (TT)	10	Rubber band, medium	4-2 (Lab)	5
Filter paper	4-3 (TT)	1	Salt (Sodium chloride), noniodized, 100g	1-1 (TT), 4-4 (Lab)	5
Filter paper strips	3-4 (DIS)	5			
Food coloring, red, 30 mL	4-2 (Lab), 4-3 (TT)	5	Sand, bag	4-1 (DIS)	1
Foam pieces, plastic	2-1 (CP)	1	Screen, roll, 5 sq ft	3-1 (Lab)	1
* Gloves, plastic, pair	4-2 (DIS)	30	Seeds, bean (white), pkg/100	1-1 (Lab)	1
* Glue stick	1-1 (DIS), 5-2 (Lab)	30	Seeds, corn pkg/100	2-3 (DIS)	1
* Graph paper, sheet	1-2 (Lab), 3-1 (DIS), 4-2 (DIS)	5	Seeds, impatiens pkg/100	2-4 (Lab)	1
Gravel, bag, 3 lb	1-1 (Lab), 4-2 (Lab)	5	Seeds, lima bean, 1 lb	2-4 (Lab)	1
Grass clippings	2-1 (CP)	2	Seeds, mixture, 1 lb	3-3 (DIS)	1
* Herbal tea	4-3 (TT)		Seeds, radish, pkg/100	1-1 (CP), 4-4 (Lab)	1
Leaves, chopped	2-1 (CP)	1	Seeds, rye grass, pkg/200	2-4 (Lab)	2
* Lemon juice, 5 mL	4-4 (TT)		Seeds. sunflower	4-1 (DIS)	1
* Magazines	1-1 (DIS)	1	* Soil, garden, 1 lb	2-1 (CP)	
* Marking pen, black	2-4 (DIS), 3-4 (DIS)	5	Soil, potting, 1 lb bag	1-1 (CP, 1-1 (Lab), 2-4 (Lab), 4-1 (DIS), 4-2 (Lab), 4-4 (Lab)	5
Microscope slides, box of 72	2-5 (Lab), 3-1 (Lab)	5			
* Milk, 100 mL	4-3 (DIS)	2	Sponge	4-2 (Lab)	5
* Newspaper	3-2 (Lab), 4-2 (Lab)	1	Spoon, plastic	1-1 (LAb)	5
* Oil, vegetable, 100 mL	4-4 (Lab)	15	* Spring water, 1 gallon	1-1 (TT)	5

KEY: **CP:** Chapter Project; **DIS:** Discover; **SA:** Skills Activity; **TT:** Try This; **Lab:** Skills, Consumer, Design Your Own, & Technology and * items are school supplied.

Quantities based on five groups of six students per class.

Consumable Materials con't

Description	Textbook Section(s)	Quantity per class	Description	Textbook Section(s)	Quantity per class
Stirrers, wooden	1-1 (TT), 5-2 (Lab)	3	* Trash bag	4-2 (DIS)	1
Straw, drinking	2-4 (DIS)	15	* Vegetables, frozen, bag	5-2 (Lab)	5
* Sugar, 100g	4-3 (TT)		Vinegar, 500 mL	4-4 (Lab)	1
T-shirt fabric, pieces	4-5 (DIS)	1	Water	3-4 (DIS), 4-2 (Lab)	1
Tape, adding machine, roll	2-4 (DIS)		Water, day-old tap	4-4 (Lab)	
Tape, masking, roll	1-2(TT), 1-2(TT), 1-3(DIS), 2-4(Lab), 3-4(DIS), 4-4(Lab), 5-2(Lab), 2-3 (DIS), 5-2(TT)	1	Water, hot	5-4 (Lab)	
			Water, ice	5-4 (Lab)	
			Water, spring, 2 L	1-1 (TT)	
Timothy hay, 2 oz	2-5 (Lab)	2	Yarn, spool	2-1 (TT)	

Nonconsumable Materials

Description	Textbook Section(s)	Quantity per class	Description	Textbook Section(s)	Quantity per class
* Apron, lab	1-1 (Lab)	30	* Jar, baby-food	2-5 (Lab)	5
Beads, UV detection, pkg/100	4-5 (DIS)		Jar, plastic, wide-mouthed	1-2 (DIS), 4-2 (Lab)	5
Beaker, low form, 600 mL	1-1 (TT), 5-4 (lab)	1	Jigsaw puzzle, small	1-2 (TT)	5
Beaker, polypropylene, 150 mL	1-2 (DIS)	5	* Lamp	4 (DIS)	5
Boreal forest biome map	2-4 (SA)	5	Lignite coal	5-1 (DIS)	5
Bottle caps	5-2 (TT)		Measuring cup	4-2 (Lab)	5
Bottle, spray	1-1 (Lab), 4-4 (DIS)	5	Meter stick	1 (Lab)	5
Book, heavy	3-1 (Lab)	1	* Microscope, compound	2-5 (Lab), 3-1 (Lab)	
• Bowl, mixing	3-1 (Lab)	5	* Mirror, small	2-2 (DIS)	5
* Calculator	1-2 Lab, 3-2 (SA), 5-1 (SA), 5-3 (SA)	5	Pan, aluminum	4-1 (DIS), 3-1 (Lab)	5
			Pan, shallow	2-3 (DIS)	5
* Clock	1-2 (DIS), 1-2 (TT), 5-4 (Lab), 5-4 (DIS), 5-2 (Lab)	5	* Pinwheel	5-2 (TT)	
* Compass, directional	3-1 (Lab)	5	Planting container (large margarine tub or half-gallon milk carton)	1-1 (CP)	5
Cylinder, graduated, polypropylene, 10 mL	4-4 (Lab)	5	Protractor	4-2 (SA)	5
* Dominoes, set of 15	5-3 (DIS)	5	Ruler, 12 in	1-1 (CP), 2-2 (DIS), 3-1 (Lab), 3-2 (Lab), 4-2 (Lab), 4-4 (Lab)	5
Drawing compass	4-2 (SA)	5	* Scissors	1-1 (DIS), 1-3 (DIS), 2-4 (TT), 2-4 (Lab), 4-2 (Lab), 5-2 (Lab)	5
* Eggbeater	3-1 (Lab)	5			
* Fan	5-2 (TT)	5			
Field guides	3-1 (Lab)		Spoon, large metal	4-3 (TT)	5
* Flashlight	4-3 (DIS)	1	Stakes, small	3-1 (Lab)	20
Funnel, small	4-3 (TT)	10	String, 25 meters	3-1 (Lab)	
* Hammer	3-1 (Lab)	5	Thermometer, -25 to 100 degrees C	3-1 (Lab), 5-2 (DIS), 5-2 (Lab), 5-4 (Lab), 5-4 (DIS)	5
Hand lens	1-1 (TT), 2-4 (TT), 3-1 (Lab), 3-3 (DIS), 5-1 (DIS)	5	Timer	1-2 (DIS)	5
Household waste (4 paper items, 2 yard waste items, 1 piece of rubber, cloth, or wood waste, 1 soda can or other metal item, 1 glass jar or bottle, 1 plastic item, 1 food waste item, such as an orange peel	4-2 (DIS)	5	Tray, foam	2-3 (DIS)	15
			Tree cookie	3-2 (Lab)	5
			Trowel	1-1 (CP), 3-1 (Lab)	5
			Tweezers	4-1 (DIS), 4-2 (Lab)	5
			Watering can	1-1 (CP)	5

KEY: CP: Chapter Project; **DIS:** Discover; **SA:** Skills Activity; **TT:** Try This; **Lab:** Skills, Consumer, Design Your Own, & Technology and * items are school supplied.

Quantities based on five groups of six students per class.

Prentice Hall Science Explorer

Environmental Science

Book-Specific Resources

Student Edition
Interactive Textbook
Teacher's Edition
All-in-One Teaching Resources
Guided Reading and Study Workbook
Student Edition on Audio CD
Discovery Channel Video
Lab Activity Video
Consumable and Nonconsumable Materials Kits

Program Print Resources

Integrated Science Laboratory Manual
Computer Microscope Lab Manual
Inquiry Skills Activity Books
Test Preparation Blackline Masters
Test Preparation Workbook
Test-Taking Tips With Transparencies
Teacher's ELL Handbook
Reading in the Content Area

Program Technology Resources

Teacher Express™ CD-ROM
Interactive Textbook
Presentation Pro CD-ROM
Exam*View*®, Computer Test Bank CD-ROM
Lab zone™ Easy Planner CD-ROM
Student Edition Worksheet Library CD-ROM
Probeware Lab Manual With CD-ROM
Computer Microscope and Lab Manual
Materials Ordering CD-ROM
Discovery Channel DVD Library
Lab Activity DVD Library
Web Site at PHSchool.com

Spanish Print Resources

Spanish Student Edition
Spanish Guided Reading and Study Workbook
Spanish Teaching Guide With Tests

Acknowledgments appear on p. 230, which constitutes an extension of this copyright page.

Cover
Mosses drape the trees of this temperate rain forest in Washington State (top). Hundreds of butterfly species live in the tropical rain forests of Ecuador (bottom).

ISBN 0-13-115090-1

1 2 3 4 5 6 7 8 9 10   08 07 06 05 04

Program Authors

Michael J. Padilla, Ph.D.
Professor of Science Education
University of Georgia
Athens, Georgia

Michael Padilla is a leader in middle school science education. He has served as an author and elected officer for the National Science Teachers Association and as a writer of the National Science Education Standards. As lead author of Science Explorer, Mike has inspired the team in developing a program that meets the needs of middle grades students, promotes science inquiry, and is aligned with the National Science Education Standards.

Ioannis Miaoulis, Ph.D.
President
Museum of Science
Boston, Massachusetts

Originally trained as a mechanical engineer, Ioannis Miaoulis is in the forefront of the national movement to increase technological literacy. As dean of the Tufts University School of Engineering, Dr. Miaoulis spearheaded the introduction of engineering into the Massachusetts curriculum. Currently he is working with school systems across the country to engage students in engineering activities and to foster discussions on the impact of science and technology on society.

Martha Cyr, Ph.D.
Director of K–12 Outreach
Worcester Polytechnic Institute
Worcester, Massachusetts

Martha Cyr is a noted expert in engineering outreach. She has over nine years of experience with programs and activities that emphasize the use of engineering principles, through hands-on projects, to excite and motivate students and teachers of mathematics and science in grades K–12. Her goal is to stimulate a continued interest in science and mathematics through engineering.

Book Authors

Marylin Lisowski, Ph.D.
Professor of Science and
    Environmental Education
Eastern Illinois University
Charleston, Illinois

Linda Cronin Jones, Ph.D.
Associate Professor of Science
    and Environmental Education
University of Florida
Gainesville, Florida

Contributing Writer

Thomas R. Wellnitz
Science Instructor
The Paideia School
Atlanta, Georgia

Consultants

Reading Consultant

Nancy Romance, Ph.D.
Professor of Science
    Education
Florida Atlantic University
Fort Lauderdale, Florida

Mathematics Consultant

William Tate, Ph.D.
Professor of Education and
    American Culture Studies
Washington University
St. Louis, Missouri

Reviewers

Tufts University Content Reviewers

Faculty from Tufts University in Medford, Massachusetts, participated in the development of *Science Explorer* chapter projects, reviewed the student books for content accuracy, and helped coordinate field testing.

Astier M. Almedom, Ph.D.
Department of Biology

Wayne Chudyk, Ph.D.
Department of Civil and Environmental
   Engineering

John Durant, Ph.D.
Department of Civil and Environmental
   Engineering

George S. Ellmore, Ph.D.
Department of Biology

David Kaplan
Department of Chemical Engineering

Samuel Kounaves, Ph.D.
Department of Chemistry

David H. Lee, Ph.D.
Department of Chemistry

Doug Matson, Ph.D.
Department of Mechanical Engineering

Karen Panetta, Ph.D.
Department of Electrical Engineering and
   Computer Science

John C. Ridge, Ph.D.
Department of Geology

William Waller, Ph.D.
Department of Astronomy

Content Reviewers

Jeff Bodart, Ph.D.
Chipola Junior College
Marianna, Florida

Michael Castellani, Ph.D.
Department of Chemistry
Marshall University
Huntington, West Virginia

Eugene Chiang, Ph.D.
Department of Astronomy
University of California – Berkeley
Berkeley, California

Charles C. Curtis, Ph.D.
Department of Physics
University of Arizona
Tucson, Arizona

Daniel Kirk-Davidoff, Ph.D.
Department of Meteorology
University of Maryland
College Park, Maryland

Diane Doser, Ph.D.
Department of Geological Sciences
University of Texas at El Paso
El Paso, Texas

Richard Duhrkopf, Ph.D.
Department of Biology
Baylor University
Waco, Texas

Michael Hacker
Co-director, Center for
   Technological Literacy
Hofstra University
Hempstead, New York

Michael W. Hamburger, Ph.D.
Department of Geological Sciences
Indiana University
Bloomington, Indiana

Alice Hankla, Ph.D.
The Galloway School
Atlanta, Georgia

Donald Jackson, Ph.D.
Department of Molecular Pharmacology,
   Physiology, & Biotechnology
Brown University
Providence, Rhode Island

Jeremiah Jarrett, Ph.D.
Department of Biological Sciences
Central Connecticut State University
New Britain, Connecticut

Becky Mansfield, Ph.D.
Department of Geography
Columbus, Ohio

Joe McCullough, Ph.D.
Department of Natural and
   Applied Sciences
Cabrillo College
Aptos, California

Robert J. Mellors, Ph.D.
Department of Geological Sciences
San Diego State University
San Diego, California

Joseph M. Moran, Ph.D.
American Meteorological Society
Washington, D.C.

David J. Morrissey, Ph.D.
Department of Chemistry
Michigan State University
East Lansing, Michigan

Philip A. Reed, Ph.D.
Department of Occupational & Technical
   Studies
Old Dominion University
Norfolk, Virginia

Scott M. Rochette, Ph.D.
Department of Earth Sciences
State University of New York, College at
   Brockport
Brockport, New York

Laurence D. Rosenheim, Ph.D.
Department of Chemistry
Indiana State University
Terre Haute, Indiana

Ronald Sass, Ph.D.
Department of Ecology & Evolutionary
   Biology
Rice University
Houston, Texas

George Schatz, Ph.D.
Department of Chemistry
Northwestern University
Evanston, Illinois

Sara Seager, Ph.D.
Carnegie Institution of Washington
Washington, D.C.

John R. Villarreal, Ph.D.
College of Science and Engineering
The University of Texas – Pan American
Edinburg, Texas

Kenneth Welty, Ph.D.
School of Education
University of Wisconsin–Stout
Stout, Wisconsin

Edward J. Zalisko, Ph.D.
Department of Biology
Blackburn College
Carlinville, Illinois

Teacher Reviewers

Steve Barbato
Lower Merion School
Ardmore, Pennsylvania

David R. Blakely
Arlington High School
Arlington, Massachusetts

Jane Callery
Two Rivers Magnet Middle
    School
East Hartford, Connecticut

Melissa Lynn Cook
Oakland Mills High School
Columbia, Maryland

James Fattic
Southside Middle School
Anderson, Indiana

Wayne Goates
Goddard Middle School
Goddard, Kansas

Katherine Bobay Graser
Mint Hill Middle School
Charlotte, North Carolina

Darcy Hampton
Deal Junior High School
Washington, D.C.

Karen Kelly
Pierce Middle School
Waterford, Michigan

David Kelso
Manchester High School Central
Manchester, New Hampshire

John G. Little
St. Mary's High School
Stockton, California

Benigno Lopez, Jr.
Sleepy Hill Middle School
Lakeland, Florida

Angie L. Matamoros, Ph.D.
ALM Consulting
Weston, Florida

Tim McCollum
Charleston Middle School
Charleston, Illinois

Bruce A. Mellin
Brooks School
North Andover, Massachusetts

Ella Jay Parfitt
Southeast Middle School
Baltimore, Maryland

Kathleen Poe
Duncan Fletcher Middle School
Jacksonville, Florida

Shirley Rose
Lewis and Clark Middle School
Tulsa, Oklahoma

Linda Sandersen
Greenfield Middle School
Milwaukee, Wisconsin

Mary E. Solan
Southwest Middle School
Charlotte, North Carolina

Mary Stewart
University of Tulsa
Tulsa, Oklahoma

Paul Swenson
Billings West High School
Billings, Montana

Thomas Vaughn
Arlington High School
Arlington, Massachusetts

Steve Wright
Butler Middle School
Waukesha, Wisconsin

Safety Reviewers

W. H. Breazeale, Ph.D.
Department of Chemistry
College of Charleston
Charleston, South Carolina

Ruth Hathaway, Ph.D.
Hathaway Consulting
Cape Girardeau, Missouri

Douglas Mandt
Science Education Consultant
Edgewood, Washington

Activity Field Testers

Nicki Bibbo
Russell Street School
Littleton, Massachusetts

Connie Boone
Fletcher Middle School
Jacksonville Beach, Florida

Rose-Marie Botting
Broward County School District
Fort Lauderdale, Florida

Colleen Campos
Laredo Middle School
Aurora, Colorado

Elizabeth Chait
W. L. Chenery Middle School
Belmont, Massachusetts

Holly Estes
Hale Middle School
Stow, Massachusetts

Laura Hapgood
Plymouth Community
    Intermediate School
Plymouth, Massachusetts

Sandra M. Harris
Winman Junior High School
Warwick, Rhode Island

Jason Ho
Walter Reed Middle School
Los Angeles, California

Joanne Jackson
Winman Junior High School
Warwick, Rhode Island

Mary F. Lavin
Plymouth Community
    Intermediate School
Plymouth, Massachusetts

James MacNeil, Ph.D.
Concord Public Schools
Concord, Massachusetts

Lauren Magruder
St. Michael's Country
    Day School
Newport, Rhode Island

Jeanne Maurand
Austin Preparatory School
South Hamilton, Massachusetts

Warren Phillips
Plymouth Community
    Intermediate School
Plymouth, Massachusetts

Carol Pirtle
Hale Middle School
Stow, Massachusetts

Kathleen M. Poe
Kirby-Smith Middle School
Jacksonville, Florida

Cynthia B. Pope
Ruffner Middle School
Norfolk, Virginia

Anne Scammell
Geneva Middle School
Geneva, New York

Karen Riley Sievers
Callanan Middle School
Des Moines, Iowa

David M. Smith
Eyer Middle School
Allentown, Pennsylvania

Gene Vitale
Parkland School
McHenry, Illinois

Zenovia Young
Meyer Levi Jr. HS/IS-285
Brooklyn, New York

Contents

Environmental Science

Reference Section

VIDEO

Enhance understanding through dynamic video.

Preview Get motivated with this introduction to the chapter content.

Field Trip Explore a real-world story related to the chapter content.

Assessment Review content and take an assessment.

Web Links

Get connected to exciting Web resources in every lesson.

$SC\overbrace{}^{}$*i*$_{LINKS_{TM}}$ **NSTA** Find Web links on topics relating to every section.

Active Art Selected visuals from every chapter become interactive online.

Planet Diary® Explore news and natural phenomena through weekly reports.

Science News® Keep up to date with the latest science discoveries.

Interactive Textbook

Experience the complete text-book online and on CD-ROM.

Activities Practice skills and learn content.

Videos Explore content and learn important lab skills.

Audio Support Key terms are spoken and defined.

Self-Assessment Instant feed-back helps you track your progress.

Activities

Chapter **Project**   Opportunities for long-term inquiry

Discover **Activity**   Exploration and inquiry before reading

Try This **Activity**   Reinforcement of key concepts

Skills **Activity**   Practice of specific science inquiry skills

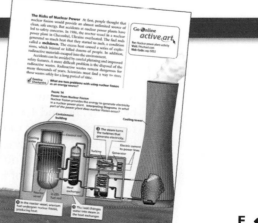

Treetop Scientist

Inquiry and Botany

Rain forest botanist Margaret Lowman conducts research on the trees of the rain forest. By reading about her work, students will gain insights about how research is done. They will read about how Dr. Lowman plans and conducts her research. They will also learn about fieldwork, sampling, and collecting. The skills that Dr. Lowman uses every day are the same inquiry skills that students need to become successful young scientists.

Build Background Knowledge

Knowledge About Rain Forests Have students write *What I Know About Tropical Rain Forests* on the top of a sheet of paper. Give them five minutes to record whatever facts and information they know about tropical rain forests. At the end of five minutes have students share the items on their lists, making a cumulative list on the board.

Introduce the Career

Before students read the feature, remind students that the canopy of the rain forest is between 10 and 40 meters above the ground. Ask: **Suppose you want to observe life in the canopy of the rain forest. How would you do this?** *(Student responses will vary but may include ideas such as building a watch tower in the canopy, climbing a tree and sitting in top branches, or flying over in a helicopter or hot-air balloon.)* **How might you move from one tree to the next without climbing down?** *(Student responses will vary but may include ideas such as swinging on a rope between trees or building a walkway between trees.)*

Careers in Science

Treetop Scientist

It is shortly after daybreak when biologist Margaret Lowman begins her climb. She moves quickly up the ladder attached to the giant tree in the rain forest of Belize in Central America. Five meters, ten meters, fifteen—within minutes, she is ten stories up. As she clambers onto a wooden platform, she stops to admire the forest. Brilliantly colored macaws fly overhead while spider monkeys swing through the branches above her.

"It is a fantastic feeling," Meg says. "Almost every organism in the world sees the forest canopy from the inside or from above. But humans are an exception. Most of the time we can do no better than look up at it from below."

The rain forest canopy is the dense covering formed by the leafy tops of tall trees. It can be 20 to 40 meters above the ground. Working as a field biologist, Meg studies the insects that feed on the plants in the canopy.

Meg Lowman climbs high into the rain forest canopy in Belize. ▶

x ◆ E

Background

Facts and Figures Tropical rain forests cover about 5 percent of Earth's surface. They are found in equatorial latitudes that receive large amounts of rain annually, between 200 and 400 centimeters. Tropical rain forests have the most biodiversity of any of Earth's biomes. It is estimated that tropical rain forests contain more than 2 million species, at least half of Earth's terrestrial plant and animal species. Tropical rain forests can be divided into four distinct layers. The emergent layer is the highest, with treetops reaching up to 70 meters high. The canopy layer ranges from 10 to 40 meters above ground. The understory is between ground level and 10 meters high, and very little light reaches the understory. The forest floor is dark and humid.

Talking With
Dr. Margaret Lowman

A macaw bursts into flight in the canopy.

? How did you get interested in science?

I probably got started at about age 3 by making forts in bushes. My friends and I made nature trails. We made zoos with earthworms, and I collected everything from birds and insects to twigs. By the fifth grade I had accumulated quite a wildflower collection. I carefully pressed and identified the wildflowers on cards by habitat, color, size, and so on. That collection won me second place in the New York state science fair. I felt proud to be among all those boys with their electronic and chemistry experiments.

? Why did you choose to study forests?

In college, I started out as a geology major. But I found myself looking at the living things while everyone else was looking at rocks. Fortunately, the college that I attended had a research forest that interested me. When it came time to do the research for my doctorate, I had thought I would study butterflies. But they can be quite difficult to track, so I chose to focus on something much less mobile—trees.

Meg Lowman, on a canopy sled, collects insect specimens in Cameroon.

Career Path

Margaret Lowman grew up in upstate New York and attended Williams College in Massachusetts. She received a Ph.D. in botany from the University of Sydney in Australia. Formerly the director of the Marie Selby Botanical Gardens in Sarasota, Florida, she is now a professor at the New College of Florida. The mother of two boys, she juggles career and family.

E ◆ 1

Explore the Career

Choose from among the teaching strategies on these pages as you help your students explore the practical application of inquiry skills.

Use Maps Use a map that shows the distribution of Earth's biomes to review the location of tropical rain forests worldwide. Ask: **What climate conditions do tropical rain forests need to survive?** *(High amounts of annual rainfall, warm temperatures, and high humidity)*

Connect Culture There are many indigenous groups of people that live in tropical rain forests worldwide. These groups use the resources including food, raw materials for structures, tools, and clothes, and medicinal plants of the forest to survive, without making a detrimental impact on the forests. Many of these groups are being displaced physically and culturally as deforestation of tropical rain forests occurs.

Build Inquiry Skills Point out the net in the photo of Dr. Lowman. Ask: **Why might a net be helpful when doing research on insects in the rain forest?** *(The net can be used to capture and collect insects for identification and further study.) What other instruments or items may be necessary for the observation or collection of insects in the rain forest? (collection jars, microscope, gloves, sheets, flashlights, tweezers, alcohol to preserve collected specimens)*

Research Interested students may want to investigate the different methods used to collect insects in the rain forest. Have students share the results of their research with the class. *(Collection methods include using ultraviolet lights at night to attract insects and then capturing them in a net or sheet; placing sheets under trees, and then shaking the insects out of the trees; using funnels and screens to sieve and collect insects from soil or leaf litter; collecting slow-moving insects with tweezers; skimming the surface of water with a net; or using a neurotoxin to "fog" a specific area so that the insects drop from the trees and are collected on sheets placed on the ground under the trees.)*

Discuss Ask: **Why do you think it is important to make observations and/or collect data on plants and animals in the least disruptive way possible?** *(When doing field investigations involving animals, you want to be able to observe the natural behavior of the animal, not have the behavior of the animal altered in some way because of your presence. You also do not want to do anything that will affect how the plant or animal lives after you are gone.)* Despite the difficulties of doing research in the rain forest, why is it important that research in this area continue? *(The rain forest is home to many indigenous peoples; it is the most diverse biome on the planet, and many species have yet to be identified; it is disappearing rapidly to cropland.)*

Use Visuals Show students photos of the rain forest at different levels. Ask: **Why do you think it would be difficult to collect data under these conditions?** *(Many rain forest areas are remote and difficult to reach through normal routes of travel. Many areas within the rain forest itself are hard to reach due to height as well as the density of plant and tree growth. Also it may be difficult to carry heavy equipment to different sites in the forest.)*

Discuss Some people may think that being a scientist is a boring job that involves sitting in a laboratory all day. Have students examine the photos of Dr. Lowman in this feature. Ask: **What about Dr. Lowman's job as a scientist seems exciting?** *(She travels all over the world to beautiful tropical rain forest locations. She hovers over the top of the rain forest on hot-air balloons, canopy sleds, or bridges in the treetops.)*

A balloon tows a canopy sled that can rest in the upper rain forest canopy.

? What are the challenges of studying the canopy?

When the canopy is far above the ground, it is not easy to study. I started out in Australia using a rope to climb into the canopy. Then another scientist and I came up with a different approach. On the back of a napkin, we drew a plan to build a bridge between trees.

The idea of a bridge between trees evolved into what I call my little "highways in the sky." I've built them in several places. They are collections of platforms and bridges that are strung together through the treetops. The platforms allow a group of people to stop and examine the canopy in detail, while the bridges allow people to keep moving.

Besides these walkways, we've used hot-air balloons and large cranes to get us up into the canopy. But these technologies are expensive.

? What did you want to learn about rain forests?

There are two questions in particular that I have been asking throughout my career. First, how many leaves on a tree do insects consume? And, second, how does insect damage affect the health of the trees?

2 ◆ E

? How much do insects consume?

One dramatic discovery was in the rain forest of Australia. Every spring something was eating up to 50 percent of the young leaves of the Antarctic beech trees and then mysteriously disappearing. I watched the trees for two years before I was able to capture the beetle larvae that were responsible for the damage. There was a reason I had missed the larvae for so long: After the larvae feed on the leaves, they fall off the trees into the leaves and soil on the ground below.

Once I raised the larvae to adult beetles, I found that I had uncovered a previously unknown species—*Nothofagus novacastria*. I called it the gul beetle.

? How do the insects affect the health of the forests?

The most surprising thing I learned is that trees can put up with a lot more insect damage than we ever dreamed. Before scientists were able to access the canopy, they had to make estimates based on what they could learn from working on the ground. Those studies found that insects damaged about 5 to 7 percent of a tree's leaves in any given year. But once we got up into the canopy, we realized that there are a lot more insects and a lot more leaves damaged—nearly four or five times what we had originally thought.

Meg discovered beetle larvae that feed on young leaves of the Antarctic beech. The scientific name of the beetle is *Nothofagus novacastria*.

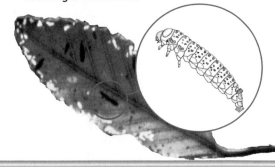

Background

Integrating Science In many cases insects help a particular species of plant as much as the plant helps them. Many rain forest plants rely on insects for pollination. The gongora orchid attracts carpenter bees by emitting a strong scent. The bees pollinate the orchids as they move from one flower to another. Although the orchids do not produce any nectar, the bees benefit by picking up the strong scent. The highly aromatic male bees fly together in swarm, attracting female bees for mating. Bullet ants feed on the nectar of the *Costus* flower. These ants have such a nasty sting that other insects and animals of the rain forest avoid these flowers altogether. The flowers are protected by the ants and the ants receive food in the form of nectar in return.

Meg carefully collects and records data on plant and animal species.

How do forests grow back?

Along with my work as a leaf detective, I got interested in yet another question: What forces affect the regrowth of a rain forest? Once the trees and other plants are killed in an area of the forest, whether by natural forces such as lightning-triggered fires or by people cutting trees, what does it take to return the forest to its natural state?

We've learned that once the canopy is seriously damaged, it will take far longer for it to grow back than we imagined. For over 30 years, we have been monitoring the regrowth of the canopy in Australia. It is surprising how slowly it grows back. We have seen four-inch-high seedlings that are 50 years old. In the tropics we're not looking at a hundred years, we're looking at a thousand years to grow again.

What are some memorable moments in the canopy?

Some memories are of little things, such as watching a yellow-bellied sapsucker eating a gypsy moth. It was very messy, like a child eating a caramel apple with his hands. Other memories are the moments of discovery—like finally finding that gul beetle larvae munching on the Antarctic beech leaves.

Writing in Science

Career Link Meg says that one of her greatest challenges as a field biologist is to find ways of getting into the canopy. In a paragraph, describe several methods that Meg uses to solve the problem. Then add a method of your own for reaching the canopy.

Go Online
PHSchool.com

For: More on this career
Visit: PHSchool.com
Web Code: ceb-5000

Discuss Ask: **Why is it important that we understand how long it takes for the forest to return to its natural state after it has been seriously damaged?** *(Rain forests are a valuable ecosystem on Earth for many different reasons. Humans are contributing to the destruction of rain forests by clearing them for farmland. It is important that we fully understand the consequences of this before continuing to deforest large portions of rain forest.)*

Research Have student groups research more information about the conservation of rain forests worldwide and what efforts are being made to reduce the amount of deforestation.

Writing in Science

Writing Skill descriptive writing
Scoring Rubric
4 Includes a thorough description of methods used to get into the canopy as well as an original idea for getting into the canopy
3 Includes a description of methods used to get into the canopy as well as an original idea for getting into the canopy
2 Includes a description of methods used to get into the canopy but does not include an original idea for getting into the canopy
1 Includes a description of some of the methods used to get into the canopy but does not include an original idea for getting into canopy

Go Online
PHSchool.com

For: More on this career
Visit: PHSchool.com
Web Code: ceb-5000

Students can do further research on this career and others that are related to the study of earth science.

Populations and Communities

Chapter at a Glance

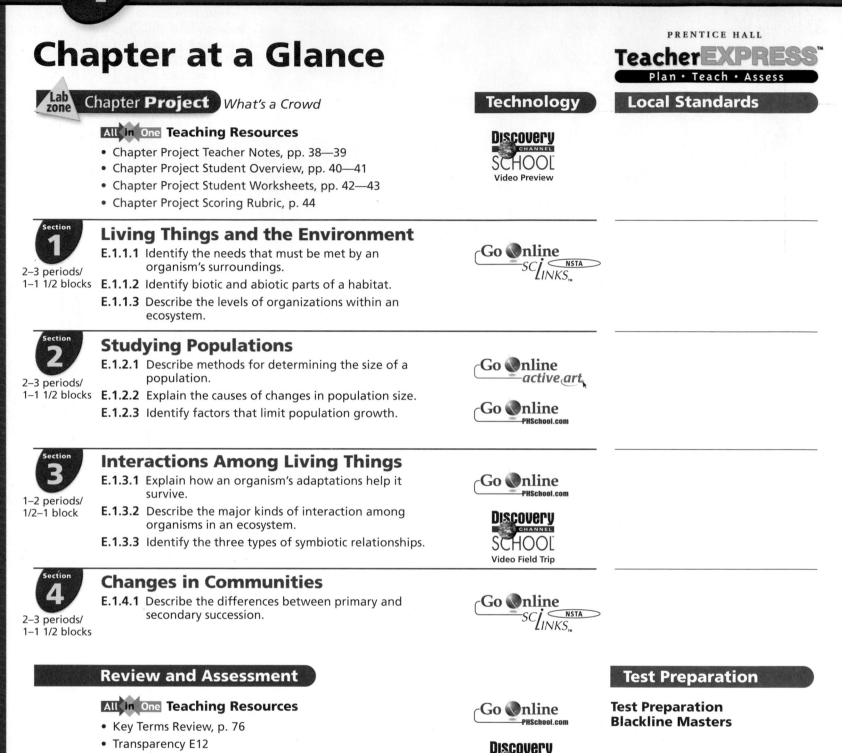

PRENTICE HALL

TeacherEXPRESS™
Plan • Teach • Assess

	Technology	**Local Standards**

Lab zone Chapter **Project** *What's a Crowd*

All in One Teaching Resources
- Chapter Project Teacher Notes, pp. 38—39
- Chapter Project Student Overview, pp. 40—41
- Chapter Project Student Worksheets, pp. 42—43
- Chapter Project Scoring Rubric, p. 44

Discovery CHANNEL SCHOOL Video Preview

Section 1 **Living Things and the Environment**

2–3 periods/
1–1 1/2 blocks

E.1.1.1 Identify the needs that must be met by an organism's surroundings.

E.1.1.2 Identify biotic and abiotic parts of a habitat.

E.1.1.3 Describe the levels of organizations within an ecosystem.

Go Online SCI LINKS™ NSTA

Section 2 **Studying Populations**

2–3 periods/
1–1 1/2 blocks

E.1.2.1 Describe methods for determining the size of a population.

E.1.2.2 Explain the causes of changes in population size.

E.1.2.3 Identify factors that limit population growth.

Go Online *active art*

Go Online PHSchool.com

Section 3 **Interactions Among Living Things**

1–2 periods/
1/2–1 block

E.1.3.1 Explain how an organism's adaptations help it survive.

E.1.3.2 Describe the major kinds of interaction among organisms in an ecosystem.

E.1.3.3 Identify the three types of symbiotic relationships.

Go Online PHSchool.com

Discovery CHANNEL SCHOOL Video Field Trip

Section 4 **Changes in Communities**

2–3 periods/
1–1 1/2 blocks

E.1.4.1 Describe the differences between primary and secondary succession.

Go Online SCI LINKS™ NSTA

Review and Assessment

All in One Teaching Resources
- Key Terms Review, p. 76
- Transparency E12
- Performance Assessment Teacher Notes, p. 84
- Performance Assessment Scoring Rubric, p. 85
- Performance Assessment Student Worksheet, p. 86
- Chapter Test, pp. 87–90

Go Online PHSchool.com

Discovery CHANNEL SCHOOL Video Assessment

Test Preparation

Test Preparation Blackline Masters

Lab zone Chapter Activities Planner

For more activities
LAB ZONE Easy Planner CD-ROM

Student Edition	Inquiry	Time	Materials	Skills	Resources
Chapter Project	Open-Ended	2 to 3 weeks	**All in One Teaching Resources** See p. 38	Developing a hypothesis, identifying and controlling variables, measuring, communicating	**Lab zone Easy Planner** **All in One Teaching Resources** Support pp. 38–44
Section 1					
Discover Activity, p. 6	Open-Ended	10 minutes	Old magazines, scissors, paste or glue, sheet of white paper, three pencils of different colors	Inferring	**Lab zone Easy Planner**
Try This, p. 9	Directed	Setup, 15 minutes, follow-up, 5 minutes per day	4 600-mL beakers, masking tape, pen, 2 L spring water, 25 g noniodized salt, stirrers, brine shrimp eggs, 4 paper squares, paper cups, hand lens (optional)	Drawing conclusions	**Lab zone Easy Planner**
Skills Lab, p. 12	Directed	Prep: 30 minutes Class: 3 minutes Follow-up, 5–10 minutes per day	gravel, soil, moss, plants, plastic spoon, charcoal, spray bottle, large rubber band, 2 vascular plants, plastic wrap, pre-cut clear plastic bottle	Making models, observing	**Lab zone Easy Planner** **All in One Teaching Resources** Skills Lab: *A World in a Bottle* pp. 53–54
Section 2					
Discover Activity, p. 13	Guided	10 minutes	2 large plastic jars, dried beans, ruler, small beaker, timer	Forming operational definitions	**Lab zone Easy Planner**
Skills Activity, p. 15	Directed	5 minutes	none	Calculating	**Lab zone Easy Planner**
Try This, p. 19	Directed	15 minutes	Masking tape, meter stick, small jigsaw puzzle, watch or clock	Making models	**Lab zone Easy Planner**
Skills Lab, p. 21	Directed	Prep: 20 minutes Class: 40 minutes	Model turtle population, paper, calculator, graph paper	Calculating, graphing, predicting	**Lab zone Easy Planner**
Section 3					
Discover Activity, p. 24	Guided	15 minutes	Sheet of white paper, colored pencils or markers, tape	Predicting	**Lab zone Easy Planner**
Skills Activity, p. 30	Directed	10 minutes	None	Classifying	**Lab zone Easy Planner**
Section 4					
Discover Activity, p. 32	Guided	10 minutes	None	Posing questions	**Lab zone Easy Planner**

Section 1 Living Things and the Environment

ABILITY LEVELS KEY
L1 Basic to Average
L2 For All Students
L3 Average to Advanced

2–3 periods, 1–1 1/2 blocks

Objectives

E.1.1.1 Identify the needs that must be met by an organism's surroundings.
E.1.1.2 Identify biotic and abiotic parts of a habitat.
E.1.1.3 Describe the levels of organization within an ecosystem.

Key Terms

• organism • habitat • biotic factor • abiotic factor • photosynthesis • species
• population • community • ecosystem • ecology

Local Standards

Preteach

Build Background Knowledge

Students identify ecosystems they are familiar with.

Lab zone Discover Activity *What's in the Scene?*

Targeted Print and Technology Resources

All in One Teaching Resources

L2 Reading Strategy Transparency E1: Identifying Main Ideas

◉ **Presentation-Pro CD-ROM**

Transparency E1

Instruct

Habitats Define *habitat* and examine what needs are met by an organism's habitat.

Biotic Factors Identify a variety of biotic factors in a habitat.

Abiotic Factors Describe abiotic factors that are part of a habitat.

Levels of Organization Use pictures to describe the relationship among populations, communities, and ecosystems.

Lab zone Skills Lab *A World in a Bottle*

Targeted Print and Technology Resources

All in One Teaching Resources

L2 Guided Reading, pp. 47–50
L2 Transparency E2
L2 Skills Lab: *A World in a Bottle,* pp. 53–54

📼 **Lab Activity Video/DVD**
Skills Lab: *A World in a Bottle*

www.SciLinks.org Web Code: scn-0511

◉ **Student Edition on Audio CD**

Transparency E2

Assess

Section Assessment Questions

↻ Have students use their Identifying Main Ideas graphic organizers to help answer the questions.

Reteach

Use a graphic organizer to show the relationships among populations, communities, and ecosystems.

Targeted Print and Technology Resources

All in One Teaching Resources

• Section Summary, p. 46
L1 Review and Reinforce, p. 51
L3 Enrich, p. 52

Section 2 Studying Populations

🕐 *2–3 periods, 1–1 1/2 blocks*

Objectives

E.1.2.1 Describe methods for determining the size of a population.
E.1.2.2 Explain the causes of changes in population size.
E.1.2.3 Identify factors that limit population growth.

Key Terms

• estimate • birth rate • death rate • immigration • emigration
• population density • limiting factor • carrying capacity

Local Standards

Preteach

Build Background Knowledge

Describe the purpose of tagging individuals in a population study.

Lab zone Discover Activity *What's the Population of Beans in a Jar?*

Targeted Print and Technology Resources

All in One Teaching Resources
L2 Reading Strategy Transparency E3: Asking Questions

🔘 **Presentation-Pro CD-ROM**

Transparency E3

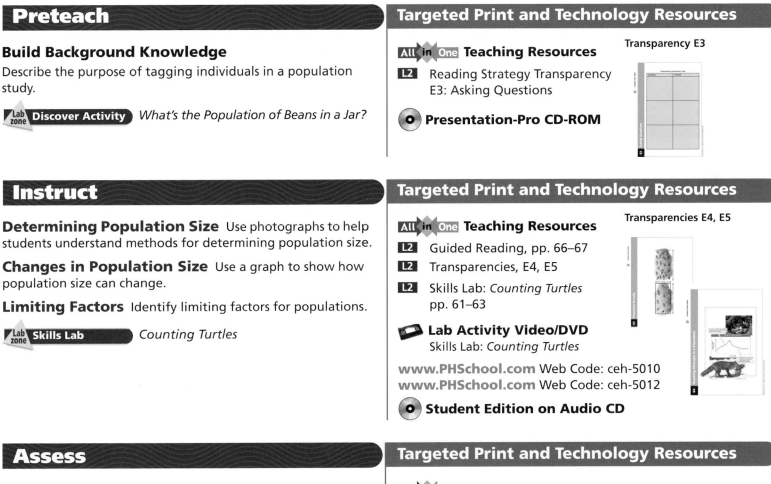

Instruct

Determining Population Size Use photographs to help students understand methods for determining population size.

Changes in Population Size Use a graph to show how population size can change.

Limiting Factors Identify limiting factors for populations.

Lab zone Skills Lab *Counting Turtles*

Targeted Print and Technology Resources

All in One Teaching Resources
L2 Guided Reading, pp. 66–67
L2 Transparencies, E4, E5
L2 Skills Lab: *Counting Turtles* pp. 61–63

📼 **Lab Activity Video/DVD**
Skills Lab: *Counting Turtles*

www.PHSchool.com Web Code: ceh-5010
www.PHSchool.com Web Code: ceh-5012

🔘 **Student Edition on Audio CD**

Transparencies E4, E5

Assess

Section Assessment Questions

↪ Have students use their Answering Questions graphic organizers to answer the questions.

Reteach

Discuss how specific limiting factors can cause populations to decrease.

Targeted Print and Technology Resources

All in One Teaching Resources
• Section Summary, p. 65
L1 Review and Reinforce, p. 68
L3 Enrich, p. 69

Section 3 Interactions Among Living Things

🕐 *1–2 periods, 1/2–1 block*

Objectives

E.1.3.1 Explain how an organism's adaptations help it survive.
E.1.3.2 Describe the major kinds of interactions among organisms in an ecosystem.
E.1.3.3 Identify the three types of symbiotic relationships.

Local Standards

Key Terms

• natural selection • adaptations • niche • competition • predation • predator
• prey • symbiosis • mutualism • commensalism • parasitism • parasite • host

Preteach

Build Background Knowledge

Identify how different organisms have adapted to their environment.

Lab zone **Discover Activity** *Can You Hide a Butterfly?*

Targeted Print and Technology Resources

All in One Teaching Resources

L2 Reading Strategy Transparency E6: Using Prior Knowledge

💿 **Presentation-Pro CD-ROM**

Transparency E6

Instruct

Adapting to the Environment Use an illustration to explore how natural selection has resulted in organisms that are adapted to their environment.

Competition Discuss reasons for competition.

Predation Define *predation* and discuss the effect it has on population size.

Symbiosis Compare and contrast the three types of symbiosis.

Targeted Print and Technology Resources

All in One Teaching Resources

L2 Guided Reading, pp. 66–67
L2 Transparency E7

www.PHSchool.com Web Code: ced-5013

💿 **Student Edition on Audio CD**

Transparency E7

Assess

Section Assessment Questions

Have students use their Using Prior Knowledge graphic organizers to answer the questions.

Reteach

Review and summarize information about competition, predation, and symbiosis.

Targeted Print and Technology Resources

All in One Teaching Resources

• Section Summary, p. 65
L1 Review and Reinforce, p. 68
L3 Enrich, p. 69

Section 4 Changes in Communities

🕐 *2–3 periods, 1–1 1/2 blocks*

Objectives

E.1.4.1 Describe the differences between primary and secondary succession.

Local Standards

Key Terms

• succession • primary succession • pioneer species • secondary succession

---

Preteach

Build Background Knowledge

Observe over time a vacant lot or unattended garden and describe any changes.

Lab zone Discover Activity *What Happened Here?*

Targeted Print and Technology Resources

All in One Teaching Resources

L2 Reading Strategy Transparency E7: Comparing and Contrasting

💿 **Presentation-Pro CD-ROM**

Transparency E8

Instruct

Primary Succession Use labeled illustrations to describe the process of primary succession.

Secondary Succession Use labeled illustrations to compare and contrast the processes of secondary and primary succession.

Targeted Print and Technology Resources

All in One Teaching Resources

L2 Guided Reading, pp. 72–73
L2 Transparencies E9, E10

www.SciLinks.org Web Code: scn-0514

💿 **Student Edition on Audio CD**

Transparencies E9, E10

Assess

Section Assessment Questions

Have students use their Comparing and Contrasting graphic organizers to answer the questions.

Reteach

Summarize the processes of primary and secondary succession.

Targeted Print and Technology Resources

All in One Teaching Resources

• Section Summary, p. 71
L1 Review and Reinforce, p. 74
L3 Enrich, p. 75

Go Online
NSTA-PDi LINKS

For: Professional development support
Visit: www.SciLinks.org/PDLinks
Web Code: scf-0110

Professional Development

Section 1 Living Things and the Environment

Carbon Dioxide Carbon dioxide is an abiotic factor that all plants and some algae require to carry out photosynthesis. Chlorophyll, the green pigment in plants and some algae, absorbs energy in sunlight. The organism uses this energy to combine carbon dioxide (CO_2) and water (H_2O) in a chemical reaction that produces sugars, including glucose ($C_6H_{12}O_6$). Water and oxygen (O_2) are produced as byproducts of the reaction. The sugars provide energy for sustaining the organism's life processes. Other organisms obtain this energy when they eat plants or algae. The energy is released during cellular respiration when glucose is broken down into carbon dioxide and water.

Biosphere All of Earth's communities are part of a higher level of organization, the biosphere. The organizations that make up the biosphere interact with each other. But they also interact in various ways with Earth's other "spheres." These include the atmosphere (the gases that envelop Earth), the hydrosphere (Earth's water), and the lithosphere (Earth's rocky outer covering and soils). While scientists study the relationships among organisms of the biosphere, they also consider the biosphere in relation to the other spheres of the physical environment.

Section 2 Studying Populations

Principle of Competitive Exclusion The Gause principle, which is also known as the principle of competitive exclusion, was named for G.F. Gause, a Soviet biologist. Gause was the first to suggest that species cannot coexist for long in the same niche. Gause developed his ideas by studying two similar species of *Paramecium*. When he grew populations of the two species separately, both grew rapidly and then leveled off at a population size that could be supported by available resources in the growing medium. However, when Gause grew the two species together, one species survived and the other species died out. Gause concluded that the surviving species had a competitive advantage in obtaining food and other resources. His work was later confirmed by other studies.

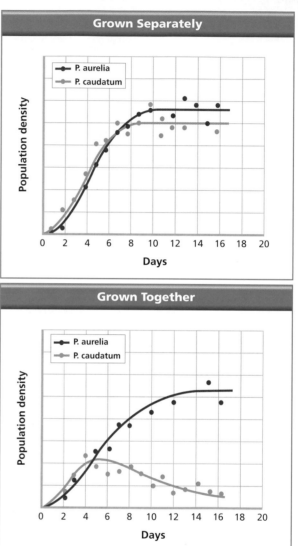

Section 3 Interactions Among Living Things

Moose and Wolves on Isle Royale When a population grows beyond the carrying capacity of its habitat, a population crash may occur. One example of such a crash occurred with the moose population on Isle Royale before wolves arrived in 1949. Moose came to Isle Royale around 1900 by walking across the frozen lake in winter. Over the next 35 years, the moose population increased to about 3,000. As a result, the food supply became exhausted, and 90 percent of the moose starved. The population increased again until 1948 and then declined sharply once more because of lack of food.

After the introduction of wolves to Isle Royale, the wolf and moose populations on Isle Royale cycled up and down for decades. Then in the early 1980s, the wolf population declined sharply. Biologists hypothesize that the extreme genetic uniformity of the wolf population is one of the reasons for the decline. Populations that lack genetic variability often have low reproductive success. For example, in 1994, only two wolf pups were born on the island. Genetic uniformity also makes a population more susceptible to disease. Analysis of the wolves' blood has revealed antibodies to canine parvovirus, indicating that the wolves have been exposed to this lethal disease. More recently, scientists have been encouraged as the wolf population has begun to increase slowly.

Address Misconceptions

Adaptation occurs in species, not in individuals. Although individual traits enable certain individuals to survive and reproduce, these traits are not a result of an individual adapting in order to survive. Instead, individuals survive *because of* their traits. For a strategy for clarifying natural selection and adaptations, see **Address Misconceptions** on page 25.

Section 4 Changes in Communities

Lichens Lichens are an example of one type of symbiotic relationship—mutualism. In this type of association, both organisms depend on each other and cannot live independently. In the lichen, one organism, the algae, produces during photosynthesis the food the other organism, the fungus, requires. The fungus absorbs vital nutrients and water for the process. Notice in the cross-section diagram that the fungus provides a top layer (1) that protects the algae directly beneath (2). Fungal filaments (3) lie below the algae. The bottom protective layer and the rootlike structures that anchor the lichen are provided by the fungus.

Cross-Section of a Lichen

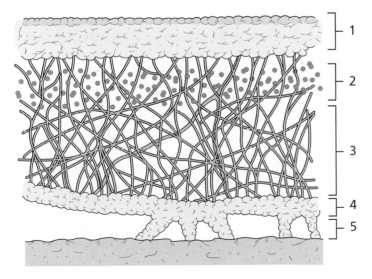

Lichens occur in most habitats, especially those unsuitable for plant growth. In arid habitats they have a ball-like shape, so they blow about and disperse in the wind. They have been found growing on the shells of tortoises in the Galapagos and on beetles in New Guinea.

Lichens are very sensitive to sulfur dioxide, which makes them good indicators of pollution and acid rain. Because they also tolerate and accumulate metals, they can be an indicator of industrial pollutants. Lichens also are used in traditional dyes, in herbal medicines, and as human and animal food. In the arctic, they are the main source of food for caribou and reindeer.

Think Aloud
Verbalize Thought Processes While Reading

Strategy Model cognitive and metacognitive processes that students can use to build meaning, self-correct, and monitor their own comprehension. Choose part of a section from the chapter and preview it. As you do so, imagine that you are reading these paragraphs for the first time, just as your students will be. Make a copy of the section, and on it write comments and questions that you can use as "think-aloud" models.

Example
1. Read several paragraphs aloud and have your students follow along silently. Have them listen to how you pause to check your own comprehension and to determine meaning at trouble spots. You might model some of the following strategies aloud as you read:
- Make a prediction, and then revise or verify it.
- Describe mental pictures as they form.
- Connect new information with prior knowledge or related ideas; share an analogy.
- Verbalize confusing points and work out steps to clarify their meanings; adjust your reading pace if needed.

2. Select a logical stopping point. Then have students read the next paragraph silently and apply similar strategies internally. Afterwards, ask students to share the strategies they used. Repeat this several times.

3. Have students work in pairs, taking turns applying think-aloud strategies to the next several paragraphs.

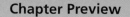

Interactive Textbook
- Complete student edition
- Video and audio
- Simulations and activities
- Section and chapter activities

Chapter 1

Populations and Communities

Chapter Preview

Interactive Textbook

A population of Grant's zebras roams on the Masai Mara Reserve in Kenya. ▶

Chapter Project

Objectives
In addition to giving students an opportunity to observe the effect of crowding on plant growth, this project will enhance understanding of the procedure involved in scientific experimentation. After this Chapter Project, students will be able to
- design an experiment to test the effect of crowding on plant growth
- identify and control variables
- measure plant growth, record data, and analyze results
- communicate experimental procedures and results in a written report and graph

Skills Focus
Developing a hypothesis, identifying and controlling variables, measuring, communicating

Project Time Line 2 to 3 weeks

All in One Teaching Resources
- Chapter Project Teacher Notes
- Chapter Project Worksheet 1
- Chapter Project Worksheet 2
- Chapter Project Worksheet 3
- Chapter Project Scoring Rubric

Safety
 Review the Safety Guidelines in Appendix A.

Developing a Plan
During the first phase of the project, each group should plan an experiment and submit the plan for your review.

Possible Materials
- Wisconsin Fast Plants™ *(Brassica rapa),* a strain of radishlike plants specifically developed for their short life cycle, are preferred for this project. They germinate within 24 hours, develop leaves within one week and flowers in about two weeks, and can be grown easily in a small space. They are available from biological supply houses.

Populations and
Communities
▶ Video Preview
Video Field Trip
Video Assessment

Chapter **Project**

What's a Crowd?

In this chapter, you will explore how living things obtain the things they need from their surroundings. You will also learn how living things interact with the living and nonliving things around them. As you work on this chapter project, you will observe interactions among growing plants.

Your Goal To design and conduct an experiment to determine the effect of crowding on plant growth

To complete this project, you must

- develop a plan for planting different numbers of seeds in identical containers
- observe and collect data on the growing plants
- present your results in a written report and a graph
- follow the safety guidelines in Appendix A

Plan It! With your group, brainstorm ideas for your plan. What conditions do plants need to grow? How will you arrange your seeds in their containers? What types of measurements will you make when the plants begin to grow? Submit your draft plan to your teacher. When your teacher has approved your plan, plant your seeds. Then collect and analyze the growth data and present your results.

Chapter 1 E ◆ 5

- Each group will need several identical planting containers. Possibilities include large margarine tubs or half-gallon milk cartons with one of the sides removed.
- Provide potting soil, trowels or large spoons, watering cans or spray bottles, and rulers.
- Set aside a location where the plant containers will receive direct sunlight or strong indirect sunlight for several hours a day. If sunlight is limited, set up lamps on tables.

Launching the Project

To introduce the project, ask: **What do plants need to grow?** (*Students may mention sunlight, water, a certain temperature, soil, or nutrients in the soil.*) **Do you think that every seed that germinates grows into a mature plant? Why or why not?** (*Most students will realize that many plants do not mature because their needs are not met.*) Discuss with students how overcrowding of plants might affect growth.

*Video
Preview*

Populations and Communities

Show the Video Preview to introduce the Chapter Project and present an overview of the chapter content. Ask: **What are some of the characteristics of the cheetah population?** (*Accept all student responses that show an understanding of the characteristics of a population.*)

Performance Assessment

The Chapter Scoring Rubric will help you evaluate how well students complete the Chapter Project. You may want to share the rubric with students so that they will know what is expected. Students will be assessed on

- how well they design an experiment to test the effect of crowding on plant growth
- how carefully they identify and control variables, make observations, and record data
- how well they communicate their procedures, results, and conclusion to the class
- how well they participate in their groups

Portfolio

Objectives

After this lesson, students will be able to

E.1.1.1 Identify the needs that must be met by an organism's surroundings.

E.1.1.2 Identify biotic and abiotic parts of a habitat.

E.1.1.3 Describe the levels of organization within an ecosystem.

Target Reading Skill

Identifying Main Ideas Explain that identifying main ideas and details helps students sort the facts from the information into groups. Each group can have a main topic, subtopics, and details.

Answers

One way students might map the information is:

Main Idea: An organism obtains food, water, shelter, and other things it needs from its environment.

Detail: Each organism must live in a specific type of environment, called its habitat.

Detail: Organisms live in different habitats because they have different requirements for survival.

Detail: One area may contain many habitats.

All in One Teaching Resources

• Transparency E1

Preteach

Build Background Knowledge   L2

Experience with Ecosystems

Ask: **What is an ecosystem?** (*Students may say that it is a particular type of place with different kinds of organisms living in it. Accept all responses without comment at this time.*)
What kinds of ecosystems do you know of? (*Students may mention a swamp, desert, seashore, forest, and so on.*)

Reading Preview

Key Concepts

• What needs are met by an organism's surroundings?

• What are the two parts of an organism's habitat with which it interacts?

• What are the levels of organization within an ecosystem?

Key Terms

• organism • habitat
• biotic factor • abiotic factor
• photosynthesis • species
• population • community
• ecosystem • ecology

Target Reading Skill

Identifying Main Ideas As you read the Habitats section, write the main idea—the biggest or most important idea—in a graphic organizer like the one below. Then write three supporting details that give examples of the main idea.

Main Idea

An organism obtains food . . .

Detail	Detail	Detail

Lab zone Discover **Activity**

What's in the Scene?

1. Choose a magazine picture of a nature scene. Paste the picture onto a sheet of paper, leaving space all around the picture.
2. Locate everything in the picture that is alive. Use a colored pencil to draw a line from each living thing. If you know its name, write it on the line.
3. Using a different colored pencil, label each nonliving thing.

Think It Over

Inferring How do the living things in the picture depend on the nonliving things? Using a third color, draw lines connecting the living things to the nonliving things they need.

As the sun rises on a warm summer morning, the Nebraska town is already bustling with activity. Some residents are hard at work building homes for their families. They are working underground, where it is dark and cool. Other inhabitants are collecting seeds for breakfast. Some of the town's younger residents are at play, chasing each other through the grass.

Suddenly, an adult spots a threatening shadow—an enemy has appeared in the sky! The adult cries out several times, warning the others. Within moments, the town's residents disappear into their underground homes. The town is silent and still, except for a single hawk circling overhead.

Have you guessed what kind of town this is? It is a prairie dog town on the Nebraska plains. As these prairie dogs dug their burrows, searched for food, and hid from the hawk, they interacted with their environment, or surroundings.

Black-Tailed Prairie Dog ▶

Lab zone Discover **Activity**

Skills Focus Inferring

Materials old magazines, scissors, paste or glue, sheet of white paper, three pencils of different colors

Time 10 minutes

Tips Encourage students to look for pictures with close-enough views to allow them to distinguish various living and nonliving things.

Expected Outcome The specific living things shown will vary. Students should identify water, soil, sunlight, and air among the nonliving things.

Think It Over Students should indicate that living things needs water and air and that plants also need sunlight.

Habitats

A prairie dog is one type of **organism,** or living thing. Each organism must live in a specific type of environment. **An organism obtains food, water, shelter, and other things it needs to live, grow, and reproduce from its environment.** An environment that provides the things the organism needs to live, grow, and reproduce is called its **habitat.**

One area may contain many habitats. For example, in a forest, mushrooms grow in the damp soil, bears live on the forest floor, and woodpeckers build nests in tree trunks.

Organisms live in different habitats because they have different requirements for survival. A prairie dog obtains the food and shelter it needs from its habitat. It could not survive in a tropical rain forest or on the rocky ocean shore. Likewise, the prairie would not meet the needs of a spider monkey or hermit crab.

Reading Checkpoint Why do different organisms live in different habitats?

Biotic Factors

To meet its needs, a prairie dog must interact with more than just the other prairie dogs around it. **An organism interacts with both the living and nonliving parts of its habitat.** The living parts of a habitat are called **biotic factors** (by AHT ik). Biotic factors in the prairie dogs' habitat include the grass and plants that provide seeds and berries. The hawks, ferrets, badgers, and eagles that hunt the prairie dogs are also biotic factors. In addition, worms, fungi, and bacteria are biotic factors that live in the soil underneath the prairie grass.

Reading Checkpoint Name a biotic factor in your environment.

FIGURE 1
An Organism in Its Habitat
Like all organisms, this red-tailed hawk obtains food, water, and shelter from its habitat. Prairie dogs are a major source of food for the red-tailed hawk.

Habitats

Teach Key Concepts L2
Definition of Habitat

Focus Ask: **Are all parts of the forest where organisms live the same?** *(No)* **How do they differ?** *(Possible answers: Some parts get more sunlight than others; some organisms live on the ground, others in the treetops.)*

Teach Explain that the type of place where an organism lives—a forest or a prairie, for example—is an ecosystem. The specific part of the ecosystem that meets the organism's needs and in which it lives is its habitat. Ask: **What are some habitats in a forest?** *(Answers might include: a tree branch; a sunny patch on the forest floor.)*

Apply Ask: **Why do you find different kinds of organisms in different habitats?** *(Each kind of organism has specific needs. Different habitats provide different things.)* **learning modality: verbal**

Biotic Factors

Teach Key Concepts L2
Identifying Biotic Factors

Focus Remind students that an organism's habitat includes living and nonliving parts.

Teach Explain that the living parts of a habitat are called biotic factors.

Apply Ask: **What are some biotic factors in the habitat of a field mouse?** *(Answers might include: grass and other plants, insects, snakes, or gophers.)* **learning modality: verbal**

Independent Practice

All in One Teaching Resources
• Guided Reading and Study Worksheet: *Living Things and the Environment*

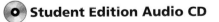 **Student Edition Audio CD**

Monitor Progress L1
Answers

Reading Checkpoint Different kinds of organisms have different requirements. Their habitats must meet the requirements.

Reading Checkpoint Students may name another living organism such as a person, tree, dog, bird, grass, flower.

Differentiated Instruction

Less Proficient Readers L1
Building Vocabulary Before students begin reading the lesson, have them skim the text for unfamiliar words. Tell them to record the words and as they read they can write definitions as they encounter the words. After reading, students can use a dictionary to check any definitions they are uncertain of. **learning modality: visual**

Gifted and Talented L3
Comparing Habitats Have students describe their own habitat and make a list of its biotic factors. Then tell students to explain how these factors differ from those of organisms living in natural habitats. **learning modality: logical/mathematical**

Abiotic Factors

Help Students Read

Word-Part Analysis Explain that knowing the meanings of prefixes and root words can help students figure out and remember the meaning of key concept words. Write the word *biotic* on the board and ask student to identify the root word. *(Bio)* Tell students that *bio* comes from the Greek *bios,* which means "life." Next write the word *abiotic* on the board and point out that *a-* is a prefix meaning "not" or "opposite of." Ask students to use the meanings of the prefix and root word to construct a meaning for *abiotic.* *("Not living")*

Teach Key Concepts L2

Identifying Abiotic Factors

Focus Remind students that biotic factors are the living parts of an organism's habitat.

Teach Ask: **What are some nonliving parts of a habitat?** *(Water, sunlight, oxygen, temperature, soil)* Discuss how each factor helps an organism survive.

Apply Ask: **Does a squirrel need all the abiotic factors in its habitat to survive?** *(No)* Help students identify those that are essential to the squirrel's survival. *(Water, oxygen, temperature)* Ask students what might happen to a squirrel if its habitat did not provide sufficient amounts of a factor. *(It might die.)* **learning modality: verbal**

Lab zone Build **Inquiry** L1

Observing Soil Components

Materials soil sample, jar with screw-on lid, water, metric ruler

Time 10 minutes

Focus Discuss with students the different materials that they might find in soil.

Teach Have small groups of students put about 200 mL of soil into a jar, add water to about 3 cm from the top, and screw on the lid tightly. Tell students to shake the jar thoroughly to mix the soil and water and then place the jar on the desk. When the soil has settled, have students observe the layers of separated soil. Remind student to wash their hands after completing the activity.

Apply Challenge students to identify the materials that make up the soil and to tell which are biotic and which are abiotic. **learning modality: kinesthetic**

FIGURE 2
Abiotic Factors

The nonliving things in an organism's habitat are abiotic factors. **Applying Concepts** *Name three abiotic factors you interact with each day.*

▲ This orangutan is enjoying a drink of water.

▲ Sunlight enables this plant to make its own food.

▲ This banjo frog burrows in the soil to stay cool.

Abiotic Factors

Abiotic factors (ay by AHT ik) are the nonliving parts of an organism's habitat. They include water, sunlight, oxygen, temperature, and soil.

Water All living things require water to carry out their life processes. Water also makes up a large part of the bodies of most organisms. Your body, for example, is about 65 percent water. Plants and algae need water, along with sunlight and carbon dioxide, to make their own food in a process called **photosynthesis** (foh toh SIN thuh sis). Other living things depend on plants and algae for food.

Sunlight Because sunlight is needed for photosynthesis, it is an important abiotic factor for most living things. In places that do not receive sunlight, such as dark caves, plants and algae cannot grow. Because there are no plants or algae to provide food, few other organisms can live in such places.

Oxygen Most living things require oxygen to carry out their life processes. Oxygen is so important to the functioning of the human body that you can live only a few minutes without it. Organisms that live on land obtain oxygen from air, which is about 20 percent oxygen. Fish and other water organisms obtain oxygen that is dissolved in the water around them.

Temperature The temperatures that are typical of an area determine the types of organisms that can live there. For example, if you took a trip to a warm tropical island, you might see colorful orchid flowers and tiny lizards. These organisms could not survive on the frozen plains of Siberia.

Some animals alter their environments so they can survive very hot or very cold temperatures. Prairie dogs, for example, dig underground dens to find shelter from the hot summer sun and cold winter winds.

Soil Soil is a mixture of rock fragments, nutrients, air, water, and the decaying remains of living things. Soil in different areas consists of varying amounts of these materials. The type of soil in an area influences the kinds of plants that can grow there. Many animals, such as the prairie dogs, use the soil itself as a home. Billions of microscopic organisms such as bacteria also live in the soil.

✓ **Reading Checkpoint** How do abiotic factors differ from biotic factors?

FIGURE 3
A Population
All these garter snakes make up a population.

Levels of Organization

Of course, organisms do not live all alone in their habitat. Instead, organisms live together in populations and communities, and with abiotic factors in their ecosystems.

Populations In 1900, travelers saw a prairie dog town in Texas that covered an area twice the size of the city of Dallas. The town contained more than 400 million prairie dogs! These prairie dogs were all members of one species, or single kind, of organism. A **species** (SPEE sheez) is a group of organisms that are physically similar and can mate with each other and produce offspring that can also mate and reproduce.

All the members of one species in a particular area are referred to as a **population.** The 400 million prairie dogs in the Texas town are one example of a population. All the pigeons in New York City make up a population, as do all the bees that live in a hive. In contrast, all the trees in a forest do not make up a population, because they do not all belong to the same species. There may be pines, maples, birches, and many other tree species in the forest.

Communities A particular area usually contains more than one species of organism. The prairie, for instance, includes prairie dogs, hawks, grasses, badgers, and snakes, along with many other organisms. All the different populations that live together in an area make up a **community.**

To be considered a community, the different populations must live close enough together to interact. One way the populations in a community may interact is by using the same resources, such as food and shelter. For example, the tunnels dug by prairie dogs also serve as homes for burrowing owls and black-footed ferrets. The prairie dogs share the grass with other animals. Meanwhile, prairie dogs themselves serve as food for many species.

Lab zone Try This Activity

With or Without Salt?
In this activity you will explore salt as an abiotic factor.

1. Label four 600-mL beakers A, B, C, and D. Fill each with 500 mL of room-temperature spring water.
2. Set beaker A aside. Add 2.5 grams of noniodized salt to beaker B, 7.5 grams of salt to beaker C, and 15 grams of salt to beaker D. Stir each beaker.
3. Add $\frac{1}{8}$ spoonful of brine shrimp eggs to each beaker.
4. Cover each beaker with a square of paper. Keep them away from direct light or heat. Wash your hands.
5. Observe the beakers daily for three days.

Drawing Conclusions In which beakers did the eggs hatch? What can you conclude about the amount of salt in the shrimps' natural habitat?

Levels of Organization

Teach Key Concepts L2
Identifying Species, Populations, and Communities

Focus Write the names of these organisms on the board: grass, grasshoppers, field mouse, red-tailed hawks. Ask: **Where might you find these organisms living together?** *(In a grassland)*

Teach Tell students that the members of each single kind of organism make up a species. Although the members of a species might have some small differences, they are physically similar and can mate with each other. Ask: **Do all members of each species, such as the red-tailed hawk, live in the same grassland?** *(No)* **What do we call the members of a single species living in this grassland?** *(Population)* **What do we call all the species living together in a grassland?** *(Community)*

Apply Ask: **Would white-tailed deer living in a forest in Pennsylvania be members of the same population as white-tailed deer living in Illinois? Why or why not?** *(No, a population is composed of individuals that live in a particular area.)* **learning modality: logical/mathematical**

Use Visuals: Figure 3 L1
Identifying Populations

Focus Have students study Figure 3 and read the caption.

Teach Ask: **Why is this group of garter snakes a population?** *(Because all the individuals are the same species and they live in the same area)*

Apply Ask students what other populations they might find living in a community with these snakes. *(Possible answers: plants, including grasses; mice; insects)* **learning modality: verbal**

Lab zone Try This Activity

Skills Focus Drawing conclusions
Materials 4 600-mL beakers, masking tape, pen, 2 L spring water, 25 g noniodized salt, stirrers, brine shrimp eggs, 4 paper squares, paper cups, hand lens (optional)
Time setup—15 minutes; follow-up—5 minutes per day

Tips Allow the water to sit overnight. Put brine shrimp eggs in a paper cup for each group. Add 1/2 teaspoon of dry yeast to each beaker to feed the shrimp.
Expected Outcome Beaker A, no eggs hatch; beaker B, eggs hatch well; beaker C, less well; beaker D, little or no hatching. **learning modality: kinesthetic**

Monitor Progress L2

Skills Check Have students make a chart that lists abiotic factors in the first column. In the second column they should tell why each factor is necessary for life.

Answers
Figure 2 Answers might include: oxygen, water, temperature, sunlight.

✓ **Reading Checkpoint** Biotic factors are living; abiotic factors are nonliving.

Use Visuals: Figure 4 L2

Diagram Levels of Organization

Focus Review with students the definitions of *population* and *community*.

Teach Have students study Figure 4. Ask: **Which level has the most different kinds of individuals?** *(Ecosystem)* **How many different species are in the population?** *(One)* **What do the organisms in the community have in common?** *(They all live in the same place.)*

Apply Tell students to think of a different ecosystem. Then have each student create a diagram that shows the levels of organization for the chosen ecosystem. **learning modality: visual**

All in One **Teaching Resources**

• Transparency E2

Ecosystems The community of organisms that live in a particular area, along with their nonliving surroundings, make up an **ecosystem.** A prairie is just one of the many different ecosystems found on Earth. Other ecosystems in which living things make their homes include mountain streams, deep oceans, and dense forests.

Figure 4 shows the levels of organization in the prairie ecosystem. **The smallest level of organization is a single organism, which belongs to a population that includes other members of its species. The population belongs to a community of different species. The community and abiotic factors together form an ecosystem.**

Because the populations in an ecosystem interact with one another, any change affects all the different populations that live there. The study of how living things interact with each other and with their environment is called **ecology.** Ecologists are scientists who study ecology. As part of their work, ecologists study how organisms react to changes in their environment. An ecologist, for example, may look at how a fire affects a prairie ecosystem.

✓ **Reading Checkpoint** What is ecology?

Section 1 Assessment

Target Reading Skill Identifying Main Ideas Use your graphic organizer to help you answer Question 1 below.

Reviewing Key Concepts

1. **a. Listing** What basic needs are provided by an organism's habitat?
   b. Predicting What might happen if an organism's habitat could not meet one of its needs?
2. **a. Defining** Define the terms *biotic factors* and *abiotic factors.*
   b. Interpreting Illustrations List all the biotic and abiotic factors in Figure 4 on page 11.
   c. Making Generalizations Explain why water and sunlight are two abiotic factors that are important to all organisms.
3. **a. Sequencing** List these terms in order from the smallest level to the largest: *population, organism, ecosystem, community.*
   b. Classifying Would all the different kinds of organisms in a forest be considered a population or a community? Explain.
   c. Relating Cause and Effect How might a change in one population affect other populations in a community?

Writing in Science

Descriptive Paragraph What habitat do you live in? Write a one-paragraph description of your habitat. Describe how you obtain the food, water, and shelter you need from your habitat. How does this habitat meet your needs in ways that another would not?

Differentiated Instruction

English Learners/Beginning L1
Vocabulary: Link to Visual Use Figure 4 to explain levels of organization. Have students identify each kind of organism (species) in their home language and in English. Then pronounce aloud the picture labels: Organism, Population, Community and Ecosystem. Ask students how each level differs. **learning modality: visual**

English Learners/Intermediate L2
Vocabulary: Link to Visual Repeat the Beginning activity but have students write a sentence to describe what they see in each level. **learning modality: visual**

FIGURE 4
Ecological Organization
The smallest level of organization is the organism. The largest is the entire ecosystem.

Organism: Prairie dog

Population: Prairie dog town

Community: All the living things that interact on the prairie

Ecosystem: All the living and nonliving things that interact on the prairie

E ◆ 11

Monitor Progress L1
Answer

✓ **Reading Checkpoint** Ecology is the study of how living things interact with each other and with their environment.

Assess

Reviewing Key Concepts
1. a. A habitat provides food, water, shelter, and other things an organism needs to grow and reproduce. **b.** The organism might die.
2. a. Biotic factors are the living parts of a habitat that an organism interacts with; abiotic factors are the nonliving parts. **b.** Biotic—grass, birds, snake, badger, bison, prairie dogs; abiotic—soil, air, temperature, sunlight **c.** All organisms need water to carry on life processes. Plants and algae need sunlight to make food in photosynthesis. Other organisms depend directly or indirectly on the plants and algae for food.
3. a. Organism, population, community, ecosystem **b.** A community because a community consists of different populations living together **c.** Sample answer: If a population that is a food source for another population decreases, then the second population may decrease due to starvation.

Reteach L1
Write the word *prairie* on the board and draw a very large circle around it. Inside the circle draw smaller squares with these labels: *hawks, grasses, mice, snakes, water, air*. Inside the mice square, draw smaller triangles and label each *mouse*. Have students identify the shape that represent populations, a community, and an ecosystem.

Performance Assessment L2
Writing Ask students to choose an organism and describe its habitat. Tell them to identify the biotic and abiotic factors in the habitat.

All in One Teaching Resources
- Section Summary: *Living Things and the Environment*
- Review and Reinforce: *Living Things and the Environment*
- Enrich: *Living Things and the Environment*

Lab zone Chapter **Project**

Keep Students on Track Make sure students have identified the major variables that affect plant growth: size of the containers, amount of soil in each, density and depth for planting the seeds, amount and frequency of watering, and location in which the containers will be placed. Also review students' data tables to make sure they will be recording all relevant data.

Writing in Science

Writing Mode Description
Scoring Rubric
4 Includes detailed descriptions of what student needs, how the student will get it, and how another habitat would not meet the student's needs
3 Includes incomplete descriptions of all three factors
2 Includes only two of the three factors
1 Includes only one of the factors

A World in a Bottle

Prepare for Inquiry

Skills Objectives

After this lab, student will be able to
- make a model of a closed system
- observe the interactions of biotic and abiotic factors in a closed system

🕐 **Prep Time** 30 minutes

Class Time 30 minutes followed by 5–10 minutes per day for observations

Safety

 **Be sure students wear lab aprons to protect their clothing from soil stains.** Students who are allergic to molds should not handle the soil. Remind students to wash their hands after they finish the activity. Review the safety guidelines in Appendix A.

All in One Teaching Resources
- Lab Worksheet: *A World in a Bottle*

Guide Inquiry

Introducing the Procedure

Have students study the picture of the lab setup in their books. Ask: **Why do you think a layer of gravel is included in the setup?** *(The gravel will help prevent the soil from becoming too wet, which could harm the plant.)*

Expected Outcome

The plants will grow and thrive as long as not too little and not too much water is provided, and plants receive sunlight. Plants may outgrow the container and become root bound. Plants may start to decline if they become too crowded, or if nutrients in the soil decline.

Analyze and Conclude

1. Biotic factors: plants, any microscopic organisms in the soil; abiotic factors: gravel, soil, charcoal, water, air, light

2. Yes, light

3. Diagrams should show plants taking in carbon dioxide, water, and sunlight and giving off oxygen gas and water.

Skills Lab

A World in a Bottle

Problem

How do organisms survive in a closed ecosystem?

Skills Focus

making models, observing

Materials

- gravel • soil • moss plants • plastic spoon
- charcoal • spray bottle • large rubber band
- 2 vascular plants • plastic wrap
- pre-cut, clear plastic bottle

Procedure

1. In this lab, you will place plants in moist soil in a bottle that then will be sealed. This setup is called a terrarium. Predict whether the plants can survive in this habitat.

2. Spread about 2.5 cm of gravel on the bottom of a pre-cut bottle. Then sprinkle a spoonful or two of charcoal over the gravel.

3. Use the spoon to layer about 8 cm of soil over the gravel and charcoal. After you add the soil, tap it down to pack it.

4. Scoop out two holes in the soil. Remove the vascular plants from their pots. Gently place their roots in the holes. Then pack the loose soil firmly around the plants' stems.

5. Fill the spray bottle with water. Spray the soil until you see water collecting in the gravel.

6. Cover the soil with the moss plants, including the areas around the stems of the vascular plants. Lightly spray the mosses with water.

7. Tightly cover your terrarium with plastic wrap. Secure the cover with a rubber band. Place the terrarium in bright, indirect light.

8. Observe your terrarium daily for two weeks. Record your observations in your notebook. If its sides fog, move the terrarium to an area with a different amount of light. You may need to move it a few times. Note any changes you make in your terrarium's location.

12 ◆ E

Analyze and Conclude

1. **Making Models** List all of the biotic factors and abiotic factors that are part of your ecosystem model.

2. **Observing** Were any biotic or abiotic factors able to enter the terrarium? If so, which ones?

3. **Inferring** Draw a diagram showing the interactions between the terrarium's biotic and abiotic factors.

4. **Predicting** Suppose a plant-eating insect were added to the terrarium. Predict whether it would be able to survive. Explain your prediction.

5. **Communicating** Write a paragraph that explains how your terrarium models an ecosystem on Earth. How does your model differ from that ecosystem?

Design an Experiment

Plan an experiment that would model a fresh-water ecosystem. How would this model be different from the land ecosystem? *Obtain your teacher's approval before carrying out your plan.*

---

4. Sample answer: The insect probably would not survive because it would eat the plants faster than they could grow.

5. Paragraphs should explain that the model shows how biotic and abiotic factors interact within an ecosystem. The model is closed, not as complex, contains fewer organisms than an ecosystem.

Extend the Inquiry

Design an Experiment Students should include both plants and animals in their ecosystem. Make sure students let the water stand uncovered for a few days before adding it to the ecosystem to get rid of dissolved chemicals in the water. Water temperature should be maintained around 23°C.

Studying Populations

Reading Preview

Key Concepts
- How do ecologists determine the size of a population?
- What causes populations to change in size?
- What factors limit population growth?

Key Terms
- estimate • birth rate
- death rate • immigration
- emigration
- population density
- limiting factor
- carrying capacity

Target Reading Skill

Asking Questions Before you read, preview the red headings. In a graphic organizer like the one below, ask a question for each heading. As you read, write the answers to your questions.

Determining Population Size

Question	Answer
How do you determine population size?	Some methods of determining population size are . . .

Lab zone — Discover **Activity**

What's the Population of Beans in a Jar?

1. Fill a plastic jar with dried beans. This is your model population.
2. Your goal is to determine the bean population size, but you will not have time to count every bean. You may use any of the following to help you: a ruler, a small beaker, another large jar. Set a timer for two minutes when you are ready to begin.
3. After two minutes, record your answer. Then count the beans. How close was your answer?

Think It Over
Forming Operational Definitions In this activity, you came up with an estimate of the size of the bean population. Write a definition of the term *estimate* based on what you did.

How would you like to be an ecologist today? Your assignment is to study the albatross population on an island. One question you might ask is how the size of the albatross population has changed over time. Is the number of albatrosses on the island more than, less than, or the same as it was 50 years ago? To answer this question, you must first determine the current size of the albatross population.

FIGURE 5
Studying Populations
These young albatrosses are part of a larger albatross population in the Falkland Islands.

E ◆ 13

Lab zone — Discover **Activity**

Skills Focus Forming operational definitions

Materials 2 large plastic jars, dried beans, ruler, small beaker, timer

Time 10 minutes

Expected Outcome Possible methods: (1) Fill the small beaker with beans, count the beans, estimate how many small beakers would fit into the large jar, multiply the bean count by that number. (2) Put a 1-cm layer of beans in the second large jar, count the beans, measure the height of the jar, multiply the height by the number of beans in one layer.

Think It Over Definitions should focus on the idea of making an informed or educated guess.

Objectives

After this lesson, students will be able to
E.1.2.1 Describe methods for determining the size of a population.
E.1.2.2 Explain the causes of changes in population size.
E.1.2.3 Identify factors that limit population growth.

Target Reading Skill

Asking Questions Explain that changing a head into a question helps students anticipate the ideas, facts, and events they are about to read.

Answers

Possible student question and answers are these: **How do you determine population size?** (*Some methods of determining population size are direct observation, indirect observation, sampling, and mark-and-recapture studies.*) **What causes populations to change in size?** (*Some factors include birth, death, immigration, and emigration.*) **What are limiting factors?** (*These are factors that can limit population growth if they are unfavorable for the organisms in the population. Food and water, space, and weather conditions can be limiting factors.*)

All in One Teaching Resources
- Transparency E3

Preteach

Build Background Knowledge   L2

Experience with Mark-and-Recapture
Ask: **Have you ever seen scientists in a television documentary capture a wild animal, such as a wolf, bear, or bird, and then tag it with a specific color or mark and release it? What was the purpose of this procedure?** (*Answers might include to count the number of individuals in a population.*) Tell students that this is only one technique that scientists use to find the number of individuals in a population.

Determining Population Size

Teach Key Concepts **L2**
Estimating

Focus Remind students that a population is all the members of a species living in a particular area.

Teach Ask: **Why might scientists want to determine the number of individuals in a population?** *(Possible answer: To see if a population is increasing or decreasing)* Review the techniques for determining population size by direct and indirect observation, sampling, and mark-and-capture studies.

Apply Ask students what method they would use to count the number of individuals in the following populations: grizzly bears in a national park, grasshoppers in a field, and herons on a large pond. Have students give reasons for their answers. *(Possible answers: grizzly bears: mark-and-recapture because they would be spread over a large area; grasshoppers: sampling because there would be too many to count individually; herons: direct observation because only a few would live in the same pond)* **learning modality: logical/mathematical**

Independent Practice

All in One Teaching Resources

• Guided Reading and Study Worksheet: *Studying Populations*

O Student Edition Audio CD

FIGURE 6
Determining Population Size

Scientists use a variety of methods to determine the size of a population.

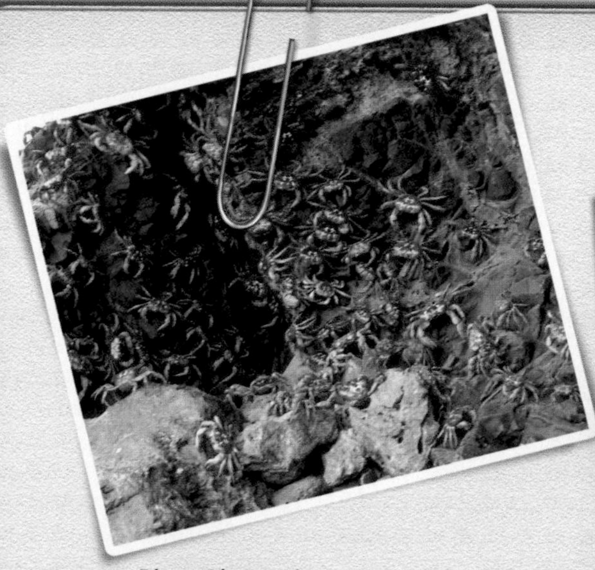

Direct Observation
Counting these crabs one by one is an example of direct observation.

Determining Population Size

Some methods of determining the size of a population are direct and indirect observations, sampling, and mark-and-recapture studies.

Direct Observation The most obvious way to determine the size of a population is to count all of its members. For example, you could try to count all the crabs in a tide pool.

Indirect Observation Sometimes it may be easier to observe signs of organisms rather than the organisms themselves. Look at the mud nests built by cliff swallows in Figure 6. Each nest has one entrance hole. By counting the entrance holes, you can determine the number of swallow nests in this area. Suppose that the average number of swallows per nest is four: two parents and two offspring. If there are 120 nests, you can multiply 120 by 4 to determine that there are 480 swallows.

Sampling In many cases, it is not even possible to count signs of every member of a population. The population may be very large or spread over a wide area. In such cases, ecologists usually make an estimate. An **estimate** is an approximation of a number, based on reasonable assumptions.

Indirect Observation
One way to determine this cliff swallow population is to count their cone-shaped nests.

Differentiated Instruction

Gifted and Talented **L3**
Researching Population Studies Have students research specific population studies around the world. Ask them to prepare a 10–15 minute oral report for the class that tells what is being studied, where and why the study is taking place, and who is doing the study. Tell them to include a description of the methods that are being used. Encourage students to use presentation software and to include pictures, diagrams, and graphs to explain their information. **learning modality: logical/mathematical**

Special Needs **L1**
Practice Calculations For students who need extra help with the Math Skills activity, provide additional examples so that they can practice the calculations; for example, 144 dandelion plants in a lawn 12 m long and 6 m wide. *(2 plants per m²)* You may want to let students use calculators to solve the problems. Also, invite students to make up problems for the class to solve.

One way to estimate the size of a population is to count the number of organisms in a small area (a sample), and then multiply to find the number in a larger area. To get the most accurate estimate, your sample area should be typical of the larger area. Suppose you count 8 birch trees in 100 square meters of a forest. If the entire forest were 100 times that size, you would multiply your count by 100 to estimate the total population, or 800 birch trees.

Mark-and-Recapture Studies Another estimating method is called "mark and recapture." Here's an example showing how mark and recapture works. First, turtles in a bay are caught in a way that does not harm them. Ecologists count the turtles and mark each turtle's shell with a dot of paint before releasing it. Two weeks later, the researchers return and capture turtles again. They count how many turtles have marks, showing that they have been recaptured, and how many are unmarked. Using a mathematical formula, the ecologists can estimate the total population of turtles in the bay. You can try this technique for yourself in the Skills Lab at the end of this section.

Reading Checkpoint When might an ecologist use indirect observation to estimate a population?

Sampling
To estimate the birch tree population in a forest, count the birches in a small area. Then multiply to find the number in the larger area.

Mark and Recapture
This researcher is releasing a marked turtle as part of a mark-and-recapture study.

E ◆ 15

Lab zone Skills Activity

Calculating
An oyster bed is 100 meters long and 50 meters wide. In a 1-square-meter area you count 20 oysters. Estimate the population of oysters in the bed. (*Hint:* Drawing a diagram may help you set up your calculation.)

Lab zone Build Inquiry L2

Estimating a Population

Materials 500 wooden toothpicks

Time 15 minutes

Focus Tell students that in this activity they will estimate the population of toothpicks.

Teach Scatter 500 toothpicks over a rectangular area large enough to provide a 1-square-meter section for each student, or use a floor with 1-ft-square tiles, allowing one tile per student. Tell students the total area but not the number of toothpicks you used. Have each student estimate the number of toothpicks in his or her "sample" and then calculate the total "population" of toothpicks. Write the estimates on the board.

Apply Ask: **Why did the estimates vary?** (*Sampling methods may have varied slightly. Different samples contained different numbers of toothpicks.*) **Which techniques does this activity model?** (*Sampling*) **Do you think this is the best way to determine the population of toothpicks? Why?** (*Accept all answers that show logical thinking. Most students will agree that sampling is the best method for counting the toothpicks because the total number is large, and it would take a lot of time to count individuals.*) **learning modality: kinesthetic**

Lab zone Skills Activity

Skills Focus Calculating

Materials none

Time 5 minutes

Tips If necessary, review the formula for finding area: length × width = area.

Expected Outcome The total population is 100,000 oysters (100 m × 50 m = 5,000 m^2 × 20 oysters per m^2).

Extend Ask: **Why is your answer only an estimate of the total population?** (*Every square meter may not have exactly 20 oysters.*) **learning modality: logical/mathematical**

Monitor Progress L2

Oral Presentation Write descriptions of various populations on index cards. Have each student choose a card and tell what method they would use to determine the population size.

Answer

Reading Checkpoint Scientists might use indirect observation when a population is small or difficult to find.

Changes in Population Size

Teach Key Concepts
Emigration and Immigration

Focus Ask: **What might happen to the size of a particular population over time?** (*It might increase or decrease.*)

Teach Discuss with students the meanings of *immigration* and *emigration*. Ask: **What might cause individuals to immigrate?** (*Possible answers might include an abundant food supply.*) **Why might individuals emigrate?** (*Students might suggest drought, food scarcity, or habitat destruction.*)

Apply Ask: **Why might scientists want to monitor the size of a population?** (*Possible answers: To make sure the population isn't getting too large, which could lead to habitat destruction; to see if a population is at risk of becoming endangered*)

Extend The Active Art shows students how populations change over time. **learning modality: verbal**

 **Teaching Resources**
- Transparency E4

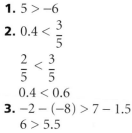

Math Skill Inequalities

Focus Ask students what the term *inequality* means. (*Not equal in amount, size, value, and so on*)

Teach Direct students' attention to the symbols for "greater than" and "less than." Point out that the smaller value appears on the side of the symbol that forms the point. The larger value is placed on the side with the open end.

Answers
1. $5 > -6$

2. $0.4 < \dfrac{3}{5}$

 $\dfrac{2}{5} < \dfrac{3}{5}$

 $0.4 < 0.6$

3. $-2 - (-8) > 7 - 1.5$

 $6 > 5.5$

Inequalities

The population statement is an example of an inequality. An inequality is a mathematical statement that compares two expressions. Two signs that represent inequalities are

  < (is less than)

  > (is greater than)

For example, an inequality comparing the fraction to the decimal 0.75 would be written

$$\frac{1}{2} < 0.75$$

Practice Problems Write an inequality comparing each pair of expressions below.

1. 5 ▧ −6
2. 0.4 ▧ $\dfrac{3}{5}$
3. −2 − (−8) ▧ 7 − 1.5

Changes in Population Size

By returning to a location often and using one of the methods described on the previous page, ecologists can monitor the size of a population over time. **Populations can change in size when new members join the population or when members leave the population.**

Births and Deaths The main way in which new individuals join a population is by being born into it. The **birth rate** of a population is the number of births in a population in a certain amount of time. For example, suppose that a population of 100 cottontail rabbits produces 600 young in a year. The birth rate in this population would be 600 young per year.

The main way that individuals leave a population is by dying. The **death rate** is the number of deaths in a population in a certain amount of time. If 400 rabbits die in a year in the population, the death rate would be 400 rabbits per year.

The Population Statement When the birth rate in a population is greater than the death rate, the population will generally increase. This can be written as a mathematical statement using the "is greater than" sign:

  If birth rate > death rate, population size increases.

However, if the death rate in a population is greater than the birth rate, the population size will generally decrease. This can also be written as a mathematical statement:

  If death rate > birth rate, population size decreases.

Immigration and Emigration The size of a population also can change when individuals move into or out of the population, just as the population of your town changes when families move into town or move away. **Immigration** (im ih GRAY shun) means moving into a population. **Emigration** (em ih GRAY shun) means leaving a population. For instance, if food is scarce, some members of an antelope herd may wander off in search of better grassland. If they become permanently separated from the original herd, they will no longer be part of that population.

Graphing Changes in Population Changes in a population's size can be displayed on a line graph. Figure 7 shows a graph of the changes in a rabbit population. The vertical axis shows the numbers of rabbits in the population, while the horizontal axis shows time. The graph shows the size of the population over a ten-year period.

Differentiated Instruction

English Learners/Beginning
Vocabulary: Word Analysis Write the words *immigration* and *emigration* on the board and circle *migration* in each. Explain that *migration* means "traveling from one place to another." Tell students that the prefix *im-* is similar in meaning to the word *in*, so *immigration* means "in-migration." Then explain that when they see the prefix *e-*, students can think of *exit*, so *emigration* means "out-migration." Demonstrate these meanings by leaving the room and walking back into it, stating the words as you do each act. **learning modality: verbal**

English Learners/Intermediate
Vocabulary: Word Analysis Use the procedure for Beginning students, but have students use the words *immigration* and *emigration* to write sentences describing your actions. **learning modality: verbal**

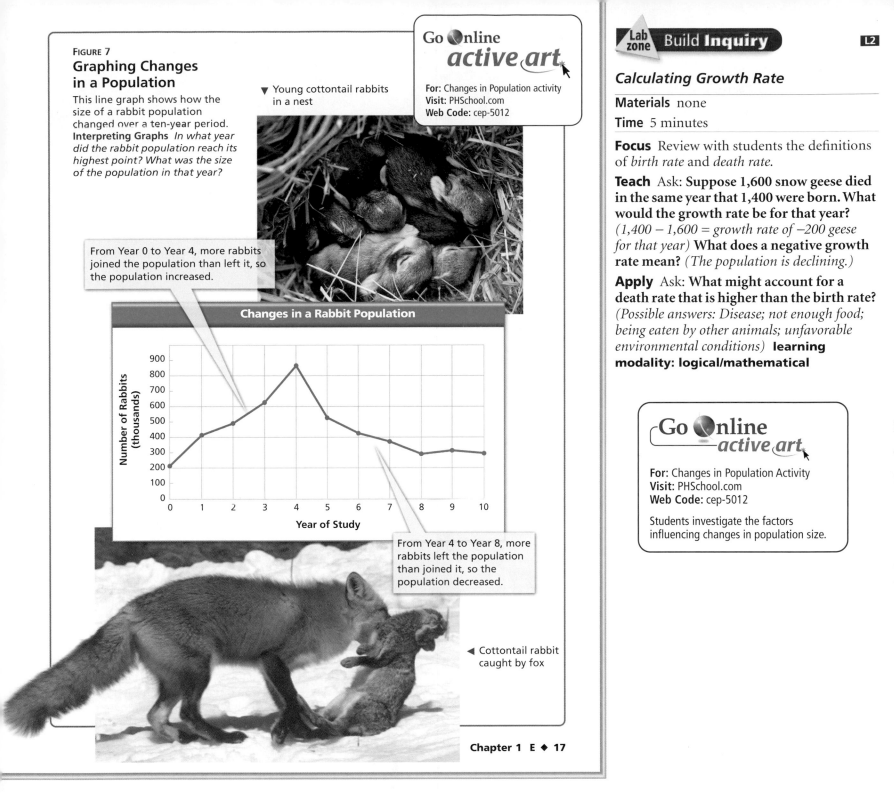

FIGURE 7
Graphing Changes in a Population

This line graph shows how the size of a rabbit population changed over a ten-year period. **Interpreting Graphs** *In what year did the rabbit population reach its highest point? What was the size of the population in that year?*

▼ Young cottontail rabbits in a nest

Go Online
active art

For: Changes in Population activity
Visit: PHSchool.com
Web Code: cep-5012

From Year 0 to Year 4, more rabbits joined the population than left it, so the population increased.

Changes in a Rabbit Population

Number of Rabbits (thousands)

Year of Study

From Year 4 to Year 8, more rabbits left the population than joined it, so the population decreased.

◄ Cottontail rabbit caught by fox

Lab zone   Build Inquiry   L2

Calculating Growth Rate

Materials none

Time 5 minutes

Focus Review with students the definitions of *birth rate* and *death rate*.

Teach Ask: **Suppose 1,600 snow geese died in the same year that 1,400 were born. What would the growth rate be for that year?** *(1,400 − 1,600 = growth rate of −200 geese for that year)* **What does a negative growth rate mean?** *(The population is declining.)*

Apply Ask: **What might account for a death rate that is higher than the birth rate?** *(Possible answers: Disease; not enough food; being eaten by other animals; unfavorable environmental conditions)* **learning modality: logical/mathematical**

Go Online
active art

For: Changes in Population Activity
Visit: PHSchool.com
Web Code: cep-5012

Students investigate the factors influencing changes in population size.

Differentiated Instruction

Gifted and Talented   L3
Calculating Growth Rate Tell students that ecologists use the birth and death rates to calculate a population's growth rate, the rate at which the population is changing. The birth rate *(b)* minus the death rate *(d)* equals the growth rate *(g): b − d = g.* Have students use this formula to calculate the growth rate of rabbits discussed in the text. *(600 births − 400 deaths = a growth rate of 200 rabbits per year)* **learning modality: logical/mathematical**

Monitor Progress _____   L2

Writing Have each student write a paragraph explaining how birth rate and death rate affect the size of a population. Students can save their paragraphs in their portfolios.

Answer
Figure 7 Fourth year of the study; about 850

Limiting Factors

Teach Key Concepts L2

Inferring Limiting Factors of Plants

Focus Review with students the biotic and abiotic factors that might be found in an organism's habitat. Help students identify the factors that are essential for all living things, such as food, water, space, and temperature.

Teach Ask: **If all the needs of a population are met, what will most likely happen to the size of the population?** *(It will increase.)* **Can the size of the population continue to increase indefinitely? Why?** *(No, because at some time one or more of the factors will become insufficient for the size of the population)* Tell students that any factor that causes a population to decrease is a limiting factor.

Apply Ask: **Is food a limiting factor for plants?** *(No)* **Why not?** *(Plants make their own food.)* **What factors do limit the size of plant populations?** *(The amounts of sunlight, carbon dioxide in the air, water, and nutrients in the soil)* **How do these factors limit plant populations?** *(Plants need light, carbon dioxide, and water to conduct photosynthesis, and they need nutrients for their own life processes.)* **learning modality: logical/mathematical**

All in One Teaching Resources
• Transparency E5

← 4 meters → ← 4 meters →

2 meters

FIGURE 8
Population Density
In the pond on the left, there are ten flamingos in 8 square meters. The population density is 1.25 flamingos per square meter.
Calculating *What is the population density of the flamingos in the pond on the right?*

◄ Greater flamingo

Population Density Sometimes an ecologist may need to know more than just the total size of a population. In many situations, it is helpful to know the **population density**—the number of individuals in a specific area. Population density can be written as an equation:

$$\text{Population density} = \frac{\text{Number of individuals}}{\text{Unit area}}$$

For example, suppose you counted 20 monarch butterflies in a garden measuring 10 square meters. The population density would be 20 monarchs per 10 square meters, or 2 monarchs per square meter.

Reading Checkpoint What is meant by the term *population density*?

Limiting Factors

When the living conditions in an area are good, a population will generally grow. But eventually some environmental factor will cause the population to stop growing. A **limiting factor** is an environmental factor that causes a population to decrease. **Some limiting factors for populations are food and water, space, and weather conditions.**

Food and Water Organisms require food and water to survive. Since food and water are often in limited supply, they are often limiting factors. Suppose a giraffe must eat 10 kilograms of leaves each day to survive. The trees in an area can provide 100 kilograms of leaves a day while remaining healthy. Five giraffes could live easily in this area, since they would only require a total of 50 kilograms of food. But 15 giraffes could not all survive—there would not be enough food. No matter how much shelter, water, and other resources there were, the population would not grow much larger than 10 giraffes.

18 ◆ E

The largest population that an area can support is called its **carrying capacity.** The carrying capacity of this environment would be 10 giraffes. A population can only grow so large because of the carrying capacity of its environment.

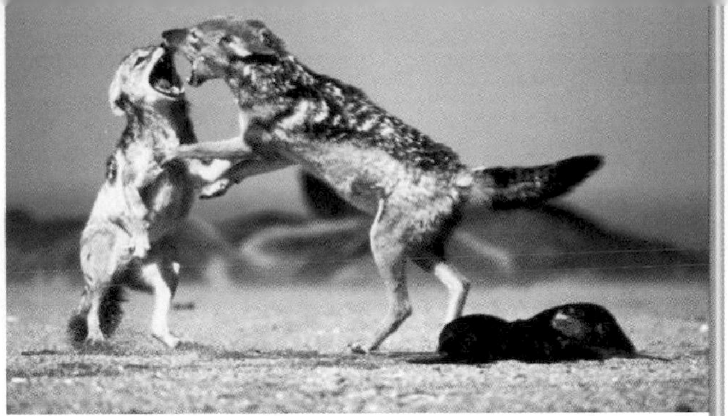

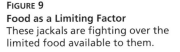

FIGURE 9
Food as a Limiting Factor
These jackals are fighting over the limited food available to them.

Space Space is another limiting factor for populations. Gannets are seabirds that are usually seen flying over the ocean. They come to land only to nest on rocky shores. But the nesting shores get very crowded. If a pair does not find room to nest, they will not be able to lay eggs or add any offspring to the gannet population. So nesting space is a limiting factor for gannets. If there were more nesting space on the shore, more gannets would be able to nest there, and the population would increase.

Space is also a limiting factor for plants. The amount of space in which a plant grows determines whether the plant can obtain the sunlight, water, and soil nutrients it needs. For example, many pine seedlings sprout each year in a forest. But as the seedlings grow, the roots of those that are too close together run out of space. Branches from other trees may block the sunlight the seedlings need. Some of the seedlings then die, limiting the size of the pine population.

FIGURE 10
Space as a Limiting Factor
Could any more sunflower plants grow in this field? If not, the field has reached its carrying capacity for sunflowers.

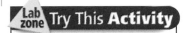

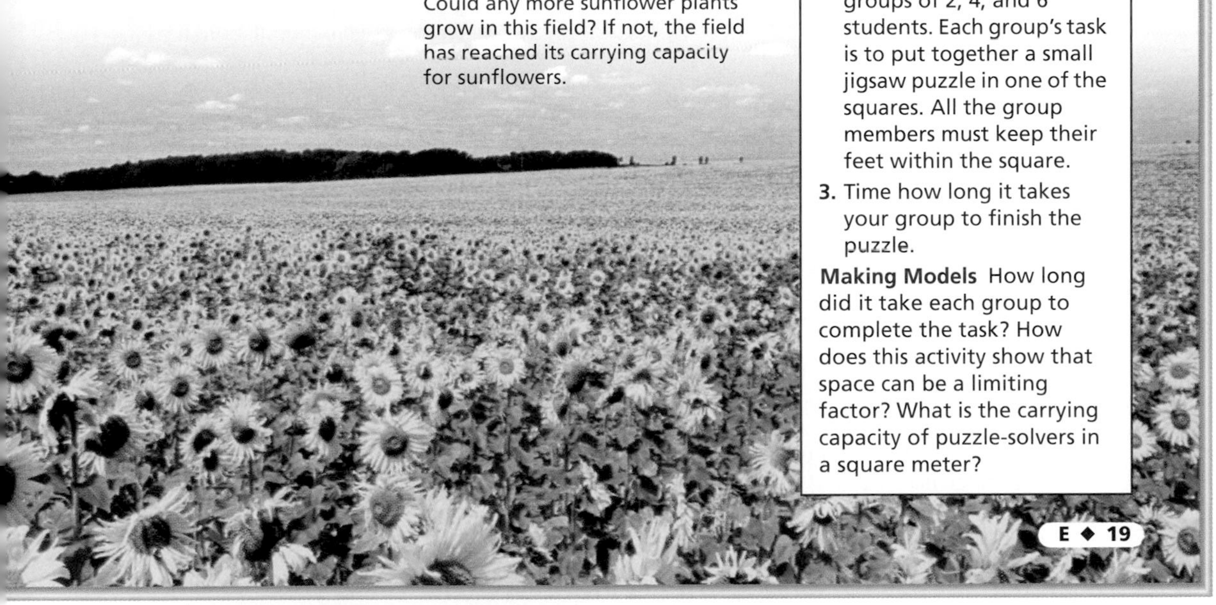

Lab zone Try This Activity

Elbow Room

1. Using masking tape, mark off several one-meter squares on the floor of your classroom.
2. Your teacher will set up groups of 2, 4, and 6 students. Each group's task is to put together a small jigsaw puzzle in one of the squares. All the group members must keep their feet within the square.
3. Time how long it takes your group to finish the puzzle.

Making Models How long did it take each group to complete the task? How does this activity show that space can be a limiting factor? What is the carrying capacity of puzzle-solvers in a square meter?

Lab zone Build Inquiry L2

Exponential Growth

Materials 2 boxes of small paper clips
Time 15 minutes

Focus Tell students that limiting factors help control population growth.

Teach Give small groups of students boxes of paper clips. Tell students that each paper clip represents an amoeba, a one-celled organism that reproduces by splitting in half. Have students show uncontrolled population growth by laying out the paper clips to show growth through six generations. *(The results: Generation 1—1 amoeba; Generation 2—2 amoebas; Generation 3—4 amoebas; Generation 4—8 amoebas; Generation 5—16 amoebas; Generation 6—32 amoebas)* Then tell students that the food supply for the amoebas has become scarce, and some members of each generation will die. Tell students to remove one "amoeba" and its resulting offspring from Generations 4, 5, and 6. Have students compare the numbers of organisms in the last generation of both models.

Apply Discuss how limiting factors help to keep populations from growing out of control. Tell students that under laboratory conditions, a common bacterium, *E. coli*, can reproduce once every 20 minutes. Explain that unchecked, one *E. coli* could multiply to a mass twice that of Earth in 48 hours.
learning modality: kinesthetic

Lab zone Try This Activity

Skills Focus Making models
Materials masking tape, meter stick, small jigsaw puzzle, watch or clock
Time 15 minutes
Tips Use very simple puzzles so that puzzle difficulty is not a factor.

Expected Outcome Smaller groups will probably finish their puzzles before groups of six. Crowding in groups of six made the task more difficult.
Extend Invite students to suggest other simple models of space as a limiting factor.
learning modality: kinesthetic

Monitor Progress L2

Writing Have students write a few sentences telling in their own words what a limiting factor is.

Answers
Figure 8 2.5 flamingos/m^2

Reading Checkpoint Population density is the number of individuals in a specific area.

Answers

Figure 11 Temperature, amount of rainfall (too much or too little), storms, floods

✓ **Reading Checkpoint** Possible answers: A cold snap in late spring, a hurricane, a flood

Assess

Reviewing Key Concepts

1. a. direct observation, indirect observation, sampling, mark and recapture **b.** Sampling; there would be too many mushrooms over too large an area to count them individually.
2. a. Join—birth, immigration; leave—death, emigration **b.** 500 mice **c.** Some mice may have immigrated into the population.
3. a. Food and water, space, weather **b.** Any of the following: A population cannot grow beyond the number that can be supported by the amount of food and water available; if organisms do not have enough space, some will not be able to reproduce or survive; severe weather conditions can kill members of a population. **c.** Sample answer: A severely cold winter could kill large numbers of pigeons and reduce the population.
4. a. If population size > carrying capacity, then population size will decrease. The carrying capacity is the largest population an area can support. If there are more individuals than an area can support, then they won't survive and the population will decrease.

Reteach   L1

As a class make a two-column chart. In the first column, list the limiting factors for populations. In the second column, tell how the factor can limit populations.

Performance Assessment   L2

Oral Presentation Call on students to identify a factor that affects the size of a population. *(Birth/death rates, immigration, emigration, limiting factors)*

All in One Teaching Resources

- Section Summary: *Studying Populations*
- Review and Reinforcement: *Studying Populations*
- Enrich: *Studying Populations*

FIGURE 11
Weather as a Limiting Factor
A snowstorm can limit the size of an orange crop.
Applying Concepts *What other weather conditions can limit population growth?*

Weather Weather conditions such as temperature and the amount of rainfall can also limit population growth. A cold snap in late spring can kill the young of many species of organisms, including birds and mammals. A hurricane or flood can wash away nests and burrows. Such unusual events can have long-lasting effects on population size.

✓ **Reading Checkpoint** What is one weather condition that can limit the growth of a population?

Section 2 Assessment

🔵 **Target Reading Skill** **Asking Questions** Use the answers to the questions you wrote about the headings to help you answer the questions below.

Reviewing Key Concepts

1. a. Listing What are four methods of determining population size?
   b. Applying Concepts Which method would you use to determine the number of mushrooms growing on the floor of a large forest? Explain.
2. a. Identifying Name two ways organisms join a population and two ways organisms leave a population.
   b. Calculating Suppose a population of 100 mice has produced 600 young. If 200 mice have died, how many mice are in the population now? (Assume for this question that no mice have moved into or out of the population for other reasons.)
   c. Drawing Conclusions Suppose that you discovered that there were actually 750 mice in the population. How could you account for the difference?

3. a. Reviewing Name three limiting factors for populations.
   b. Describing Choose one of the limiting factors and describe how it limits population growth.
   c. Inferring How might the limiting factor you chose affect the pigeon population in your town?

Math Practice

4. Inequalities Complete the following inequality showing the relationship between carrying capacity and population size. Then explain why the inequality is true.

> **If population size ■ carrying capacity, then population size will decrease.**

Math Practice

Math Skill Inequalities

Answer

If population size > carrying capacity, then population size will decrease. The carrying capacity is the largest population an area can support. If there are more individuals than an area can support, then they won't survive and the population will decrease.

Counting Turtles

Problem
How can the mark-and-recapture method help ecologists monitor the size of a population?

Skills Focus
calculating, graphing, predicting

Materials
• model paper turtle population • calculator
• graph paper

Procedure
1. The data table shows the results from the first three years of a population study to determine the number of turtles in a pond. Copy it into your notebook.

Data Table

Year	Number Marked	Total Number Captured	Number Recaptured (With Marks)	Estimated Total Population
1	32	28	15	
2	25	21	11	
3	23	19	11	
4	15			

2. Your teacher will give you a box representing the pond. Fifteen of the turtles have been marked, as shown in the data table for Year 4.

3. Capture a member of the population by randomly selecting one turtle. Set it aside.

4. Repeat Step 3 nine times. Record the total number of turtles you captured.

5. Examine each turtle to see whether it has a mark. Count the number of recaptured (marked) turtles. Record this number in your data table.

Analyze and Conclude
1. **Calculating** Use the equation below to estimate the turtle population for each year. The first year is done for you as a sample. If your answer is a decimal, round it to the nearest whole number. Record the population for each year in the last column of the data table.

$$\text{Total population} = \frac{\text{Number marked} \times \text{Total number captured}}{\text{Number recaptured (with marks)}}$$

Sample (Year 1):

$$\frac{32 \times 28}{15} = 59.7 \text{ or } 60 \text{ turtles}$$

2. **Graphing** Graph the estimated total populations for the four years. Mark years on the horizontal axis. Mark population size on the vertical axis.

3. **Interpreting Data** Describe how the turtle population has changed over the four years of the study. Suggest three possible causes for the changes.

4. **Predicting** Use your graph to predict what the turtle population will be in Year 5. Explain your prediction.

5. **Communicating** Write a paragraph that explains why the mark-and-recapture method is a useful tool for ecologists. When is this technique most useful for estimating a population's size?

More to Explore
Suppose that only six turtles had been recaptured in Year 2. How would this change your graph?

Analyze and Conclude
1. The estimated totals for Years 1–3 are 60, 48, and 40. Total number captured for Year 4 is 10. If 0 are recaptured, the total population cannot be determined. If 1 is recaptured, the estimated total is 150; if 2, 75; if 3, 50; if 4, 38; if 5, 30; if 6, 25; if 7, 21; if 8, 19; if 9, 17; if 10, 15.

2. Year 4 will vary.

3. The turtle population declined steadily from Year 1 to Year 3. Possible causes include limited food, overcrowding, weather conditions, disease, predation, and use of chemicals in the pond.

4. Most students will probably predict a continuing decline in the population.

5. Sample answer: Mark and recapture is useful because it allows scientists to study a population over time. It is most useful when a population is fairly large, concentrated in one area, and can't be observed directly or indirectly.

Counting Turtles

Prepare for Inquiry

Skills Objectives
After this lab, students will be able to
• calculate the size of a population
• graph population estimates
• predict the size of a future population

Prep Time 20 minutes
Class Time 40 minutes

Advance Planning
Prepare a model population for each group. Use 30 paper squares to represent turtles. Mark a dot on one side of 15 cards. Spread all 30 cards in a box, marked sides down.

All in One Teaching Resources
• Lab Worksheet: *Counting Turtles*

Guide Inquiry

Invitation
Review with students the mark-and-recapture method for determining population size.

Introducing the Procedure
Tell students that each square represents a turtle and that some of the "turtles" have been marked with a dot on one side.

Troubleshooting the Experiment
• In Step 2, clarify that the 15 marked turtles refer to the bottom box in the second column of the table, "Numbered Marked."
• Students may assume that more turtles recaptured with marks means a bigger population, and fewer turtles with marks means a smaller population. Point out that the opposite is true because unmarked turtles could be new turtles added (birth, immigration) since the last count.

Expected Outcome
The number of marked turtles recaptured will vary. Therefore, students' estimates of the total population of Year 4 will also vary.

More to Explore
The estimated total population would increase to 88.

Science and Society

Animal Overpopulation: How Can People Help?

Key Concept
Food has become a limiting factor for the rapidly growing populations of white-tailed deer in many parts of the United States. People must decide how to reduce the deer populations.

Build Background Knowledge

Recalling Limiting Factors
Help students recall that several factors can limit populations. Ask: **What are some limiting factors for populations?** *(Food, water, space, weather)* **What would be the effect on a population if the food supply is insufficient to support all the individuals?** *(Some individuals will die of starvation.)*

Introduce the Debate
Direct attention to the large picture of the white-tailed deer. Explain that in many areas of the country these animals have no natural predators and, as a result, their populations have increased rapidly. Point out that, in addition, many of their habitats have been destroyed due to land development. Explain that these conditions have made the food supply for many of these populations inadequate. Ask: **What are some ways that the deer population might be controlled?** *(Accept any reasonable responses at this point.)*

Facilitate the Debate
Have students read the feature and answer the You Decide questions individually as a homework assignment. The next day, organize the class into small groups for discussion. Have students consider these questions: **What are the advantages and disadvantages of each proposed action? Which action do you think is in the best interests of the deer? Of other populations in the area? Which solution would you support if your area had a deer overpopulation problem? Why would you choose that solution?** Organize the class into three groups. Arbitrarily assign each group to argue each proposed action. Alternately call on students from each group to state the group's position or refute an idea from someone in the other group.

White-Tailed Deer
To obtain food, deer are moving into people's yards.

Animal Overpopulation: How Can People Help?

Populations of white-tailed deer are growing rapidly in many parts of the United States. As populations soar, food becomes a limiting factor. Many deer die of starvation. Others grow up small and unhealthy. In search of food, hungry deer move closer to where humans live. There they eat farm crops, garden vegetables, shrubs, and even trees. In addition, increased numbers of deer near roads can cause automobile accidents.

People admire the grace and swiftness of deer. Most people don't want these animals to suffer from starvation or illness. Should people take action to limit growing deer populations?

Wildlife Technician
This wildlife researcher in Virginia studies white-tailed deer populations. Here he prepares to tag a young deer.

The Issues

Should People Take Direct Action?
Many people argue that hunting is the best way to reduce animal populations. Wildlife managers look at the supply of resources in an area and determine its carrying capacity. Then hunters are issued licenses to help reduce the number of deer.

Other people favor nonhunting approaches to control deer populations. One plan is to trap the deer and relocate them. But this method is expensive and requires finding another location that can accept the deer without upsetting the balance of its own ecosystem.

Scientists are also working to develop chemicals to reduce the birth rate in deer populations. But this plan is effective for only one year at a time.

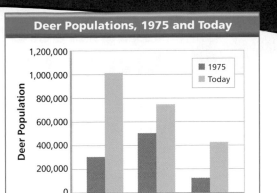

Deer Populations, 1975 and Today

White-Tailed Deer Populations
This graph shows how the deer populations have grown in North Carolina, Florida, and Oklahoma.

Should People Take Indirect Action?

Some suggest bringing in natural predators of deer, such as wolves, mountain lions, and bears, to areas with too many deer. But these animals could also attack cattle, dogs, cats, and even humans. Other communities have built tall fences around areas to keep out the deer. However, this solution is impractical for farmers or ranchers.

Should People Do Nothing?

Some people oppose any kind of action. They support leaving the deer alone and allowing nature to take its course. Animal populations in an area naturally cycle up and down over time. Doing nothing means that some deer will die of starvation or disease. But eventually, the population will be reduced to a size within the carrying capacity of the environment.

You Decide

1. Identify the Problem
In your own words, explain the problem created by the overpopulation of white-tailed deer.

2. Analyze the Options
List the ways that people can deal with the overpopulation of white-tailed deer. State the positive and negative points of each method.

3. Find a Solution
Suppose you are an ecologist in an area that has twice as many deer as it can support. Propose a way for the community to deal with the problem.

Go Online
PHSchool.com

For: More on white-tailed deer overpopulation
Visit: PHSchool.com
Web Code: ceh-5010

You Decide

1. Possible response: Overpopulation results in starvation for many animals; others may grow up unhealthy. In search of limited food, the deer may destroy crops and landscape plants in areas where human live and grow crops, which can affect other organisms dependent on those plants. Increased numbers of deer also can cause more automobile accidents.

2. Direct actions—*hunting*: inexpensive but many people object to this method and it is impractical in suburban areas where deer are most troublesome; *trapping and relocating*: animals are not killed but the method is expensive and requires finding another location to accept the deer, which can upset the existing balance in the new location; *using chemicals to reduce birth rates*: the chemicals are only effective for one year at a time. Indirect action—*bringing in natural enemies*: predators could attack other animals in the area; *building fences*: impractical for large areas. Do nothing—some deer will die but eventually the population will reduce to within the carrying capacity.

3. Encourage students to provide reasons for their plans.

For: More on white-tailed deer overpopulation
Visit: PHSchool.com
Web Code: ceh-5010

Extend

If your community has a problem with animal overpopulation—with deer, gypsy moths, or skunks, for example—suggest that students discuss the issue with family members and, if possible, consult with community and state agencies to find out how people are dealing with the problem.

Background

Facts and Figures Deer overpopulation can also be hazardous to human health, as shown by the increasing occurrence of Lyme disease in the United States. White-tailed deer may carry tiny ticks that are smaller than the head of a pin. The ticks in turn carry a bacterium, *Borrelia burgdorferi,* which causes Lyme disease. The ticks attach themselves to people walking through infested areas.

The ticks' bite transfers the bacteria to humans.

A reddish rash shaped like a bull's eye usually appears within days of the tick's bite. Other early symptoms of Lyme disease may include fatigue, fever, chills, and headache. Left untreated, the disease can inflame the heart muscle and nerves or cause painful arthritis in the joints. Antibiotics, if taken soon after symptoms

appear, are an effective treatment for Lyme disease. In 1998, the U.S. FDA approved a vaccine for Lyme disease.

Objectives
After this lesson, students will be able to

E.1.3.1 Explain how an organism's adaptations help it survive.

E.1.3.2 Describe the major kinds of interaction among organisms in an ecosystem.

E.1.3.3 Identify the three types of symbiotic relationships.

Target Reading Skill

Using Prior Knowledge Explain that using prior knowledge helps students connect what they already know to what they are about to read.

Answers
Possible answers:

What You Know

1. Organisms interact in different ways.

What You Learned

1. Organisms are adapted to their environments.

2. Organisms have niches, which are their roles.

3. Organisms compete for resources. Some organisms eat others, and this affects the size of populations.

4. Some organisms live together in symbiotic relationships, of which there is mutualism (both benefit), commensalism (one benefits, the other is not helped or harmed), and parasitism (one benefits, the other is harmed).

All in One Teaching Resources
• Transparency E6

Preteach

Build Background Knowledge L1

Identifying Adaptations
Ask: **What features enable fish to survive in an underwater environment?** *(Students most likely will mention fins and tails for moving through the water and gills for breathing oxygen dissolved in the water.)* Encourage students to think of other examples of how organisms are adapted to their environments.

Section

Interactions Among Living Things

Reading Preview

Key Concepts
• How do an organism's adaptations help it to survive?
• What are the major ways in which organisms in an ecosystem interact?
• What are the three types of symbiotic relationships?

Key Terms
• natural selection
• adaptations • niche
• competition • predation
• predator • prey • symbiosis
• mutualism • commensalism
• parasitism • parasite • host

Target Reading Skill
Using Prior Knowledge Your prior knowledge is what you already know before you read about a topic. Before you read, look at the section headings and visuals to see what this section is about. Then write what you know about how living things interact in a graphic organizer like the one below. As you read, continue to write in what you learn.

What You Know
1. Organisms interact in different ways.
2.

What You Learned
1.
2.

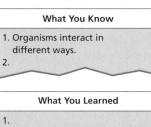

Lab zone Discover Activity

Can You Hide a Butterfly?

1. Trace a butterfly on a piece of paper, using the outline shown here.
2. Look around the classroom and pick a spot where you will place your butterfly. You must place your butterfly out in the open. Color your butterfly so it will blend in with the spot you choose.
3. Tape your butterfly to its spot. Someone will now have one minute to find all the butterflies he or she can. Will your butterfly be found?

Think It Over
Predicting Over time, how do you think the population size would change for butterflies that blend in with their surroundings?

Can you imagine living in a cactus like the one in Figure 12? Ouch! You probably wouldn't want to live in a house covered with sharp spines. But many species live in, on, and around saguaro cactuses.

As day breaks, a twittering sound comes from a nest tucked in one of the saguaro's arms. Two young red-tailed hawks are preparing to fly for the first time. Farther down the stem, a tiny elf owl peeks out of its nest in a small hole. This owl is so small it could fit in your palm! A rattlesnake slithers around the base of the saguaro, looking for lunch. Spying a shrew, the snake strikes it with its needle-like fangs. The shrew dies instantly.

Activity around the saguaro continues after sunset. Long-nosed bats come out to feed on the nectar from the saguaro's blossoms. The bats stick their faces into the flowers to feed, dusting their long snouts with white pollen. As they move from plant to plant, they carry the pollen to other saguaros. This enables the cactuses to reproduce.

Lab zone Discover Activity

Skills Focus Predicting

Materials Sheet of white paper, colored pencils or markers, tape

Time 15 minutes

Tips Tell students that the butterflies do not have to be colored realistically. Arrange to have another staff member or a student from another class look for the butterflies.

Expected Outcome Butterflies whose colors and patterns closely match their background will be most difficult to see.

Think It Over Butterflies that blend well with their surroundings will escape predators and survive to reproduce, thus increasing the population.

Adapting to the Environment

Each organism in the saguaro community has unique characteristics. These characteristics affect the individual's ability to survive in its environment.

Natural Selection A characteristic that makes an individual better suited to its environment may eventually become common in that species through a process called **natural selection.** Natural selection works like this: Individuals whose unique characteristics are best suited for their environment tend to survive and produce offspring. Offspring that inherit these characteristics also live to reproduce. In this way, natural selection results in **adaptations,** the behaviors and physical characteristics that allow organisms to live successfully in their environments.

Individuals with characteristics that are poorly suited to the environment are less likely to survive and reproduce. Over time, poorly suited characteristics may disappear from the species.

Niche **Every organism has a variety of adaptations that are suited to its specific living conditions.** The organisms in the saguaro community have adaptations that result in specific roles. The role of a organism, or how it makes its living, is called its **niche.** A niche includes the type of food the organism eats, how it obtains this food, and which other organisms use the organism as food. A niche also includes when and how the organism reproduces and the physical conditions it requires to survive.

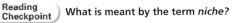 **Reading Checkpoint** What is meant by the term *niche*?

FIGURE 12
Saguaro Community
The organisms in the saguaro community are well adapted to their desert environment.
Observing *Identify two interactions taking place in this scene.*

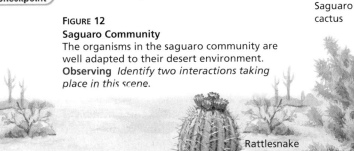

Red-tailed hawk

Flycatcher

Purple martin

Hawk nest

Woodpecker

Elf owl

Wasps

Saguaro cactus

Gila monster

Rattlesnake

Roadrunner

Scorpion

 E ◆ 25

Differentiated Instruction

English Learners/Beginning L1
Comprehension: Link to Visual Use Figure 12 to help students understand the meaning of *adaptations*. Point to an organism and ask: How does this [name organism] live? What body parts or behaviors does it have that enable it to do these tasks? How does each help the organism survive? **learning modality: visual**

English Learners/Intermediate L2
Comprehension: Link to Visual Have each student make a two-column chart. Tell them to choose an organism from Figure 12. In the first column of the chart they should list the organism's adaptations. In the second column they should tell how each adaptation helps the organism survive. **learning modality: logical/mathematical**

Instruct

Adapting to the Environment

Teach Key Concepts L2
Describing Niches

Focus Have students note the organisms living in the community shown in Figure 12. Ask: **Give examples of how the roles of these organisms differ in the community.** (*Possible answer: The hawk preys on other animals. The cactus makes food that stores energy, which other organisms can use.*)

Teach Ask: **What are adaptations?** (*The characteristics that enable each organism to survive in its niche*)

Apply Ask: **What is the niche of the rattlesnake?** (*Possible answer: It lives on the ground where it preys on small animals, uses oxygen, releases carbon dioxide, and is prey for the hawk.*) **learning modality: verbal**

Address Misconceptions L2
Changes Within Species

Focus Emphasize that the changes within a species are not deliberate or conscious.

Teach Explain that organisms do not decide to develop characteristics that enable them to survive more successfully. Also point out that individuals do not develop new characteristics within their own lifetimes, but species change over time.

Apply Ask: **If a squirrel gives birth to two offspring, one that can run much faster than the other, which offspring is more likely to pass its traits on to its offspring? Why?** (*The faster squirrel is more likely to escape predators and survive to produce offspring with the same trait.*) **learning modality: logical/mathematical**

Independent Practice

All in One Teaching Resources
• Guided Review and Study Worksheet: *Interactions Among Living Things*

Student Edition Audio CD

Monitor Progress L2

Answers
Figure 12 Possible answer: Owl nesting in cactus; woodpecker eating insects

Reading Checkpoint An organism's role

Competition

Teach Key Concepts
Limited Resources

Focus Remind students that in any community, organisms interact.

Teach Tell students that in a community, there is a limited amount of some resources. Ask: **What happens when more than one species requires the same limited resource?** *(Competition)* Refer students to Figure 13, and point out that each bird species feeds in a different part of the tree. Ask: **What advantage is this for the three birds?** *(The three species do not compete with each other for the same food and space.)*

Apply Ask: **For what resources do the tree and the grass in Figure 13 compete?** *(Sunlight, water, minerals, space)* **learning modality: visual**

Teaching Resources L2
• Transparency E7

Build Inquiry

Observing Cricket Competition

Materials several male crickets (from a pet store), terrarium, soil, materials to provide hiding places (rocks, leaves, pieces of bark, small branches), paint of different colors

Time 15 minutes for setup

Focus Ask students what they know about crickets.

Teach Tell students that male crickets compete for territories. Have volunteers set up a cricket habitat in a terrarium. Tell them to cover the bottom of the terrarium with soil and then add several items under which the crickets can hide. Before students place the crickets in the terrarium, have them mark each cricket's back with a different color dot of paint for identification. Caution students to handle the crickets carefully and wash their hands afterward. When the crickets are first introduced into the terrarium, they will fight. In time, each will establish its own territory, remain in it most of the time, and defend it against other males. After the activity, you can release the crickets.

Apply Ask: **What is the advantage of having a territory?** *(It reduces competition.)* **learning modality: visual**

Cape May Warbler
This species feeds at the tips of branches near the top of the tree.

Bay-Breasted Warbler
This species feeds in the middle part of the tree.

Yellow-Rumped Warbler
This species feeds in the lower part of the tree and at the bases of the middle branches.

FIGURE 13
Niche and Competition
Each of these warblers occupies a different niche in its spruce tree habitat. By feeding in different areas of the tree, the birds avoid competing for food.
Comparing and Contrasting *How do the niches of these three warblers differ?*

Go Online
PHSchool.com
For: More on population interactions
Visit: PHSchool.com
Web Code: ced-5013

Competition

During a typical day in the saguaro community, a range of interactions takes place among organisms. **There are three major types of interactions among organisms: competition, predation, and symbiosis.**

Different species can share the same habitat and food requirements. For example, the roadrunner and the elf owl both live on the saguaro and eat insects. However, these two species do not occupy exactly the same niche. The roadrunner is active during the day, while the owl is active mostly at night. If two species occupy the same niche, one of the species will eventually die off. The reason for this is **competition,** the struggle between organisms to survive as they attempt to use the same limited resource.

In any ecosystem, there is a limited amount of food, water, and shelter. Organisms that survive have adaptations that enable them to reduce competition. For example, the three species of warblers in Figure 13 live in the same spruce forest habitat. They all eat insects that live in the spruce trees. How do these birds avoid competing for the limited insect supply? Each warbler "specializes" in feeding in a certain part of a spruce tree. This is how the three species coexist.

Reading Checkpoint Why can't two species occupy the same niche?

Go Online
PHSchool.com
For: More on population interactions
Visit: PHSchool.com
Web Code: ced-5013

Students can review population interactions in an online interactivity.

Predation

A tiger shark lurks below the surface of the clear blue water, looking for shadows of albatross chicks floating above. The shark spots a chick and silently swims closer. Suddenly, the shark bursts through the water and seizes the albatross with one snap of its powerful jaw. This interaction between two organisms has an unfortunate ending for the albatross.

An interaction in which one organism kills another for food is called **predation**. The organism that does the killing, in this case the tiger shark, is the **predator**. The organism that is killed, in this case the albatross, is the **prey**.

The Effect of Predation on Population Size Predation can have a major effect on the size of a population. Recall from Section 2 that when the death rate exceeds the birth rate in a population, the size of that population usually decreases. So if predators are very effective at hunting their prey, the result is often a decrease in the size of the prey population. But a decrease in the number of prey results in less food for their predators. Without adequate food, the predator population starts to decline. So, generally, populations of predators and their prey rise and fall in related cycles.

FIGURE 14
Predation
This green tree python and mouse are involved in a predator-prey interaction.

Math — Analyzing Data

Predator-Prey Interactions

On Isle Royale, an island in Lake Superior, the populations of wolves (the predator) and moose (the prey) rise and fall in cycles. Use the graph to answer the questions.

1. **Reading Graphs** What variable is plotted on the *x*-axis? What two variables are plotted on the *y*-axis?

2. **Interpreting Data** How did the moose population change between 1965 and 1975? What happened to the wolf population from 1973 through 1976?

3. **Inferring** How might the change in the moose population have led to the change in the wolf population?

4. **Drawing Conclusions** What is one likely cause of the dip in the moose population between 1974 and 1981?

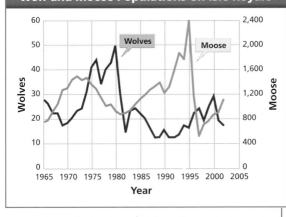

Wolf and Moose Populations on Isle Royale

5. **Predicting** How might a disease in the wolf population one year affect the moose population the next year?

Predation

Teach Key Concepts L2
Predation in a Terrarium

Focus Have students visualize a cricket habitat set up in a terrarium.

Teach Ask: **What would happen if you added a toad to the habitat?** *(It would eat the crickets.)* **What would happen if you then added a snake?** *(It would eat the toad.)* **Which of these animals would be prey?** *(The crickets are prey for the toad, and the toad is prey for the snake.)* **Which would be a predator?** *(The toad is a predator of crickets, and the snake is a predator of toads.)*

Apply Challenge students to identify other feeding relationships in which one organism is both predator and prey. **learning modality: logical/mathematical**

Math — Analyzing Data

Math Skill Making and interpreting graphs

Focus Remind students that without enough prey, a predator population declines.

Teach Direct attention to the graph. Ask: **What does the x-axis show?** *(The years from 1965 to 2000)* **The y-axis?** *(The population of wolves and moose)* **What are the wolf and moose populations in 1970?** *(Wolves, 18; moose, 1,300)*

Answers
1. Year; numbers of wolves and moose
2. The moose population increased and then decreased; the wolf population increased.
3. As the moose population increased, more food was available to the wolf population and it increased.
4. The wolf population increased.
5. Disease would cause a decrease in the wolf population, so fewer moose would be eaten and the population could increase.

Monitor Progress _____ L2

Oral Presentation Present students with various predator-prey pairs. Have them identify the predator and prey in each.

Answers
Figure 13 Each species feeds at a different location on the tree

✔ **Reading Checkpoint** If two species occupy the same niche, they will compete directly against each other and one species will eventually die off.

Observing an Insect-Eating Plant

Materials sundew or Venus's fly-trap, cooked ground beef, tweezers

Time 5 minutes a day for several days

Focus Review with students the definitions of *predator* and *prey*.

Teach Have students take turns feeding the plant small pieces of the ground beef from time to time. (**CAUTION:** *Remind students to wash their hands afterward.*) Ask: **What did you observe after you fed the meat to the plant?** *(The plant's leaf blades snapped closed, trapping the meat.)* **What did you notice when the leaves opened again?** *(The meat was gone.)* Explain that the plant produces enzymes that digest the meat. Explain that carnivorous plants living in the wild capture and digest live insects and other small organisms.

Apply Tell students that many carnivorous plants live in areas with poor soil. Ask: **How does this adaptation enable carnivorous plants to survive in areas of poor soil?** *(The plant can get the nutrients it needs from the digested insects.)* **learning modality: visual**

Discovery CHANNEL SCHOOL™ Video Field Trip

Populations and Communities

Show the Video Field Trip to help students understand the predator–prey relationship. Discussion question: **What makes the cheetah a successful predator?** *(It can run faster over short distances than any other land animal.)*

FIGURE 15
Predator Adaptations
This greater horseshoe bat has adaptations that allow it to find prey in the dark. The bat produces pulses of sound and locates prey by interpreting the echoes.
Inferring *What other adaptations might contribute to the bat's success as a predator?*

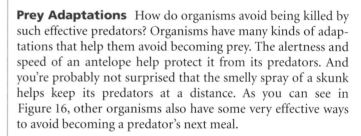

Discovery CHANNEL SCHOOL™

Populations and Communities

Video Preview
▶ Video Field Trip
Video Assessment

Predator Adaptations Predators have adaptations that help them catch and kill their prey. For example, a cheetah can run very fast for a short time, enabling it to catch its prey. A jellyfish's tentacles contain a poisonous substance that paralyzes tiny water animals. Some plants, too, have adaptations for catching prey. The sundew is covered with sticky bulbs on stalks—when a fly lands on the plant, it remains snared in the sticky goo while the plant digests it.

Some predators have adaptations that enable them to hunt at night. For example, the big eyes of an owl let in as much light as possible to help it see in the dark. Insect-eating bats can hunt without seeing at all. Instead, they locate their prey by producing pulses of sound and listening for the echoes. This precise method enables a bat to catch a flying moth in complete darkness.

Prey Adaptations How do organisms avoid being killed by such effective predators? Organisms have many kinds of adaptations that help them avoid becoming prey. The alertness and speed of an antelope help protect it from its predators. And you're probably not surprised that the smelly spray of a skunk helps keep its predators at a distance. As you can see in Figure 16, other organisms also have some very effective ways to avoid becoming a predator's next meal.

✓ **Reading Checkpoint** What are two predator adaptations?

FIGURE 16
Defense Strategies

Organisms display a wide array of adaptations that help them avoid becoming prey.

Mimicry ▶
If you're afraid of snakes, you'd probably be terrified to see this organism staring at you. But this caterpillar only looks like a snake. Its convincing resemblance to a viper tricks would-be predators into staying away.

Protective Covering ▼
Have you ever seen a pine cone with a face? This organism is actually a pangolin, a small African mammal. When threatened, the pangolin protects itself by rolling up into a scaly ball.

False Coloring ▲
If you saw this moth in a dark forest, you might think you were looking into the eyes of a large mammal. The large, false eyespots on the moth's wings scare potential predators away.

▼ Warning Coloring
A grasshopper this brightly colored can't hide. So what defense does it have against predators? Like many brightly colored animals, this grasshopper is poisonous. Its bright blue and yellow colors warn predators not to eat it.

Camouflage ▲
Is it a leaf? Actually, it's a walking leaf insect, but if you were a predator, you might be fooled into looking elsewhere for a meal.

Use Visuals: Figure 16
Identifying Defense Strategies

Focus Remind students that prey have a variety of adaptations to avoid predators.

Teach Have students look at each defense strategy. Discuss how each strategy helps protect the animal. Then ask: **What kind of defense strategy does a poison ivy plant have?** (*Chemical defense*) **What is an example of an animal using a chemical defense?** (*Students might mention a skunk spraying.*) **How does this defense help a skunk survive?** (*The foul odor repels predators that try to attack the skunk; predators that have been sprayed by a skunk will avoid skunks in the future.*)

Apply Ask students to describe other examples of each type of defense strategy shown in the pictures. **learning modality: verbal**

Monitor Progress

Writing Have students write a paragraph that identifies and describes a defense strategy used by prey. Students can place their paragraphs in their portfolios.

Answers
Figure 15 The bat's ears pick up echoes, which the bat uses to locate prey. The bat is quick, and it has teeth.

Reading Checkpoint Possible answers: Some can run fast; some produce poisons to paralyze or kill prey, some can see at night, some produce sound waves and interpret echoes.

E ● 29

Symbiosis

Teach Key Concepts L2

Identifying Relationships

Focus Have students look at Figure 17 and read the caption. Ask: **Why are these birds sitting on the hippo?** (*To feed and to hitch a ride*)

Teach Tell students that the birds and the hippo have a symbiotic relationship. Ask: **What are three types of symbiosis?** (*Mutualism, commensalism, parasitism*) Explain that this type of symbiotic relationship is mutualism. Ask: **How do the birds benefit?** (*They get food.*) **How does the hippo benefit?** (*The birds eat the ticks that feed on the hippo's blood.*)

Apply Ask: **What type of relationship do the tick and the hippo have?** (*A parasitic relationship*) **Which animal is the parasite?** (*The tick*) **learning modality: visual**

Integrating Health

Students are probably unaware that their own bodies are inhabited by other living things. Tell students that microscopic mites (*Demodex folliculorum*) live at the base of eyelashes, where they feed on tiny bits of dead skin and other detritus. Ask: **What type of symbiotic relationship is this? Explain your answer.** (*Commensalism because the mites benefit and human are neither harmed nor helped*) **learning modality: verbal**

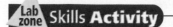
Classifying

Classify each interaction as an example of mutualism, commensalism, or parasitism. Explain your answers.

- A remora fish attaches itself to the underside of a shark without harming the shark, and eats leftover bits of food from the shark's meals.
- A vampire bat drinks the blood of horses.
- Bacteria living in cows' stomachs help them break down the cellulose in grass.

FIGURE 17
Mutualism
Three yellow-billed oxpeckers get a cruise and a snack aboard an obliging hippopotamus. The oxpeckers eat ticks living on the hippo's skin. Since both the birds and the hippo benefit from this interaction, it is an example of mutualism.

30 ◆ E

Symbiosis

Many of the interactions in the saguaro community you read about are examples of symbiosis. **Symbiosis** (sim bee OH sis) is a close relationship between two species that benefits at least one of the species. **The three types of symbiotic relationships are mutualism, commensalism, and parasitism.**

Mutualism A relationship in which both species benefit is called **mutualism** (MYOO choo uh liz um). The relationship between the saguaro and the long-eared bats is an example of mutualism. The bats benefit because the cactus flowers provide them with food. The saguaro benefits as its pollen is carried to another plant on the bat's nose.

In some cases of mutualism, two species are so dependent on each other that neither could live without the other. This is true for some species of acacia trees and stinging ants in Central and South America. The stinging ants nest only in the acacia tree, whose thorns discourage the ants' predators. The tree also provides the ants' only food. The ants, in turn, attack other animals that approach the tree and clear competing plants away from the base of the tree. To survive, each species needs the other.

Commensalism A relationship in which one species benefits and the other species is neither helped nor harmed is called **commensalism** (kuh MEN suh liz um). The red-tailed hawks' interaction with the saguaro is an example of commensalism. The hawks benefit by having a place to build their nest, while the cactus is not affected by the hawks.

Commensalism is not very common in nature because two species are usually either helped or harmed a little by any interaction. For example, by creating a small hole for its nest in the cactus stem, the elf owl slightly damages the cactus.

Skills Focus Classifying
Materials none
Time 10 minutes
Expected Outcome Remora/shark— commensalism; the remora benefits. Vampire bat/horses—parasitism; the bat benefits, and the horses are harmed. Bacteria/cows— mutualism; the bacteria receive food and a place to live, and the bacteria help the cows digest their food.

Extend Have students classify the relationships between: clown fish and anemones (commensalism—the clown fish receives protection); termites and gut protozoa (mutualism—the protozoa enable the termites to digest wood, and the termites provide shelter and food); dogs and heartworms (parasitism). **learning modality: logical/mathematical**

Parasitism Parasitism (PA ruh sit iz um) involves one organism living on or inside another organism and harming it. The organism that benefits is called a **parasite,** and the organism it lives on or in is called a **host.** The parasite is usually smaller than the host. In a parasitic relationship, the parasite benefits from the interaction while the host is harmed.

Some common parasites are fleas, ticks, and leeches. These parasites have adaptations that enable them to attach to their host and feed on its blood. Other parasites live inside the host's body, such as tapeworms that live inside the digestive systems of dogs, wolves, and some other mammals.

Unlike a predator, a parasite does not usually kill the organism it feeds on. If the host dies, the parasite loses its source of food. An interesting example of this rule is shown by a species of mite that lives in the ears of moths. The mites almost always live in just one of the moth's ears. If they live in both ears, the moth's hearing is so badly affected that it is likely to be quickly caught and eaten by its predator, a bat.

FIGURE 18
Parasitism
This tick is feeding on a person's blood. **Classifying** *Which organism in this interaction is the parasite? Which organism is the host?*

✓ **Reading Checkpoint** Why doesn't a parasite usually kill its host?

Section 3 Assessment

🎯 **Target Reading Skill** Using Prior Knowledge Review your graphic organizer and revise it based on what you just learned in the section.

Reviewing Key Concepts

1. a. **Defining** What are adaptations?
   b. **Explaining** How are a snake's sharp fangs an adaptation that helps it survive in the saguaro community?
   c. **Developing Hypotheses** Explain how natural selection in snakes might have led to adaptations such as sharp fangs.

2. a. **Reviewing** What are three main ways in which organisms interact?
   b. **Classifying** Give one example of each type of interaction.

3. a. **Listing** List the three types of symbiotic relationships.
   b. **Comparing and Contrasting** For each type of symbiotic relationship, explain how the two organisms are affected.

c. **Applying Concepts** Some of your classroom plants are dying. Others that you planted at the same time and cared for in the same way are growing well. When you look closely at the dying plants, you see tiny mites on them. Which symbiotic relationship is likely occurring between the plants and mites? Explain.

Lab zone **At-Home Activity**

Feeding Frenzy You and your family can observe interactions among organisms at a bird feeder. With paper clips, attach a plastic plate to the neck of a clean, dry 2-liter bottle. Then fill your feeder with birdseed and hang it outside where you can see it easily. Observe the feeder at different times of the day. Keep a log of all the organisms you see near it and how they interact.

Skills Check Call on students to name a type of symbiotic relationship and give an example.

Answers
Figure 18 The tick is the parasite; the person is the host.

✓ **Reading Checkpoint** If a parasite kills its host, the parasite will no longer have a source of food.

Assess

Reviewing Key Concepts

1. **a.** Adaptations are the behaviors and physical characteristics that allow organisms to live successfully in their environments. **b.** The sharp fangs enable the snake to bite into its prey. **c.** Snakes with sharper fangs could capture more prey and thus be able to survive and reproduce. They pass this trait, sharp fangs, on to their offspring.
2. **a.** Competition, predation, and symbiosis **b.** Possible answers: Competition—Two species of birds that eat the same type of insects; predation—a snake eating a mouse; symbiosis—stinging ants nesting in an acacia tree
3. **a.** Mutualism, commensalism, and parasitism **b.** Mutualism—both species benefit; commensalism—one species benefits and the other is neither harmed nor helped; parasitism—one species is helped and the other species is harmed. **c.** Parasitism is most likely. One species is being harmed (the plant).

Reteach L1

Use Figures 13, 14, and 18 to present information about competition, predation, and symbiosis.

Performance Assessment L2

Writing Have each student explain how each type of interaction among species described in this section affects an organism's survival.

All in One Teaching Resources
- Section Summary: *Interactions Among Living Things*
- Review and Reinforcement: *Interactions Among Living Things*
- Enrich: *Interactions Among Living Things*

Lab zone **Chapter Project**

All groups should graph the data they collected for plant height. Some groups may wish to create additional graphs for the numbers of leaves and buds.

Lab zone **At Home Activity**

Feeding Frenzy Organisms seen at the feeder will vary, but most students will see several varieties of birds. Some may also see squirrels and other small animals. Suggest that students use a bird guide to identify the birds they see.

Objective

After completing this lesson, students will be able to

E.1.4.1 Describe the differences between primary and secondary succession.

Target Reading Skill

Comparing and Contrasting Explain that comparing and contrasting shows how ideas, facts, and events are similar and different. The results of the comparison can have importance.

Answers

Possible answers:

Primary Succession—volcanic eruption, no soil or organisms exist, no

Secondary Succession—fire, soil and organisms exist but have been disturbed, yes

All in One Teaching Resources

• Transparency E8

Preteach

Build Background Knowledge   L2

Changes Over Time

Ask: **Have you ever observed a vacant lot or an untended garden over time. What changes did you see?** *(Answers will depend on students' experiences. They probably will say that first small grassy weeds grew, then larger weeds and some shrubs, and finally small trees.)*

Reading Preview

Key Concept

• How do primary and secondary succession differ?

Key Terms

• succession
• primary succession
• pioneer species
• secondary succession

Target Reading Skill

Comparing and Contrasting As you read, compare and contrast primary and secondary succession by completing a table like the one below.

Factors in Succession	Primary Succession	Secondary Succession
Possible cause	Volcanic eruption	
Type of area		
Existing ecosystem?		

Changes in a
Yellowstone Community ▼

Lab zone Discover Activity

What Happened Here?

1. The two photographs at the bottom of this page show the same area in Yellowstone National Park in Wyoming. The photograph on the left was taken soon after a major fire. The photograph on the right was taken a few years later. Observe the photographs carefully.

2. Make a list of all the differences you notice between the two scenes.

Think It Over

Posing Questions How would you describe what happened during the time between the two photographs? What questions do you have about this process?

In 1988, huge fires raged through the forests of Yellowstone National Park. The fires were so hot that they jumped from tree to tree without burning along the ground. Huge trees burst into flame from the intense heat. It took months for the fires to burn themselves out. All that remained were thousands of blackened tree trunks sticking out of the ground like charred toothpicks.

Could a forest community recover from such disastrous fires? It might seem unlikely. But within just a few months, signs of life had returned. First, tiny green shoots of new grass poked through the black ground. Then, small tree seedlings began to grow. The forest was coming back! After 15 years, a lush young forest was flourishing.

Fires, floods, volcanoes, hurricanes, and other natural disasters can change communities very quickly. But even without disasters, communities change. The series of predictable changes that occur in a community over time is called **succession.**

Lab zone Discover Activity

Skills Focus Posing questions

Materials none

Time 10 minutes

Expected Outcome In Photograph A the soil is bare and scorched; trees in the background have been damaged. In Photograph B the soil is covered with small plants and the damaged trees are leafy.

Think It Over Small plants began to grow again; the existing trees recovered. Students' questions will vary. Sample questions: What kinds of plants come back first? Will the area ever look like it did before the fire? How long will that take?

FIGURE 19
Primary Succession
Primary succession occurs in an area
where no soil and no organisms exist.
Applying Concepts *What determines
the particular species that appear
during succession?*

Volcanic Eruption
Shortly after a
volcanic eruption,
there is no soil,
only ash and rock.

Pioneer Species
The first species to
grow are pioneer
species such as
mosses and lichens.

Soil Creation
As pioneer species
grow and die, soil
forms. Some plants
grow in this new soil.

Fertile Soil and Maturing Plants
As more plants die, they
decompose and make the soil
more fertile. New plants grow
and existing plants mature in
the fertile soil.

Primary Succession

Primary succession is the series of changes that occur in an area where no soil or organisms exist. Such an area might be a new island formed by the eruption of an undersea volcano or an area of rock uncovered by a melting sheet of ice.

Figure 19 shows the series of changes an area might undergo after a violent volcanic eruption. The first species to populate the area are called **pioneer species.** They are often carried to the area by wind or water. Typical pioneer species are mosses or lichens, which are fungi and algae growing in a symbiotic relationship. As pioneer species grow, they help break up the rocks. When the organisms die, they provide nutrients that enrich the thin layer of soil that is forming on the rocks.

Over time, plant seeds land in the new soil and begin to grow. The specific plants that grow depend on the climate of the area. For example, in a cool, northern area, early seedlings might include alder and cottonwood trees. Eventually, succession may lead to a community of organisms that does not change unless the ecosystem is disturbed. Reaching this mature community can take centuries.

 Reading Checkpoint What are some pioneer species?

Chapter 1 E ◆ 33

Primary Succession

Teach Key Concepts L2
Predicting Changes

Focus Remind students that the events that occur during succession are predictable.

Teach Ask: **Which stage of succession in figure 19 shows pioneer species?** *(Second stage)* **How might these species arrive at the area?** *(They could be carried by wind or water.)*

Apply Ask: **Why are the changes during succession predictable? How can ecologists tell what will happen in a particular community after a natural disaster?** *(The types of plants that will grow in the area and the types of animals that will live there are determined by climate conditions, which usually are not changed over the long term by a disaster. Certain organisms appear first because they can survive in those conditions. Other species appear later as conditions become suitable for their survival.)* **learning modality: logical/mathematical**

All in One Teaching Resources
• Transparency E9

Monitor Progress _____ L2

Answers
Figure 19 The particular species depend on the biome of the area.

Reading Checkpoint Lichens and mosses

Secondary Succession

Teach Key Concepts L2

Comparing Primary and Secondary Succession

Focus Remind students that primary succession occurs in an area where no soil or organisms exist.

Teach Have students study Figure 20. Ask: **How does secondary succession differ from primary succession?** *(Secondary succession occurs in an area where the ecosystem has been disturbed but soil and organisms still exist.)* **Which type of succession occurs more rapidly?** *(Secondary succession)*

Apply Ask: **What type of succession would occur in an area that has been damaged by floods? Explain your answer.** *(Secondary succession because most likely soil and other organisms will remain after the flood)* **learning modality: logical/mathematical**

All in One Teaching Resources

- Transparency E10

Go Online SCI LINKS NSTA
For: Links on succession
Visit: www.SciLinks.org
Web Code: scn-0514

Download a worksheet that will guide students' review of Internet sources on succession.

FIGURE 20
Secondary Succession
Secondary succession occurs following a disturbance to an ecosystem, such as clearing a forest for farmland.

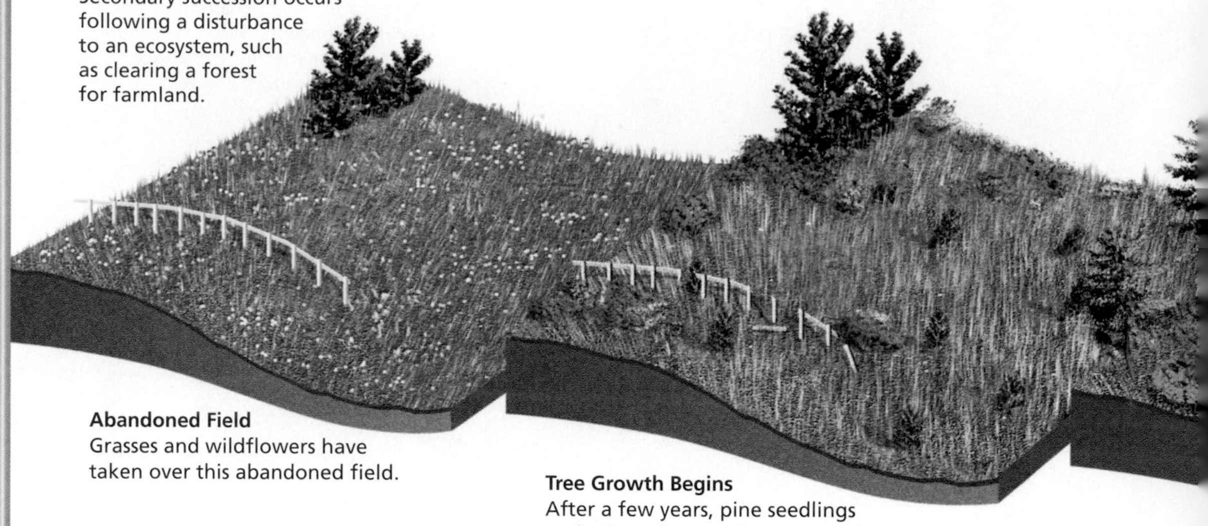

Abandoned Field
Grasses and wildflowers have taken over this abandoned field.

Tree Growth Begins
After a few years, pine seedlings and other plants replace some of the grasses and wildflowers.

Secondary Succession

The changes following the Yellowstone fire were an example of secondary succession. **Secondary succession** is the series of changes that occur in an area where the ecosystem has been disturbed, but where soil and organisms still exist. Natural disturbances that have this effect include fires, hurricanes, and tornadoes. Human activities, such as farming, logging, or mining, may also disturb an ecosystem. **Unlike primary succession, secondary succession occurs in a place where an ecosystem currently exists.**

Secondary succession occurs more rapidly than primary succession. Consider, for example, an abandoned field in the southeastern United States. You can follow the process of succession in such a field in Figure 20. After a century, a hardwood forest is developing. This forest community may remain for a long time.

Go Online SCI LINKS NSTA
For: Links on succession
Visit: www.SciLinks.org
Web Code: scn-0514

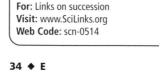

Reading Checkpoint What are two natural events that can disturb an ecosystem?

Differentiated Instruction

Less Proficient Readers L1

Interpreting Diagrams Ask students to compare the first picture in Figures 19 and 20. Help them see that the first picture of Figure 19 shows an area with no soil and no organisms, but in Figure 20 the first picture has plants already living there. Help them relate these differences to the definitions of the terms *primary* and *secondary succession.* **learning modality: visual**

Gifted and Talented L3

Researching Succession Encourage students to research examples of succession. Have them choose a location and find photos of the area, showing how it has changed. Tell students to use the photos to create a timeline that describes the changes in their location over time. **learning modality: logical/mathematical**

A Forest Develops
As tree growth continues, the trees begin to crowd out the grasses and wildflowers.

Mature Community
Eventually, a mixed forest of pine, oak, and hickory dominates the landscape.

Section 4 Assessment

🎯 **Target Reading Skill** Comparing and Contrasting
Use the information in your table to help you answer Question 1 below.

Reviewing Key Concepts

1. **a. Defining** What is primary succession? What is secondary succession?
   b. Comparing and Contrasting How do primary succession and secondary succession differ?
   c. Classifying Grass poking through a crack in a sidewalk is an example of succession. Is it primary succession or secondary succession? Explain.

Lab zone **At-Home Activity**

Community Changes Interview a family member or neighbor who has lived in your neighborhood for a long time. Ask the person to describe how the neighborhood has changed over time. Have areas that were formerly grassy been paved or developed? Have any farms, parks, or lots returned to a wild state? Write a summary of your interview. Can you classify any of the changes as examples of succession?

Answer

✓ **Reading Checkpoint** Possible answers: Fires, hurricanes, tornadoes

Assess

Reviewing Key Concepts

1. a. Primary succession occurs in an area where no soil or organisms exist. Secondary succession occurs after a disturbance in an existing ecosystem. **b.** Secondary succession generally occurs more rapidly than primary succession. **c.** Secondary succession; before the sidewalk was built, an ecosystem existed there.

Reteach   L1
Help students use Figures 19 and 20 to present the processes of primary and secondary succession.

All in One **Teaching Resources**
- Section Summary: *Changes in Communities*
- Review and Reinforce: *Changes in Communities*
- Enrich: *Changes in Communities*

Lab zone **At Home Activity**

Community Changes Suggest that students take notes so that they will remember what the person said. Have students present their summaries followed by a class discussion, focusing on any examples of succession they identified.

Interactive Textbook

- Comprehension student edition
- Section and chapter self-assessments
- Assessment reports for teachers

Help Students Read

Building Vocabulary

Word-Part Analysis Ask students what words they know that contain the key words *bio* and *photo*. *(Answers may include biology, biography, biohazard; photograph, photocopy.)* Ask them to give a definition of each key word. (*Bio* means "life," and *photo* means "light.")

Vocabulary Knowledge Rating Chart

Have students construct a chart with four columns, labeled *Term, Can Define or Use It, Have Heard or Seen It,* and *Don't Know.* They can use the chart to rate their knowledge of each vocabulary term. Ask students to share what they know about photosynthesis and the other terms in this chapter. Help students establish a purpose for reading by using the terms to predict the text content. After students have read the section, have them re-rate themselves.

All in One Teaching Resources

- Key terms Review: *Populations and Communities*

Connecting Concepts

Concepts Map Help students develop one way to show how the information in this chapter is related. Living things interact with the living and nonliving parts of their environment. Have students brainstorm to identify Key Concepts, Key Terms, details, and examples. Then write each item on a self-stick note and attach it at random to chart paper or to the board.

Tell students that this concept map will be organized in hierarchical order and to begin at the top with the Key Concepts. Ask students these questions to guide them to categorize the information on the self-stick notes: **What are some biotic and abiotic**

1 Living Things and the Environment

Key Concepts

- An organism obtains food, water, shelter, and other things it needs to live, grow, and reproduce from its environment.
- An organism interacts with both the living and nonliving parts of its habitat.
- The smallest unit of organization is a single organism, which belongs to a population that includes other members of its species. The population belongs to a community of different species. The community and abiotic factors together form an ecosystem.

Key Terms

organism	species
habitat	population
biotic factor	community
abiotic factor	ecosystem
photosynthesis	ecology

2 Studying Populations

Key Concepts

- Some methods of determining the size of a population are direct and indirect observations, sampling, and mark-and-recapture studies.
- Populations can change in size when new members join the population or when members leave the population.
- Population density can be determined using the following equation:

$$\text{Population density} = \frac{\text{Number of individuals}}{\text{Unit area}}$$

- Some limiting factors for populations are food and water, space, and weather conditions.

Key Terms

estimate	emigration
birth rate	population density
death rate	limiting factor
immigration	carrying capacity

3 Interactions Among Living Things

Key Concepts

- Every organism has a variety of adaptations that are suited to its specific living conditions.
- There are three major types of interactions among organisms: competition, predation, and symbiosis.
- The three types of symbiotic relationships are mutualism, commensalism, and parasitism.

Key Terms

natural selection	symbiosis
adaptations	mutualism
niche	commensalism
competition	parasitism
predation	parasite
predator	host
prey	

4 Changes in Communities

Key Concept

- Unlike primary succession, secondary succession occurs in a place where an ecosystem currently exists.

Key Terms

succession
primary succession
pioneer species
secondary succession

factors in the environment? How do organisms interact with them?

Prompt students by using connecting words or phrases, such as "leads to" and "results in" to indicate the basis for the organization of the map. The phrases should form a sentence between or among a set of concepts.

Answer

Accept logical presentations by students.

Review and Assessment

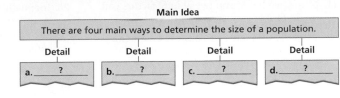

Go Online
PHSchool.com

For: Self-Assessment
Visit: PHSchool.com
Web Code: cea-5010

Organizing Information

Identifying Main Ideas Copy the graphic organizer about determining population size onto a separate sheet of paper. Then complete it and add a title. (For more on Identifying Main Ideas, see the Skills Handbook.)

Main Idea

There are four main ways to determine the size of a population.

Detail	Detail	Detail	Detail
a. ___?___	b. ___?___	c. ___?___	d. ___?___

Reviewing Key Terms

Choose the letter of the best answer.

1. A prairie dog, a hawk, and a badger all are members of the same
   a. niche.
   b. community.
   c. species.
   d. population.

2. All of the following are examples of limiting factors for populations *except*
   a. space.
   b. food.
   c. time.
   d. weather.

3. In which type of interaction do both species benefit?
   a. predation
   b. mutualism
   c. commensalism
   d. parasitism

4. Which of these relationships is an example of parasitism?
   a. a bird building a nest on a tree branch
   b. a bat pollinating a saguaro cactus
   c. a flea living on a cat's blood
   d. ants protecting a tree that produces the ants' only food

5. The series of predictable changes that occur in a community over time is called
   a. natural selection.
   b. ecology.
   c. commensalism.
   d. succession.

If the statement is true, write *true*. If it is false, change the underlined word or words to make the statement true.

6. Grass is an example of a <u>biotic factor</u> in a habitat.

7. <u>Immigration</u> is the number of individuals in a specific area.

8. An organism's specific role in its habitat is called its <u>niche</u>.

9. The struggle between organisms for limited resources is called <u>mutualism</u>.

10. A parasite lives on or inside its <u>predator</u>.

Writing in Science

Descriptive Paragraph Use what you have learned about predators and prey to write about an interaction between two organisms. For each organism, describe at least one adaptation that helps it either catch prey or fend off predators.

Discovery CHANNEL SCHOOL

Populations and Communities
Video Preview
Video Field Trip
▶ Video Assessment

Chapter 1 E ◆ 37

Go Online
PHSchool.com

For: Self-Assessment
Visit: PHSchool.com
Web Code: cea-5010

Students can take an online practice test that is automatically scored.

All in One Teaching Resources
- Transparency E11: *Identifying Main Ideas*
- Chapter Test
- Performance Assessment Teacher Notes
- Performance Assessment Student Worksheet
- Performance Assessment Scoring Rubric

ExamView® Computer Test Bank CD-ROM

Review and Assessment

Organizing Information

1. Direct observation
2. indirect observation
3. sampling
4. mark-and-recapture studies

Reviewing Key Terms

1. b **2.** c **3.** b **4.** c **5.** d
6. true
7. false; population
8. true
9. false; competition
10. false; host

Writing in Science

Writing Skill Description
Scoring Rubric
4 Includes description of interaction and several adaptations that help predator and prey
3 Includes all criteria
2 Includes incomplete description and one adaptation of each
1 Includes incomplete description and one adaptation of each

Discovery CHANNEL SCHOOL
Video Assessment

Populations and Communities
Show the Video Assessment to review chapter content and as a prompt for the writing assignment. Discussion questions: **What are some dangers cheetahs encounter in the Serengeti?** *(Lions, eagles that prey on cubs)* **What strategies do mother cheetahs use to try to keep their cubs safe?** *(Cubs stay with their mother until about 15 months; mothers distract predators from the cubs.)* **What are two traits of gazelles that help them survive?** *(They are odorless and can turn quickly.)*

Checking Concepts

11. Sample answer: Biotic—trees, birds; abiotic—sunlight, soil

12. Plants and algae use the energy of sunlight to combine water and carbon dioxide to make their own food during photosynthesis. All consumers feed directly or indirectly on plants or algae.

13. Ecologists count the number of organisms in a small area, and then multiply by the number of units in the entire area to estimate the entire population.

14. Limited space may make it impossible for all members of the population to find places to breed or make nests.

15. Any two: Camouflage—The organism blends in with its surroundings, making it difficult for predators to see. Protective covering—the organism's spines, shell, or other outer covering makes it painful or difficult for predators to eat. Warning coloring—An organism that is poisonous has bright colors to warn predators not to eat it. Mimicry—A harmless organism looks like another organism that predators have learned not to eat. False coloring—False "eyes" or other structures fool predators into attacking the wrong part of an organism.

Checking Concepts

11. Name two biotic and two abiotic factors you might find in a forest ecosystem.

12. Explain how plants and algae use sunlight. How is this process important to other living things in an ecosystem?

13. Describe how ecologists use the technique of sampling to estimate population size.

14. Give an example showing how space can be a limiting factor for a population.

15. What are two adaptations that prey organisms have developed to protect themselves? Describe how each adaptation protects the organism.

Thinking Critically

16. **Making Generalizations** Explain why ecologists usually study a specific population of organisms rather than the entire species.

17. **Problem Solving** In a summer job working for an ecologist, you have been assigned to estimate the population of grasshoppers in a field. Propose a method and explain how you would carry out your plan.

18. **Relating Cause and Effect** Competition for resources in an area is usually more intense within a single species than between two different species. Suggest an explanation for this observation. (*Hint:* Consider how niches help organisms avoid competition.)

19. **Classifying** Lichens and mosses have just begun to grow on the rocky area shown below. Which type of succession is occurring? Explain.

Math Practice

20. **Inequalities** Review the two inequalities about population size on page 16. Then revise each inequality to include immigration and emigration in addition to birth rate and death rate.

Applying Skills

Use the data in the table below to answer Questions 21–24.

Ecologists monitoring a deer population collected data during a 30-year study.

Year	0	5	10	15	20	25	30
Population (thousands)	15	30	65	100	40	25	10

21. **Graphing** Make a line graph using the data in the table. Plot years on the horizontal axis and population on the vertical axis.

22. **Interpreting Data** In which year did the deer population reach its highest point? Its lowest point?

23. **Communicating** Write a few sentences describing how the deer population changed during the study.

24. **Developing Hypotheses** In Year 16 of the study, this region experienced a very severe winter. How might this have affected the deer population?

Chapter Project

Performance Assessment Review your report and graph to be sure that they clearly state your conclusion about the effects of crowding on plant growth. With your group, decide how you will present your results. Do a practice run-through to make sure all group members feel comfortable with their parts. After your presentation, list some improvements you could have made in your experimental plan.

Chapter Project

Project Wrap-Up Review each group's written report, and let them present their results to the rest of the class in a poster, display, or oral report. As indicated in the Scoring Rubric, base your evaluation of each group's report on both the written report and the class presentation.

Reflect and Record After all groups have made their class presentations, allow time for students to compare their results and discuss the factors that may have accounted for any differences.

Standardized Test Prep

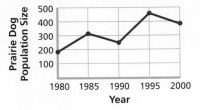
Choose the letter of the best answer.

1. According to the graph above, in what year was the prairie dog population the largest?
   A 1980   B 1990
   C 1995   D 2000

2. In general, which of the following is a true statement about population size?
   F If birth rate < death rate, population size increases.
   G If death rate < birth rate, population size decreases.
   H If birth rate > death rate, population size increases.
   J If death rate > birth rate, population size increases.

3. A freshwater lake has a muddy bottom, which is home to different types of algae and other organisms. Many species of fish feed on the algae. Which of the following is an *abiotic* factor in this ecosystem?
   A the temperature of the water
   B the color of the algae
   C the number of species of fish
   D the amount of food available to the fish

4. Although three different bird species all live in the same trees in an area, competition between the birds rarely occurs. The most likely explanation for this lack of competition is that these birds
   F occupy different niches.
   G eat the same food.
   H have a limited supply of food.
   J live in the same part of the trees.

5. During primary succession, a typical pioneer species is
   A grass.
   B lichen.
   C pine trees.
   D soil.

Constructed Response

6. Suppose that two species of squirrels living in the same habitat feed on the same type of nut. Describe two possible outcomes of competition between the two squirrel species.

Thinking Critically

16. Studying the entire population of the species usually is not possible because the population is too spread out. In addition, because the organism's interaction with other organisms and the environment is specific to that environment, studying a population produces more accurate results than studying an entire species.

17. Answers may include indirect observation (counting egg clusters), sampling (counting the number in a small area and then multiplying by the number of units in the entire area), or mark and capture.

18. Within a species, there is a smaller range of adaptation than between species. Organisms within a species share the same niche. Because individuals within a species are more similar, they will share many of the same advantages and disadvantages in surviving in a certain environment, which intensifies competition for the limited resources.

19. Primary succession; no soil and no other organisms are shown.

Math Practice

20. If immigration > emigration, population size increases. If immigration < emigration, population size decreases.

Applying Skills

21. Check graphs to make sure students have plotted the correct points.

22. Highest: year 15; lowest: year 30

23. Possible answer: Beginning with 15,000 deer at the beginning of the study, the population increased steadily through Year 15. From Year 15 through the end of the study, the deer population declined steadily, reaching the population's lowest point, 10,000 deer, in Year 30.

24. The severe winter may have killed weak or injured deer. Food shortage during this winter also may have weakened deer or caused them to starve.

E ● 39

Standardized Test Prep

1. C   **2.** H   **3.** A   **4.** F   **5.** B
6. One species may die out or the populations of both species may decrease.

Chapter at a Glance

PRENTICE HALL
TeacherEXPRESS™
Plan • Teach • Assess

Lab zone Chapter **Project** *Breaking It Down*

Technology

Local Standards

All in One Teaching Resources
- Chapter Project Teacher Notes, pp. 100–101
- Chapter Project Student Overview, pp. 102–103
- Chapter Project Student Worksheets, pp. 104–105
- Chapter Project Scoring Rubric, p. 106

Discovery CHANNEL SCHOOL
Video Preview

Section 1 Energy Flow in Ecosystems

1–2 periods
1/2–1 blocks

E.2.1.1 Name and describe the energy roles that organisms play in an ecosystem.

E.2.1.2 Explain how energy moves through an ecosystem.

E.2.1.3 Describe how much energy is available at each level of an energy pyramid.

Go Online
SciLINKS NSTA

Section 2 Cycles of Matter

1–2 periods
1/2–1 blocks

E.2.2.1 Name and describe the processes involved in the water cycle.

E.2.2.2 Explain how carbon and oxygen are recycled in ecosystems.

E.2.2.3 Define and describe the nitrogen cycle.

Go Online
active art

Section 3 Biogeography

1–2 periods
1/2–1 blocks

E.2.3.1 Explain how the movement of the continents has affected the distribution of species.

E.2.3.2 Name three ways that organism dispersal occurs.

E.2.3.3 Name and describe factors that can limit the dispersal of a species.

Go Online
active art

Section 4 Biomes

2–3 periods
1–1 1/2 blocks

E.2.4.1 Name the six major biomes found on Earth.

E.2.4.2 Describe organisms that might be found in each biome and the adaptations they possess.

E.2.4.3 Name and describe the factors that determine the type of biome found in an area.

Discovery CHANNEL SCHOOL
Video Field Trip

Go Online
active art

Section 5 Aquatic Ecosystems

2–3 periods
1–1 1/2 blocks

E.2.5.1 Name and describe the two major types of aquatic ecosystems.

E.2.5.2 Describe how organisms are adapted to each of the aquatic habitats.

Go Online
SciLINKS NSTA

Review and Assessment

Test Preparation

All in One Teaching Resources
- Key Terms Review, p. 146
- Transparency E25
- Performance Assessment Teacher Notes, p. 153
- Performance Assessment Scoring Rubric p. 154
- Performance Assessment Student Worksheet, p. 155
- Chapter Test, pp. 156–159

Discovery CHANNEL SCHOOL
Video Assessment

Go Online
PHSchool.com

Test Preparation Blackline Masters

Lab zone Chapter Activities Planner

For more activities

LAB ZONE
Easy Planner
CD-ROM

Student Edition	Inquiry	Time	Materials	Skills	Resources
Chapter Project	Open-Ended	At least 4 weeks	**All in One** Teaching Resources See p. 100	Making models, designing experiments, observing, measuring changes, recording and interpreting data, communicating	**Lab zone Easy Planner** **All in One** Teaching Resources Support pp. 100–106
Section 1					
Discover Activity, p. 42	Guided	10 minutes	Paper and pencil or pen	Classifying	**Lab zone Easy Planner**
Try This, p. 44	Directed	15 minutes	Long pieces of yarn	Making models	**Lab zone Easy Planner**
Section 2					
Discover Activity, p. 48	Directed	5 minutes	Small mirror	Inferring	**Lab zone Easy Planner**
Skills Activity, p. 49	Open-Ended	5 minutes	None	Developing hypotheses	**Lab zone Easy Planner**
Try This, p. 50	Directed	10 minutes for setup; 15 minutes total of observations over several days	Two plastic cups, bromthymol blue solution, two sprigs of *Elodea*	Inferring	**Lab zone Easy Planner**
Section 3					
Discover Activity, p. 54	Guided	15 minutes	Shallow pan, corn kernels, possible materials to move corn, such as water, straw, and tape	Predicting	**Lab zone Easy Planner**
Section 4					
Discover Activity, p. 58	Directed	20 minutes	meter stick, adding-machine paper, scissors, marker, tape	Developing hypotheses	**Lab zone Easy Planner**
Try This, p. 61	Directed	10 minutes	Small potted cactus, hand lens, scissors	Observing	**Lab zone Easy Planner**
Skills Activity, p. 64	Directed	5 minutes	Boreal forest biome map	Inferring	**Lab zone Easy Planner**
Skills Lab, p. 68–69	Guided	Prep: 30 minutes Class: 30 minutes, then 10 minutes each day for at least one week	Scissors, clear plastic wrap, index card, lamp, tape, empty and clean cardboard milk carton, stapler, about 30 rye grass seeds, 10 impatiens seeds, 5 lima bean seeds, sandy soil or potting soil	Observing, making models	**Lab zone Easy Planner** **Lab Activity Video** **All in One** Teaching Resources Skills Lab: *Biomes in Miniature,* pp. 134–136
Section 5					
Discover Activity, p. 70	Directed	15 minutes	None	Observing	**Lab zone Easy Planner**
Skills Lab, p. 74	Guided	Prep: 45 minutes Class: Day 1, set up community: 15 minutes; Days 3, 6, and 9, examine community: 20 minutes daily	Hay solution, pond water, small baby-food jar, wax pencil, plastic dropper, microscope slide, coverslip, microscope	Observing, classifying	**Lab zone Easy Planner** **Lab Activity Video** **All in One** Teaching Resources Skills Lab: *Change in a Tiny Community,* pp. 144–145

Section 1 Energy Flow in Ecosystems

🕐 *1–2 periods, 1/2–1 block*

Objectives

E.2.1.1 Name and describe the energy roles that organisms play in an ecosystem.

E.2.1.2 Explain how energy moves through an ecosystem.

E.2.1.3 Describe how much energy is available at each level of an energy pyramid.

Key Terms

• producer • consumer • herbivore • carnivore • omnivore • scavenger
• decomposer • food chain • food web • energy pyramid

Local Standards

Preteach

Build Background Knowledge

Ask students to recall from previous chapters the definition and characteristics of an ecosystem.

Lab zone Discover Activity *Where Did Your Dinner Come From?*

Targeted Print and Technology Resources

All in One Teaching Resources
• Reading Strategy: Building Vocabulary

⊙ **Presentation-Pro CD-ROM**

Instruct

Energy Roles Discuss familiar habitats and organisms to help students examine the energy roles organisms play in an ecosystem.

Food Chains and Food Webs Use text figures and transparencies to illustrate the ways that energy moves through an ecosystem.

Energy Pyramids Relate the shape of an energy pyramid to how the energy available to organisms changes as it moves up levels of a food web.

Targeted Print and Technology Resources

All in One Teaching Resources
L2 Guided Reading, pp. 109–111
L2 Transparencies E13, E14

www.SciLinks.org Web Code: scn-0521

⊙ **Student Edition on Audio CD**

Transparencies E13, E14

Assess

Section Assessment Questions

↩ Have students use their own definitions of Key Terms to help answer the questions.

Reteach

Review energy roles in an ecosystem and discuss how energy flow is represented by food chains, food webs, and energy pyramids.

Targeted Print and Technology Resources

All in One Teaching Resources
• Section Summary, p. 108
L1 Review and Reinforce, p. 112
L3 Enrich, p. 113

Section 2 Cycles of Matter

1–2 periods, 1/2–1 block

Ability Levels Key
L1 Basic to Average
L2 For All Students
L3 Average to Advanced

Objectives

E.2.2.1 Name and describe the processes involved in the water cycle.

E.2.2.2 Explain how carbon and oxygen are recycled in ecosystems.

E.2.2.3 Define and describe the nitrogen cycle.

Local Standards

Key Terms

• water cycle • evaporation • condensation • precipitation • nitrogen fixation

Preteach

Build Background Knowledge

Prompt students to define the term *cycle* and name familiar examples of cycles.

Lab zone Discover Activity *Are You Part of a Cycle?*

Targeted Print and Technology Resources

All in One Teaching Resources

L2 Reading Strategy Transparency E15: Sequencing

Presentation-Pro CD-ROM

Transparency E15

Instruct

The Water Cycle Use a diagram of the water cycle to describe its major processes.

The Carbon and Oxygen Cycles Emphasize the link between the recycling of carbon and oxygen in an ecosystem and the roles of producers and consumers.

The Nitrogen Cycle Use text figures and transparencies to illustrate the unique aspects of the nitrogen cycle and the role of decomposers in it.

Targeted Print and Technology Resources

All in One Teaching Resources

L2 Guided Reading, pp. 116–118

L2 Transparencies E16, E17, E18

www.PHSchool.com Web Code: cfp-4024

Student Edition on Audio CD

Transparencies E16, E17, E18

Assess

Section Assessment Questions

Have students use their cycle diagram or other sequencing diagrams to help answer the questions.

Reteach

Direct students to review drawings and tables that compare and contrast the cycles that are vital to ecosystem functioning.

Targeted Print and Technology Resources

All in One Teaching Resources

• Section Summary, p. 115

L1 Review and Reinforce, p. 119

L3 Enrich, p. 120

Section 3 **Biogeography**

⏱ *1–2 periods, 1/2–1 block*

Ability Levels Key
L1 Basic to Average
L2 For All Students
L3 Average to Advanced

Objectives

E.2.3.1 Explain how the movement of the continents has affected the distribution of species.

E.2.3.2 Name three ways that organism dispersal occurs.

E.2.3.3 Name and describe factors that can limit the dispersal of a species.

Local Standards

Key Terms

• biogeography • continental drift • dispersal • exotic species • climate

---

Preteach

Build Background Knowledge

Encourage students to discuss their own ideas about how and why animals move from one place to another.

Lab zone ▶ **Discover Activity** *How Can You Move a Seed?*

Targeted Print and Technology Resources

All in One Teaching Resources

L2 Reading Strategy Transparency E19: Relating Cause and Effect

💿 **Presentation-Pro CD-ROM**

Transparency E19
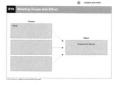

Instruct

Continental Drift Use illustrations of the movement of continents over time to explain how continental drift has affected species distributions.

Means of Dispersal Compare the ways that organisms can be dispersed.

Limits to Dispersal Ask leading questions to discuss factors that limit dispersal of a species.

Targeted Print and Technology Resources

All in One Teaching Resources

L2 Guided Reading, pp. 123–124

L2 Transparency E20

www.PHSchool.com Web Code: cfp-1015

💿 **Student Edition on Audio CD**

Transparency E20

Assess

Section Assessment Questions

🔈 Have students use their graphic organizers identifying causes of dispersal to answer the questions.

Reteach

Direct class discussion on how continental drift has affected species dispersal.

Targeted Print and Technology Resources

All in One Teaching Resources

• Section Summary, p. 122

L1 Review and Reinforce, p. 125

L3 Enrich, p. 126

Section 4 Biomes

⏱ *2–3 periods, 1–1 1/2 blocks*

Objectives

E.2.4.1 Name the six major biomes found on Earth.

E.2.4.2 Describe organisms that might be found in each biome and the adaptations they possess.

E.2.4.3 Name and describe the factors that determine the type of biome found in an area.

Local Standards

Key Terms

- biome • canopy • understory • desert • grassland • savanna • deciduous tree
- coniferous tree • tundra • permafrost

Preteach

Build Background Knowledge

Encourage students to consider how local climate conditions affect which organisms live in the area.

Lab zone Discover Activity *How Much Rain Is That?*

Targeted Print and Technology Resources

All in One Teaching Resources

L2 Reading Strategy Transparency E21: Comparing and Contrasting

⊙ **Presentation-Pro CD-ROM**

Transparency E21

Instruct

Rain Forest Biomes Use a world map to compare temperate and tropical rain forests.

Desert Biomes Discuss desert biomes in terms of adaptations that organisms there must possess.

Grassland Biomes Use a map and text figures to explore the types of grasslands, prairies and savannas.

Deciduous Forest Biomes Discuss the seasonal nature of deciduous forests and how it affects the organisms there.

Boreal Forest Biomes Describe the climate of the boreal forest and the limits placed on the biome's plants and animals.

Tundra Biomes Use a figure to describe the cold tundra biome and the adaptations of its plants and animals.

Mountains and Ice Explain the unique nature of mountain and ice habitats.

Lab zone Skills Lab *Biomes in Miniature*

Targeted Print and Technology Resources

All in One Teaching Resources

L2 Guided Reading, pp. 129–131

L2 Skills Lab: *Biomes in Miniature*, pp. 134–136

📼 **Lab Activity Video/DVD**
Skills Lab: *Biomes in Miniature*

www.PHSchool.com Web Code: cep-5024

⊙ **Student Edition on Audio CD**

Assess

Section Assessment Questions

↻ Have students use their comparing and contrasting graphic organizers to answer the questions.

Reteach

Have students prepare a table that compares the various biomes.

Targeted Print and Technology Resources

All in One Teaching Resources

- Section Summary, p. 128
- L1 Review and Reinforce, p. 132
- L3 Enrich, p. 133

Section 5 **Aquatic Ecosystems**

🕐 *2–3 periods, 1–1 1/2 blocks*

Objectives

E.2.5.1 Name and describe the two major types of aquatic ecosystems.
E.2.5.2 Describe how organisms are adapted to each of the aquatic habitats.

Key Terms

• estuary • intertidal zone • neritic zone

Local Standards

Preteach

Build Background Knowledge

Challenge students to discuss differences between aquatic ecosystems that are familiar to them.

Lab zone Discover Activity *Where Do They Live?*

Targeted Print and Technology Resources

All in One Teaching Resources

L2 Reading Strategy Transparency E22: Outlining

⊙ **Presentation-Pro CD-ROM**

Transparency E22

Instruct

Freshwater Ecosystems Use figures to prompt discussion of freshwater ecosystems and the organisms they contain.

Marine Ecosystems Compare as a class the various components of marine ecosystems.

Lab zone Skills Lab *Change in a Tiny Community*

Targeted Print and Technology Resources

All in One Teaching Resources

L2 Guided Reading, pp. 139–141
L2 Transparency E23
L2 Skills Lab: *Change in a Tiny Community*, pp. 144–145

📼 **Lab Activity Video/DVD**
Skills Lab: *Change in a Tiny Community*

www.SciLinks.org Web Code: scn-0525

⊙ **Student Edition on Audio CD**

Transparency E23

Assess

Section Assessment Questions

Have students use their outline of the types of aquatic ecosystems to answer the questions.

Reteach

Employ group presentations or a class quiz game to compare characteristics and organisms found in the various biomes.

Targeted Print and Technology Resources

All in One Teaching Resources

• Section Summary, p. 138
L1 Review and Reinforce, p. 142
L3 Enrich, p. 143

Chapter 2 Content Refresher

Go Online
NSTA-PDILINKS
For: Professional development support
Visit: www.SciLinks.org/PDLinks
Web Code: scf-0520
Professional Development

Section 1 Energy Flow in Ecosystems

Moving Through Energy Pyramids Energy in an ecosystem moves in only one direction, from the bottom (producers) to the top (top-level consumers) of an energy pyramid. Approximately 90 percent of the energy in an energy pyramid is lost from one level to the next-higher one. This fact ties into physics: the second law of thermodynamics states that it is impossible to get as much energy out of any system as is put into it. The law is as true for systems involving machines as it is for food webs.

In a food web, energy is lost not only as heat but also because not all organisms in one level are eaten by those in the next level. As a result, some energy is not transferred at all. Even those organisms that are consumed might contain parts that cannot be digested—bones, beaks, shells—which reduces the total amount of energy that can be transferred.

The narrowing of an energy pyramid from bottom to top illustrates that a smaller number of organisms in each successively higher level can be supported by the amount of available energy. This relationship also is reflected in the biomass present at each level. (Biomass in this context is a measure of the total amount of living material.) Notice in the diagram that with energy, biomass declines by 90 percent with each level up a food web. The shape of the energy pyramid and the amount of biomass at each level reflect how it takes a large number of producers to support one higher-level carnivore.

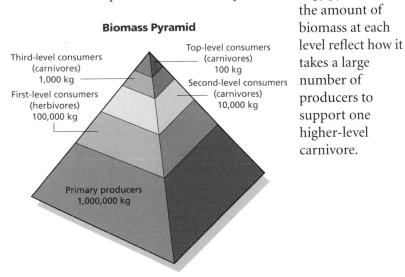

Biomass Pyramid

Third-level consumers (carnivores) 1,000 kg
First-level consumers (herbivores) 100,000 kg
Top-level consumers (carnivores) 100 kg
Second-level consumers (carnivores) 10,000 kg
Primary producers 1,000,000 kg

Section 2 Cycles of Matter

Making Nutrients Available Ecosystem cycles are critical to providing organisms, including humans, with the basic building blocks needed for survival. One important building block, nitrogen, is necessary for the formation of amino acids, which combine to form proteins. Proteins make up many human enzymes, which are catalysts for almost all of the body's chemical reactions. They also are the key components of many body tissues, such as muscle and skin. However, the body cannot use all forms of nitrogen. In an ecosystem, various organisms that are part of the nitrogen cycle make it possible for nitrogen to be converted into its usable forms.

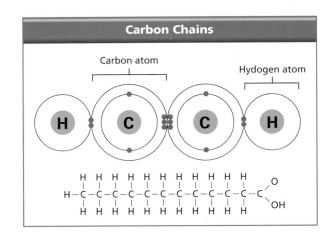

Carbon Chains

Carbon atom   Hydogen atom

H   C   C   H

In many organisms, cell function is impossible without a supply of oxygen. Millions of years ago, all the oxygen in Earth's atmosphere today was generated by producers during photosynthesis. That oxygen is now cycled through Earth's atmosphere and living organisms as part of the oxygen cycle.

Most of the material that makes up living things is based primarily on carbon, including the genetic building blocks, RNA and DNA. As you can see in the diagram, carbon atoms join together to form long chains, which are the framework for the structures of all organic materials that make up living things.

The demand for carbon in living things is great, but only producers can convert carbon dioxide gas from the atmosphere into carbon compounds that other living things can use. The carbon used by organisms is again released as carbon dioxide as living things carry on cellular respiration.

Carbon can be stored for very long periods in Earth's crust. Millions of years ago, the remains of carbon-containing plants and animals became buried under silt, mud, rocks, and in swamps. Eventually the remains formed fossil fuels. Today, these fossil fuels are a major energy source used by humans. Burning these fuels releases carbon back into the atmosphere as carbon dioxide.

Carbon can also be stored as dissolved carbon dioxide in Earth's oceans, or it can be used by marine organisms to form shells and other body parts. Ocean deposits of such materials are the largest stores of carbon on Earth.

Section 3 Biogeography

Overcoming Dispersal Barriers Long ago continental drift created continents separated by large bodies of water. These bodies of water acted as barriers to the dispersal of organisms from one continent to another. As a result, many isolated areas developed their own unique organisms. Today humans can overcome these expanses of water and other natural physical barriers that once prevented the dispersal of species. As they do so, new species can be introduced and spread across areas, and native species that previously did not have to compete for resources now must share them. Often the native species become overwhelmed.

Hawaii represents an example of an isolated location possessing many unique species. As people have accidentally or deliberately introduced new species to Hawaii's unique ecosystem, the balance of some of the existing species has been disrupted by the success of introduced species. Many native species are not equipped to compete with the exotics and may become threatened, endangered, or extinct. Coupled with the massive loss of native habitat, the introduction of species into Hawaii's ecosystems has caused hundreds of Hawaii native species to become endangered or extinct.

Address Misconceptions

All ecosystems are dependent on photosynthesis. If true, then there would be no life forms in areas that lack sunlight, which is certainly not the case. For other sources of production in ecosystems, see **Address Misconceptions** on page 44.

Section 4 Biomes

Climate and Biomes Although many factors determine the types of organisms that live in a biome, climate is especially important. The two main characteristics that determine the climate of an area—temperature and rainfall—can be summarized in a climate diagram, such as the one below. In temperate and tropical regions, the various biomes are distinguished more by amounts of precipitation than by temperature. Temperate rain forests and temperate deserts experience very different amounts of precipitation, and therefore, they vary greatly in their physical conditions and species compositions. Both tundras and boreal forests have similar levels of yearly precipitation, but their temperatures, and, therefore, their organisms differ vastly.

Many different parts of the world share similar a climate and soil, another characteristic that determines the type of organisms in a biome. As a result, they will share similar types of organisms. For example, deserts can be found in several locations across the globe. Although the specific species that live in each individual desert may be unique to that area, all share certain characteristics that enable them to survive the hot daytime temperatures, dryness, and poor soil.

Section 5 Aquatic Ecosystems

Land and Sea Estuaries are marine ecosystems that serve as bridges between freshwater and saltwater habitats. They can include bays, marshes, sounds, mangrove forests, swamps, and other habitats. Because estuaries are linked to the ocean, they are tidal. They receive and trap large deposits of decaying plant matter from the lands they are attached to as currents move the materials toward the ocean. Thus, typical estuaries offer nutrient-rich soils that support a wide array of organisms.

Many aquatic organisms cannot tolerate salinity (salt in the water) even at very low concentrations, yet several freshwater fish species join their marine counterparts in laying eggs in marshes in low-salinity areas of estuaries. The larvae and young fish can tolerate the low salinities and are protected from predators in the quiet marsh areas. As the young fish mature, the freshwater species move upstream into rivers, and the marine species move downstream into saltwater habitats.

This unique blend of marine and freshwater characteristics makes estuaries a buffer between land and sea. They absorb the impact of storms and floods, reducing potential damage to coastal communities. Estuaries also act as filters, containing river pollutants before they are released to the ocean.

Help Students Read

Asking Questions
Looking for Answers

Strategy This strategy helps students to anticipate what they will be reading and helps them look for answers in the passage as they read. With practice, students should be able to generate questions that do not simply rephrase the section headings. The headings themselves will give students the hints they need to formulate original questions about what they expect to see in the text.

Example
1. Choose a section within this chapter. A good example is "Biomes."
2. Draw a two-column chart on the board. Make the heading of the first column of your chart *Questions* and the second heading *Answers*.
3. Have students scan the section. As they encounter headings and subheadings, have them suggest ways to recast them so that they become questions. For example, "Rain Forest Biomes" might become the question "What is a rain forest?"
4. After you have several questions in the first column of your chart, ask students to read the section. You may ask a volunteer to read aloud or ask the class to read silently.
5. After students have read the section, ask volunteers to supply answers to the questions in the first column. Suggest that students make their own charts as you are writing the answers on the board. Students can use their charts to help answer assessment questions.

Chapter 2

Ecosystems and Biomes

Chapter Preview

interactive Textbook

This macaque adds to the rich diversity of organisms in the tropical rain forest. ▶

Lab zone Chapter Project

Objectives

This project will give students an opportunity to study the process of decomposition by constructing compost chambers and investigating the effects over time of environmental variables on composting. After this Chapter Project, students will be able to

- make a model compost chamber
- design an experiment to test the effect of one variable on decomposition
- observe, measure, and record changes in composted material
- communicate experimental procedures and results in a report, poster, or other product

Skills Focus

Making models, designing experiments, observing, measuring, interpreting data, communicating

Project Time Line at least 4 weeks

All in One Teaching Resources
- Chapter Project Teacher Notes
- Chapter Project Worksheet 1
- Chapter Project Worksheet 2
- Chapter Project Worksheet 3
- Chapter Project Scoring Rubric

Developing a Plan

Each student or group will first choose a variable to investigate: moisture, oxygen, temperature, or activity of soil organisms. Students will then construct compost chambers, design and launch experiments, observe the decomposition process, record and analyze data, and prepare reports.

Possible Materials

- Each student or group will need materials for the control and test compost chambers. For instructions on building compost chambers, see the Chapter Project Teacher Notes in the All-In-One Teaching Resources.
- Provide chopped leaves as the base material to be composted. Add as desired other organic waste: eggshells, paper, grass

Ecosystems and Biomes

Show the Video Preview to introduce the Chapter Project and overview the chapter content. Discussion question: **What climatic conditions are common to all deserts?** *(All get very little rain and have extreme temperature shifts.)*

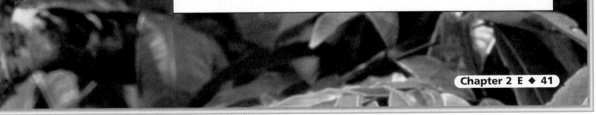

Lab zone Chapter **Project**

Breaking It Down

Nothing in an ecosystem is wasted. Even when living things die, organisms such as mushrooms recycle them. This natural process of breakdown is called decomposition. When fallen leaves and other waste products decompose, a fluffy, brown mixture called compost is formed. You can observe decomposition firsthand in this chapter project by building a compost chamber.

Your Goal To design and conduct an experiment to learn more about the process of decomposition

To complete this project, you must
● build two compost chambers
● investigate the effect of one of the following variables on decomposition: moisture, oxygen, temperature, or activity of soil organisms
● analyze your data and present your results
● follow the safety guidelines in Appendix A

Plan It! Your teacher will provide you with a sample of compost material. Observe the wastes in the mixture with a hand lens. Write a hypothesis about which kinds of waste will decay and which will not. Next, decide which variable you will test and plan how you will test it. Once your teacher approves your plan, build your compost chambers and begin your experiment.

Chapter 2 E ◆ 41

clippings, and orange peels; or inorganic waste: bottle caps or plastic foam pieces.
● Provide garden soil (not commercial potting soil) and earthworms for groups that choose to investigate the effect of soil organisms.
● Set aside protected locations in the classroom to house the compost chambers.

Launching the Project

Construct a compost chamber yourself as a prototype. Fill the chamber with the compost material, but do not add water. Set your chamber aside until the end of the project so students can compare their composted material with the original material.

Have students read the Chapter Project description. Then show and describe the compost chamber that you made. Explain that each student or group will need to make two such chambers—a control chamber and a test chamber.

If you divide the class into groups, tell students that all group members should help plan the experiment, make observations, analyze results, and develop the report.

Performance Assessment

The Chapter Project Scoring Rubric will help you evaluate how well students complete the Chapter Project. You may want to share the scoring rubric with your students so they are clear about what will be expected of them. Students will be assessed on
● their ability to design an experiment to test the effect of one variable on decomposition
● their completeness and accuracy in doing the experiment, making observations, and recording data
● their ability to draw reasonable conclusions based on experimental results and communicate their procedures, results, and conclusions
● their group participation if they worked in groups

Portfolio

E ● 41

Objectives

After completing the lesson, students will be able to

E.2.1.1 Name and describe energy roles that organisms play in an ecosystem.

E.2.1.2 Explain how energy moves through an ecosystem.

E.2.1.3 Describe how much energy is available at each level of an energy pyramid.

Target Reading Skill

Building Vocabulary Explain that knowing the definitions of key concept words helps students understand what they read.

Answers

Possible sentences:

- In a **food chain**, a **consumer** could be an **herbivore**, an **omnivore**, or a **carnivore**, including a **scavenger**.
- An **energy pyramid** shows how much energy moves from one level to another in a **food web**, beginning with the **producers**.
- **Decomposers** are nature's recyclers.

Preteach

Build Background Knowledge
L2

Recalling Ecosystems

Help students recall what they learned in the previous chapter by asking: **What is an ecosystem?** *(All the living and nonliving things that interact in a particular area)* **What are some things you know about ecosystems?** *(Responses might include information on habitat, biotic and abiotic factors, levels of organization, population size, limiting factors, adaptations, and types of interactions between organisms)*

Reading Preview

Key Concepts

- What energy roles do organisms play in an ecosystem?
- How does energy move through an ecosystem?
- How much energy is available at each level of an energy pyramid?

Key Terms

- producer
- consumer
- herbivore
- carnivore
- omnivore
- scavenger
- decomposer
- food chain
- food web
- energy pyramid

Target Reading Skill

Building Vocabulary A definition states the meaning of a word or phrase by telling about its most important feature or function. After you read the section, reread the paragraphs that contain definitions of Key Terms. Use all the information you have learned to write a definition of each Key Term in your own words.

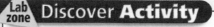

Lab zone · Discover **Activity**

Where Did Your Dinner Come From?

1. Across the top of a sheet of paper, list the different types of foods you ate for dinner last night.
2. Under each item, write the name of the plant, animal, or other organism that was the source of that food. Some foods have more than one source. For example, macaroni and cheese contains flour (which is made from a plant such as wheat) and cheese (which comes from an animal).

Think It Over
Classifying How many of your food sources were plants? How many were animals?

Do you play an instrument in your school band? If so, you know that each instrument has a role in a piece of music. For instance, the flute may provide the melody while the drum provides the beat.

Just like the instruments in a band, each organism has a role in the movement of energy through its ecosystem. A bluebird's role, for example, is different from that of the giant oak tree where it is perched. But all parts of the ecosystem, like all parts of a band, are necessary for the ecosystem to work.

Energy Roles

An organism's energy role is determined by how it obtains energy and how it interacts with other organisms. **Each of the organisms in an ecosystem fills the energy role of producer, consumer, or decomposer.**

Producers Energy enters most ecosystems as sunlight. Some organisms, such as plants, algae, and some bacteria, capture the energy of sunlight and store it as food energy. These organisms use the sun's energy to turn water and carbon dioxide into food molecules in a process called photosynthesis.

Lab zone · Discover **Activity**

Skills Focus Classifying

Materials none

Time 10 minutes

Tips Circulate among students as they work to answer questions about the sources or ingredients of some foods.

Expected Outcome As a class, students will undoubtedly cite a wide variety of foods and sources.

Think It Over Answers will vary depending on the foods eaten. Except for students whose families are strict vegetarians and eat no animal products of any kind, most students will probably cite both plant and animal sources and possibly fungi, protists, or monerans.

An organism that can make its own food is a **producer.** Producers are the source of all the food in an ecosystem. In a few ecosystems, producers obtain energy from a source other than sunlight. One such ecosystem is found in rocks deep beneath the ground. How is energy brought into this ecosystem? Certain bacteria in this ecosystem produce their own food using the energy in a gas, hydrogen sulfide, that is found in their environment.

Consumers Some members of an ecosystem cannot make their own food. An organism that obtains energy by feeding on other organisms is a **consumer.**

Consumers are classified by what they eat. Consumers that eat only plants are **herbivores.** Familiar herbivores are caterpillars and deer. Consumers that eat only animals are **carnivores.** Lions and spiders are some examples of carnivores. Consumers that eat both plants and animals are **omnivores.** Crows, bears, and most humans are omnivores.

Some carnivores are scavengers. A **scavenger** is a carnivore that feeds on the bodies of dead organisms. Scavengers include catfish and vultures.

Decomposers If an ecosystem had only producers and consumers, the raw materials of life would stay locked up in wastes and the bodies of dead organisms. Luckily, there are organisms in ecosystems that prevent this problem. **Decomposers** break down wastes and dead organisms and return the raw materials to the ecosystem.

You can think of decomposers as nature's recyclers. While obtaining energy for their own needs, decomposers return simple molecules to the environment. These molecules can be used again by other organisms. Mushrooms and bacteria are common decomposers.

✓ Reading Checkpoint What do herbivores and carnivores have in common?

Consumer—Herbivore

Producer

Consumer—Omnivore

Decomposer

FIGURE 1
Energy Roles
Each organism in an ecosystem fills a specific energy role. Producers, such as oak trees, make their own food. Consumers, such as luna moth larvae and eastern bluebirds, obtain energy by feeding on other organisms. **Classifying** *What role do decomposers play in ecosystems?*

E ◆ 43

Instruct

Energy Roles

Teach Key Concepts   L1

Playing Roles in Ecosystem

Focus Emphasize that ecosystem roles are based primarily on the way organisms obtain energy.

Teach Direct students to Figure 1. List on the board headings for energy roles. Ask: **What organisms in this ecosystem would you find in each role?** (*Producers: grass, trees; consumers: worms, birds; decomposers: mushrooms, and so on*)

Apply Instruct students to observe a habitat—their yard or the school grounds. Ask: **What are the producers, consumers, and decomposers in this ecosystem?** (*Answers will be similar to those for Figure 1.*) **learning modality: visual**

Help Students Read

Reciprocal Teaching Have students read the section with a partner. One partner reads a paragraph aloud, and then the other partner summarizes the paragraph's concepts. Have partners switch roles until they have finished the entire section.

Independent Practice   L2

All in One Teaching Resources

• Guided Reading and Study Worksheet: *Energy Flow in Ecosystems*

 **Student Edition on Audio CD**

⌐ Differentiated Instruction

Less Proficient Readers   L1
Building Vocabulary Read aloud the Target Reading Skill for students who need a more active introduction to the Key Terms. Instruct these students to list all Key Terms (*producer, consumer, herbivores, carnivores, omnivores, scavenger, decomposers*), leaving room for definitions.

Have students listen to this passage on the *Student Edition on Audio CD*. After they listen to a paragraph, have them write their own definitions of Key Terms before proceeding to the next paragraph. (*Definitions will vary but should accurately reflect text content.*) **learning modality: verbal**

Monitor Progress   L2

Answers
Figure 1 Decomposers break down wastes and dead organisms and recycle these materials.

✓ Reading Checkpoint Both herbivores and carnivores feed on other organisms.

E ● 43

Food Chains and Food Webs

Teach Key Concepts

Linking Energy Pathways

Focus Remind students that a food web includes several food chains.

Teach Call on students to identify food chains pictured in Figure 2. Ask: **With only one top consumer, the fox, how many food chains are in the web?** (*At least six*) **What are the producers in this food web?** (*Grasses, trees, other plants*) **What are the first-level consumers?** (*Rabbit, mouse, grasshopper, termite*) **The second-level consumers?** (*Mouse, garter snake, shrew, fox, woodpecker*) **The third-level consumers?** (*Garter snake, fox*) **How can the mouse be both a first- and second-level consumer?** (*It's an omnivore that eats both plants and insects*) **How do decomposers gain energy?** (*They consume wastes and remains.*)

Apply Challenge each student in a group to draw a food chain from an assigned ecosystem and then as a group to combine the food chains into a food web. **learning modality: visual**

 **Teaching Resources**

• Transparency E13

Address Misconceptions

Energy for Dark Ecosystems

Focus Tell students that not all ecosystems require light.

Teach Point out that ecosystems surrounding deep-sea hydrothermal vents are too far below the water surface to receive sunlight. Explain that bacteria living near the vents make food by harnessing energy from chemicals in the water.

Apply Ask: **How is this ecosystem similar to the one based on photosynthesis?** (*Like plants, bacteria are producers and provide food for consumers.*) **learning modality: verbal**

Lab zone Try This **Activity**

Weaving a Food Web

This activity shows how the organisms in a food web are interconnected.

1. Your teacher will assign you a role in the food web.
2. Hold one end of each of several pieces of yarn in your hand. Give the other ends of your yarn to the other organisms to which your organism is linked.
3. Your teacher will now eliminate an organism. All the organisms connected to the missing organism should drop the yarn that connects them.

Making Models How many organisms were affected by the removal of just one organism? What does this activity show about the importance of each organism in a food web?

Lab zone Try This **Activity**

Skills Focus Making models

Materials long pieces of yarn

Time 15 minutes

Tips You can use the food web shown in Figure 2. If you use another food web, be prepared to help students decide which organisms eat and are eaten by other organisms. In Step 3, eliminate either a first- or second-level consumer.

Expected Outcome The number of other organisms affected will depend on the food web you use and the organism you eliminate. In all cases, however, students should recognize that all or most of the food web is affected.

Extend Let students repeat the activity using a different food web. **learning modality: kinesthetic**

Food Chains and Food Webs

As you have read, energy enters most ecosystems as sunlight and is converted into food molecules by producers. This energy is transferred to each organism that eats a producer, and then to other organisms that feed on these consumers. **The movement of energy through an ecosystem can be shown in diagrams called food chains and food webs.**

Food Chains A **food chain** is a series of events in which one organism eats another and obtains energy. You can follow one food chain in Figure 2. The first organism in a food chain is always a producer, such as the tree. The second organism feeds on the producer and is called a first-level consumer. The termite is a first-level consumer. Next, a second-level consumer eats the first-level consumer. The second-level consumer in this example is the woodpecker.

Food Webs A food chain shows only one possible path along which energy can move through an ecosystem. But just as you do not eat the same thing every day, neither do most other organisms. Most producers and consumers are part of many food chains. A more realistic way to show the flow of energy through an ecosystem is a food web. As shown in Figure 2, a **food web** consists of the many overlapping food chains in an ecosystem.

In Figure 2, you can trace the many food chains in a woodland ecosystem. Note that an organism may play more than one role in an ecosystem. For example, an omnivore such as the mouse is a first-level consumer when it eats grass. But when the mouse eats a grasshopper, it is a second-level consumer.

Just as food chains overlap and connect, food webs interconnect as well. While a gull might eat a fish at the ocean, it might also eat a mouse at a landfill. The gull, then, is part of two food webs—an ocean food web and a land food web. All the world's food webs interconnect in what can be thought of as a global food web.

Reading Checkpoint What energy role is filled by the first organism in a food chain?

Food Chain

Woodpecker

Termite

Tree

FIGURE 2
A Food Web

A food web consists of many interconnected food chains. Trace the path of energy through the producers, consumers, and decomposers. **Interpreting Diagrams** *Which organisms in the food web are acting as herbivores? Which are carnivores?*

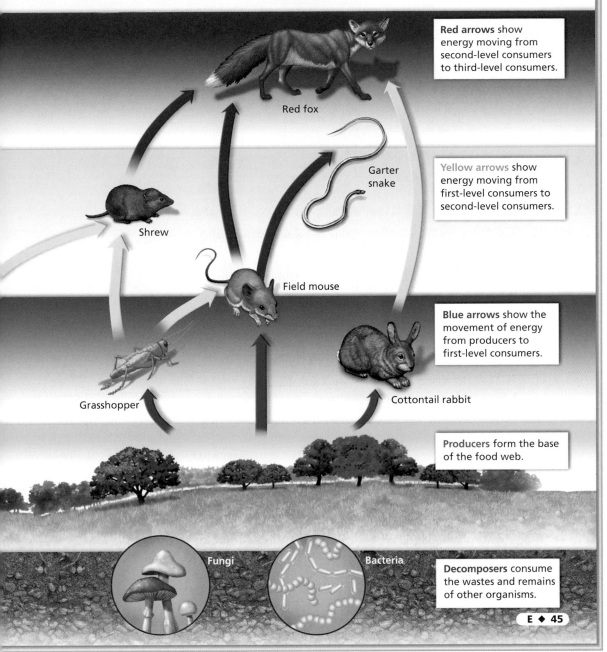

Red arrows show energy moving from second-level consumers to third-level consumers.

Red fox

Garter snake

Yellow arrows show energy moving from first-level consumers to second-level consumers.

Shrew

Field mouse

Blue arrows show the movement of energy from producers to first-level consumers.

Grasshopper

Cottontail rabbit

Producers form the base of the food web.

Fungi

Bacteria

Decomposers consume the wastes and remains of other organisms.

E ◆ 45

Observing Decomposition

Materials earthworms, terrarium, potting soil, shredded leaves or grass clippings, water

Time 15 minutes for setup

Focus Tell students that earthworms and other small animals in soil help decompose dead material by breaking it down into smaller pieces.

Teach Have students set up a class earthworm farm that they can observe closely. Fill a terrarium about two-thirds full of potting soil, mix in some shredded leaves or grass clippings, moisten the soil, and add the worms. Ask: **What do you think will happen to the food scraps?** *(The worms will break them down.)* Maintain observations throughout the study of this chapter. Students can periodically bury cut-up scraps of fruits and vegetables.

Apply When observations are complete, add the worms and soil to an outdoor garden. Ask: **How did the worms in the farm affect the soil?** *(They composted it.)* **learning modality: visual**

Monitor Progress _____ **L2**

Oral Presentation Randomly ask students to name a type of consumer and explain how it is classified.

Answers
Figure 2 Herbivores: termite, grasshopper, field mouse, rabbit; carnivores: field mouse, shrew, garter snake, fox.

Reading Checkpoint The first organisms in a food chain play the role of producer.

Energy Pyramids

Teach Key Concepts
L2

Identifying Available Energy

Focus Relate the shape of an energy pyramid to the diminishing amount of energy available, moving from bottom to top.

Teach Draw an empty pyramid on the board; divide it into four horizontal sections, numbered 1–4 from bottom to top. Ask: **Which level will include the producers?** *(Level 1)* **Which level includes the top consumer?** *(Level 4)* **Which levels include consumers?** *(Levels 2, 3, and 4)* **Which level represents the most available energy?** *(Level 1)* **The least available energy?** *(Level 4)* **Which level supports the fewest organisms?** *(Level 4)*

Apply Provide index cards bearing these energy pyramid labels: *Most Energy Available, Least Energy Available, Producers, Consumers, Top Consumer,* and the like. Assign students to attach their labels to a pyramid outline on the board. **learning modality: visual**

All in One **Teaching Resources**

• Transparency E14

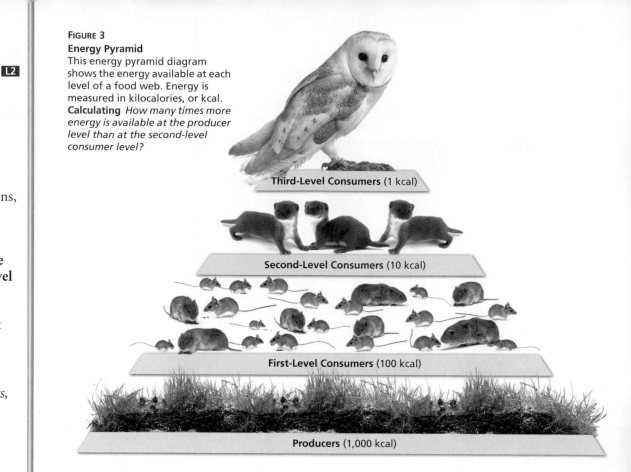

FIGURE 3
Energy Pyramid
This energy pyramid diagram shows the energy available at each level of a food web. Energy is measured in kilocalories, or kcal.
Calculating *How many times more energy is available at the producer level than at the second-level consumer level?*

Third-Level Consumers (1 kcal)

Second-Level Consumers (10 kcal)

First-Level Consumers (100 kcal)

Producers (1,000 kcal)

Energy Pyramids

When an organism in an ecosystem eats, it obtains energy. The organism uses some of this energy to move, grow, reproduce, and carry out other life activities. This means that only some of the energy it obtains will be available to the next organism in the food web.

A diagram called an **energy pyramid** shows the amount of energy that moves from one feeding level to another in a food web. You can see an energy pyramid in Figure 3. **The most energy is available at the producer level of the pyramid. As you move up the pyramid, each level has less energy available than the level below.** An energy pyramid gets its name from the shape of the diagram—wider at the base and narrower at the top.

Differentiated Instruction

Special Needs
L1
Visualizing Energy Transfers To assist students needing help visualizing energy transfers in an energy pyramid, divide the class into groups of three. Distribute scissors and graph paper. The first student, the "producer," should cut a 10-by-10 block of squares from graph paper. The block represents the total amount of food energy stored in the producer. The "producer" should then cut a row of 10 squares from the block and pass it on to the second student, the "first-level consumer." That student should cut one square from the row and pass it to the third student, the "second-level consumer." Students will see that only a small portion of the original energy stored in the producer reaches the second-level consumer. **learning modality: kinesthetic**

In general, only about 10 percent of the energy at one level of a food web is transferred to the next higher level. The other 90 percent of the energy is used for the organism's life processes or is lost to the environment as heat. Since about 90 percent of the energy is lost at each step, there is not enough energy to support many feeding levels in an ecosystem.

The organisms at higher feeding levels of an energy pyramid do not necessarily require less energy to live than do the organisms at lower levels. Since so much energy is lost at each level, the amount of energy available at the producer level limits the number of consumers that the ecosystem is able to support. As a result, there are usually few organisms at the highest level in a food web.

 Reading Checkpoint Why is the pyramid shape useful for showing the energy available at each of the levels of a food web?

FIGURE 4
Energy Flow
This barn owl will soon use the energy contained in the rat to carry out its own life processes.

Section 1 Assessment

Target Reading Skill Building Vocabulary Use your definitions to help answer the questions below.

Reviewing Key Concepts

1. **a. Identifying** Name the three energy roles that organisms fill in an ecosystem.
   b. Explaining How do organisms in each of the three energy roles obtain energy?
   c. Classifying Identify the energy roles of the following organisms in a pond ecosystem: tadpole, algae, heron.
2. **a. Defining** What is a food chain? What is a food web?
   b. Comparing and Contrasting Why is a food web a more realistic way of portraying an ecosystem than is a food chain?
3. **a. Reviewing** What does an energy pyramid show?
   b. Describing How does the amount of energy available at one level of an energy pyramid compare to the amount of energy available at the next level up?
   c. Relating Cause and Effect Why are there usually few organisms at the top of an energy pyramid?

Lab zone **At-Home Activity**

Energy-Role Walk Take a short walk outdoors with a family member to look for producers, consumers, and decomposers. Create a list of the organisms and their energy roles. For each consumer, try to classify it further according to what it eats and its level. Then explain to your family member how energy flows in ecosystems.

Lab zone **At Home Activity**

Energy-Role Walk Before students take the walk with their families, review as a class the different energy roles. Distinguish between the different types of consumers—herbivore, omnivore, carnivore, and scavenger—and discuss the different levels of consumers.

Lab zone **Chapter Project**

Keep Students on Track When students prepare their written plans, instruct them to use this format: a statement of the hypothesis, a list of materials, a step-by-step procedure, and a data table for recording results. Make sure students will keep all variables the same for both chambers except for the variable being tested with the second chamber. Also review students' planned data tables.

Monitor Progress ____ L2

Answers
Figure 3 There is 100 times more energy available at the producer level.

Reading Checkpoint The shape shows how available energy decreases at higher levels of a food web.

Assess

Reviewing Key Concepts

1. **a.** Producers, consumers, and decomposers **b.** Producers use energy, usually sunlight, to make their own food; consumers eat other organisms; decomposers break down organisms' wastes and remains. **c.** Algae: producers; tadpole and heron: consumers
2. **a.** A food chain is a series of events by which one organism eats another and obtains energy; a food web consists of many overlapping food chains. **b.** Because most organisms are part of many overlapping food chains
3. **a.** The amount of energy that moves from one feeding level to another in a food web **b.** The amount of energy available on one level of an energy pyramid is 10 times greater than that available at the next level up. **c.** Because so much energy is lost from one level to the next level up, the energy available at the top level can support few organisms.

Reteach L1
Review the different energy roles of organisms in an ecosystem, and then discuss how energy flow is represented by food chains, food webs, and energy pyramids.

Performance Assessment
Drawing Have each student draw a food chain of his or her own choice and label each organism to show (1) its energy role, (2) whether each consumer is a herbivore, and (3) the percentage of energy available at each energy level in the food chain.

All in One Teaching Resources
- Section Summary: *Energy Flow in Ecosystems*
- Review and Reinforce: *Energy Flow in Ecosystems*
- Enrich: *Energy Flow in Ecosystems*

Objectives

After completing the lesson, students will be able to

E.2.2.1 Name and describe processes involved in the water cycle.

E.2.2.2 Explain how carbon and oxygen are recycled in an ecosystem.

E.2.2.3 Define and describe the nitrogen cycle.

Target Reading Skill

Sequencing Explain that organizing information from beginning to end helps students understand a step-by-step process.

Answers
1. Water evaporates.
2. Clouds form.
3. Precipitation falls.
4. Precipitation runs off or becomes groundwater.

All in One Teaching Resources
• Transparency E15

Preteach

Build Background Knowledge   L2

Understanding a Cycle

Ask: **What is a cycle?** *(A series of things that repeat over and over again)* **What are some examples of cycles?** *(Seasons of the year, days of the week, life cycles of plants and animals, and so forth)*

Reading Preview

Key Concepts
• What processes are involved in the water cycle?
• How are carbon and oxygen recycled in ecosystems?
• What is the nitrogen cycle?

Key Terms
• water cycle   • evaporation
• condensation   • precipitation
• nitrogen fixation

Target Reading Skill

Sequencing A sequence is the order in which a series of events occurs. As you read, make a cycle diagram that shows the water cycle. Write each event of the water cycle in a separate oval.

The Water Cycle

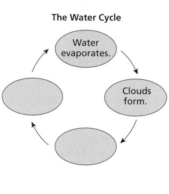

Lab zone Discover Activity

Are You Part of a Cycle?

1. Hold a small mirror a few centimeters from your mouth.
2. Exhale onto the mirror.
3. Observe the surface of the mirror.

Think It Over

Inferring What is the substance that forms on the mirror? Where did this substance come from?

A pile of crumpled cars is ready for loading into a giant compactor. The aluminum and copper pieces have already been removed so that they can be recycled, or used again. Now the steel will be reclaimed at a recycling plant. Earth has a limited supply of aluminum, copper, and the iron used in steel. Recycling old cars is one way to ensure a steady supply of these materials.

Like the supply of metal for building cars, the supply of matter in an ecosystem is limited. Matter in an ecosystem includes water, carbon, oxygen, nitrogen, and many other substances. If matter could not be recycled, ecosystems would quickly run out of the raw materials necessary for life. In this section, you will learn about some cycles of matter: the water cycle, the carbon and oxygen cycles, and the nitrogen cycle.

To understand how these substances cycle over and over through an ecosystem, you need to know a few basic terms that describe the structure of matter. Matter is made up of tiny particles called atoms. Two or more atoms that are joined and act as a unit make up a molecule. For example, a water molecule consists of two hydrogen atoms and one oxygen atom.

The Water Cycle

Water is essential for life. To ensure a steady supply, Earth's water must be recycled. The **water cycle** is the continuous process by which water moves from Earth's surface to the atmosphere and back. **The processes of evaporation, condensation, and precipitation make up the water cycle.** As you read about these processes, follow the cycle in Figure 5.

Lab zone Discover Activity

Skills Focus Inferring

Materials small mirror

Time 5 minutes

Tips If the weather is very warm and humid when students do this activity, moisture may not condense on the mirror. In this case, you can cool the mirrors in a refrigerator for a short time beforehand.

Expected Outcome As water vapor from students' breath cools, tiny droplets of liquid water will condense on the mirrors.

Think It Over The substance is water; it came from water vapor in the students' exhaled breath.

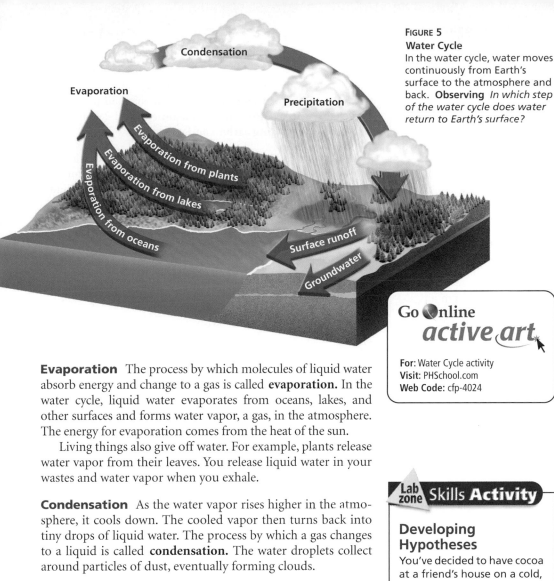

FIGURE 5
Water Cycle
In the water cycle, water moves continuously from Earth's surface to the atmosphere and back. **Observing** *In which step of the water cycle does water return to Earth's surface?*

Condensation

Evaporation

Precipitation

Evaporation from plants

Evaporation from lakes

Evaporation from oceans

Surface runoff

Groundwater

Go Online
active art

For: Water Cycle activity
Visit: PHSchool.com
Web Code: cfp-4024

Evaporation The process by which molecules of liquid water absorb energy and change to a gas is called **evaporation.** In the water cycle, liquid water evaporates from oceans, lakes, and other surfaces and forms water vapor, a gas, in the atmosphere. The energy for evaporation comes from the heat of the sun.

Living things also give off water. For example, plants release water vapor from their leaves. You release liquid water in your wastes and water vapor when you exhale.

Condensation As the water vapor rises higher in the atmosphere, it cools down. The cooled vapor then turns back into tiny drops of liquid water. The process by which a gas changes to a liquid is called **condensation.** The water droplets collect around particles of dust, eventually forming clouds.

Precipitation As more water vapor condenses, the drops of water in the cloud grow larger. Eventually the heavy drops fall back to Earth as **precipitation**—rain, snow, sleet, or hail. Most precipitation falls back into oceans or lakes. The precipitation that falls on land may soak into the soil and become groundwater. Or the precipitation may run off the land, eventually flowing back into a river or ocean.

 Reading Checkpoint What process causes water from the surface of the ocean to enter the atmosphere as water vapor?

Lab zone Skills Activity

Developing Hypotheses
You've decided to have cocoa at a friend's house on a cold, rainy day. As your friend boils some water, you notice that the inside of a window near the stove is covered with water droplets. Your friend thinks the window is leaking. Using what you know about the water cycle, can you propose another explanation for the water droplets?

Chapter 2 E ◆ 49

The Water Cycle

Teach Key Concepts ▫L2

Identifying Water Cycle Processes

Focus Explain that several processes take place in the water cycle.

Teach Direct students to Figure 5. Ask: **What is the function of the water cycle?** *(It moves water from Earth's surface to the atmosphere and back.)* **Which process includes melted snow entering rivers?** *(Surface runoff)*

Apply Ask: **How can you tell by the figure that the water cycle is continuous?** *(All three processes go on at once.)* **learning modality: visual**

All in One Teaching Resources
• Transparency E16

Go Online
active art

For: Water Cycle activity
Visit: PHSchool.com
Web Code: cfp-4024

Students can examine how water moves through the water cycle.

Independent Practice ▫L2

All in One Teaching Resources
• Guided Reading and Study Worksheet: *Cycles of Matter*

⊙ **Student Edition on Audio CD**

Monitor Progress ▫L2

Drawing Have each student draw and label a simple diagram of the water cycle without referring to Figure 5. Students can save their drawings in their portfolios.

Answers
Figure 5 Precipitation

Reading Checkpoint Evaporation (a liquid changes into a gas)

Lab zone Skills Activity

Skills Focus Developing hypotheses
Materials none
Time 5 minutes
Tips Have students do this activity after they have read the section about the water cycle.
Expected Outcome The water droplets on the cold window condensed from the

water vapor that evaporated from the boiling water.

Extend Have students draw and label a simple diagram, similar to Figure 5, which shows the water cycle operating in this example. For precipitation, students could show tiny water droplets joining to form larger drops that trickle down the window.
learning modality: logical/mathematical

The Carbon and Oxygen Cycles

Teach Key Concepts L2

Describing the Link Between Cycles

Focus Remind students that the carbon and oxygen cycles are linked and that producers and consumers all play a part.

Teach Review the basic processes of photosynthesis. Ask: **What is the role of producers in the carbon and oxygen cycles?** *(Producers take in carbon dioxide during photosynthesis and use it to make carbon-containing food molecules. They release oxygen as a product of photosynthesis.)* **How do consumers fit into the carbon and oxygen cycles?** *(Consumers take in carbon molecules by eating producers; when they break these molecules down, they release carbon. Consumers use oxygen in air to perform life functions.)*

Apply Ask: **How will depriving a closed terrarium of sunlight affect the oxygen and carbon cycles of the plants and small animals inside?** *(Without sunlight, plants can't make food and won't release oxygen; consumers will have no food sources and insufficient oxygen and will not release carbon.)* **learning modality: logical/mathematical**

All in One Teaching Resources

• Transparency E17

Help Students Read

Asking Questions Refer to the Content Refresher, which provides guidelines for asking questions. Have students make a three-column table. In the first column, have them list the heading and subheadings in this section. In the second column, have them rephrase the headings as questions. Then in the third column have them write the answers to the questions they wrote. When students are finished reading the section, have volunteers read their questions and answers.

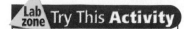
Lab zone Try This **Activity**

Carbon and Oxygen Blues

This activity explores the role of producers in the carbon and oxygen cycles.

1. Your teacher will provide you with two plastic cups containing bromthymol blue solution. Bromthymol blue solution appears blue in the absence of carbon dioxide and appears yellow in the presence of carbon dioxide. Note the color of the solution.
2. Place two sprigs of an *Elodea* plant into one of the cups. Do not put any *Elodea* into the second cup. Cover both cups with plastic wrap. Wash your hands.
3. Place the cups where they will not be disturbed. Observe the two cups over the next few days. Note any color changes.

Inferring What do your observations indicate about the role of producers in the carbon and oxygen cycles?

FIGURE 6
Rising Carbon Dioxide Levels
When forests burn, large amounts of carbon dioxide are released into the air. In addition, there are fewer trees available to absorb carbon dioxide from the air.

50 ◆ E

The Carbon and Oxygen Cycles

Two other substances necessary for life are carbon and oxygen. Carbon is an essential building block in the bodies of living things. Most organisms use oxygen for their life processes. **In ecosystems, the processes by which carbon and oxygen are recycled are linked. Producers, consumers, and decomposers play roles in recycling carbon and oxygen.**

The Carbon Cycle Producers take in carbon dioxide gas from the air during photosynthesis. They use carbon from the carbon dioxide to make food molecules—carbon-containing molecules such as sugars and starches. When consumers eat producers, they take in the carbon-containing food molecules. When consumers break down these food molecules to obtain energy, they release carbon dioxide and water as waste products. When producers and consumers die, decomposers break down their remains and return carbon compounds to the soil. Some decomposers also release carbon dioxide as a waste product.

The Oxygen Cycle Like carbon, oxygen cycles through ecosystems. Producers release oxygen as a result of photosynthesis. Most organisms take in oxygen from the air and use it to carry out their life processes.

Human Impact Human activities also affect the levels of carbon and oxygen in the atmosphere. When humans burn oil and other fuels, carbon dioxide is released into the atmosphere. When humans clear forests for lumber, fuel, and farmland, carbon dioxide levels also rise. As you know, producers take in carbon dioxide during photosynthesis. When trees are removed from the ecosystem, there are fewer producers to absorb carbon dioxide. There is a greater effect if trees are burned down to clear a forest. If trees are burned down to clear a forest, additional carbon dioxide is released in the burning process.

Reading Checkpoint What role do producers play in the carbon and oxygen cycles?

Lab zone Try This **Activity**

Skills Focus Inferring

Materials two plastic cups, bromthymol blue solution, two sprigs of *Elodea,* plastic wrap

Time 10 minutes for setup; 15 minutes of observations over several days

Tips Remind students to cover the cups and to keep them in a protected area.

Expected Outcome The solution containing *Elodea* will appear blue because the plant has taken up carbon dioxide; the solution without *Elodea* will appear yellow.

Think It Over Producers remove carbon dioxide from their environment as they make their own food and release oxygen.
learning modality: kinesthetic

FIGURE 7

Carbon and Oxygen Cycles

This scene shows how the carbon and oxygen cycles are linked. Producers, consumers, and decomposers all play a role in recycling these two substances.
Interpreting Diagrams *How do human activities affect the carbon and oxygen cycles?*

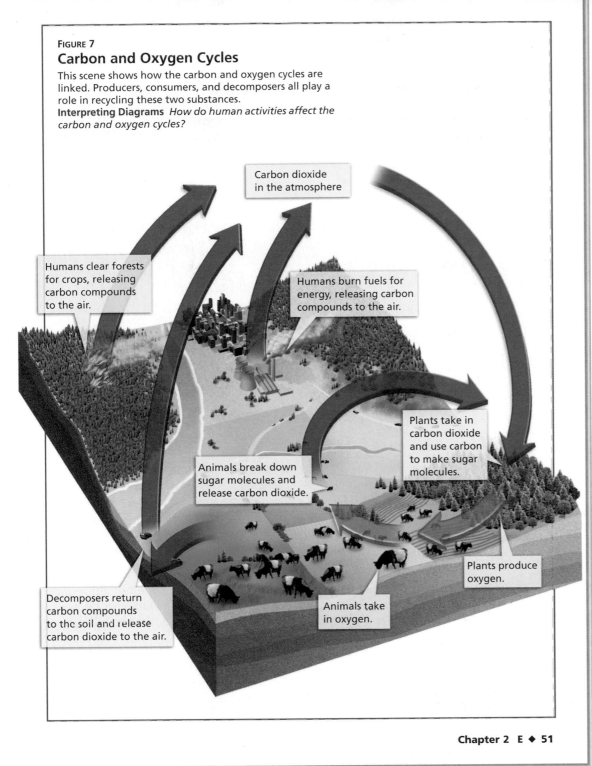

Carbon dioxide in the atmosphere

Humans clear forests for crops, releasing carbon compounds to the air.

Humans burn fuels for energy, releasing carbon compounds to the air.

Plants take in carbon dioxide and use carbon to make sugar molecules.

Animals break down sugar molecules and release carbon dioxide.

Decomposers return carbon compounds to the soil and release carbon dioxide to the air.

Animals take in oxygen.

Plants produce oxygen.

Chapter 2 E ◆ 51

Predicting Carbon and Oxygen Cycling

Materials none

Time 10 minutes

Focus Review the differing roles of producers and consumers in recycling carbon and oxygen.

Teach Describe for students a sealed jar containing guppies, plants, algae, and snails. Provide a picture if possible. Ask: **Which organisms in the jar are producers?** *(The plants and algae)* **What do the producers release when they conduct photosynthesis?** *(Oxygen)* **What happens to the oxygen?** *(It is "breathed in" by the guppies and snails.)* **Where do the producers get the carbon dioxide they need?** *(It is released by the guppies and snails.)*

Apply Ask: **Would you predict that this cycle would go on indefinitely? Why or why not?** *(Yes; as long as the producers receive sunlight and the guppies and snails receive food, the carbon and oxygen will continue to cycle between the producers and the consumers.)* **learning modality: logical/ mathematical**

Differentiated Instruction

English Learners/Beginning Comprehension: Modified Cloze L1

Distribute a simplified paragraph about carbon and oxygen cycles, leaving some strategic words blank. For example, "In photosynthesis, producers take in _____ from the air and release _____. When consumers eat _____, they take in carbon." Provide students with a list of the correct answers and have them fill in each blank with a word from the list. If necessary, read the paragraph aloud.
learning modality: visual

English Learners/Intermediate Comprehension: Modified Cloze L2

Distribute the cloze paragraph designed for Beginning students. Students can work in pairs to collaborate in writing a definition, in English, of the words that they filled in.
learning modality: verbal

Monitor Progress ———— L2

Writing Have each student write a paragraph that describes one way human activities affect the carbon and oxygen cycles.

Answer

✓ **Reading Checkpoint** Producers take in carbon dioxide gas and, through photosynthesis, release oxygen and provide carbon to consumers in the form of food sources.

The Nitrogen Cycle

Teach Key Concepts L2

Identifying Nitrogen Cycling

Focus Emphasize that most organisms cannot utilize nitrogen gas until bacteria make nitrogen available.

Teach Refer students to Figure 8. Ask: **By what process do bacteria turn nitrogen into a usable form?** (*Nitrogen fixation*) **What organisms return simple nitrogen compounds to the soil?** (*Decomposers*)

Apply Ask: **How does the nitrogen cycle differ from the carbon and oxygen cycles?** (*Nitrogen becomes available to organisms in the soil rather than in air.*) **learning modality: visual**

 **Teaching Resources**

- Transparency E18

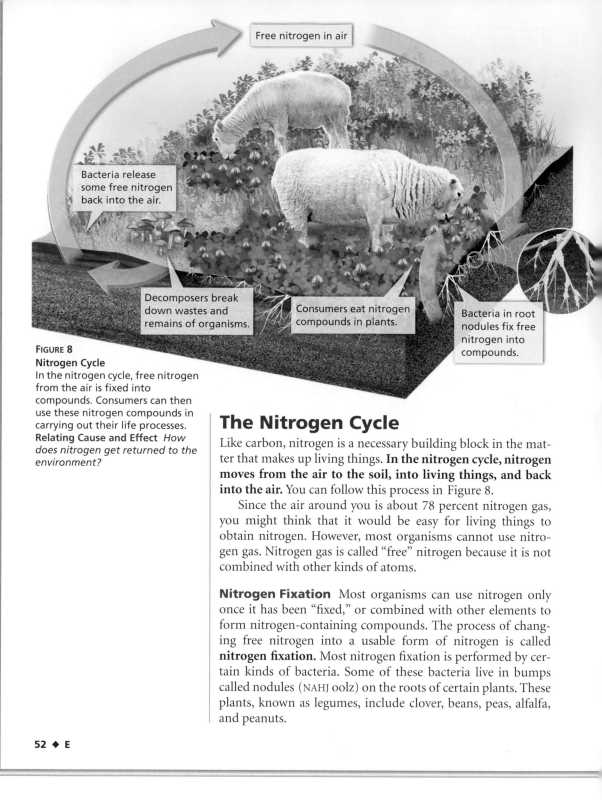

Lab zone Build Inquiry L1

Playing Nitrogen Cycle Roles

Materials blue, white index cards; tape

Time 15 minutes

Focus Let students role-play materials and organisms shown in Figure 8.

Teach Assign roles: air, clover plants, sheep, nitrogen-fixing bacteria in nodules on the clover's roots, decomposers in the soil, and bacteria in the soil. Give the "air" students white index cards to represent free nitrogen, and the "nodule bacteria" students blue index cards and tape. Begin the cycle with the air students handing white cards to the nodule bacteria students, who attach, or "fix," each white card to one of their blue cards and then hand the cards to the "clover plants." To show that some plants are eaten by consumers, some clover plants should hand their cards to "sheep." To show that some plants and animals die and decompose, other clover plants should hand their cards to "decomposers," who in turn hand the cards to "soil bacteria."

Apply Ask: **How is the cycle completed?** (*Soil bacteria release nitrogen to the air.*) **learning modality: kinesthetic**

Figure 8
Free nitrogen in air

Bacteria release some free nitrogen back into the air.

Decomposers break down wastes and remains of organisms.

Consumers eat nitrogen compounds in plants.

Bacteria in root nodules fix free nitrogen into compounds.

FIGURE 8
Nitrogen Cycle
In the nitrogen cycle, free nitrogen from the air is fixed into compounds. Consumers can then use these nitrogen compounds in carrying out their life processes.
Relating Cause and Effect How does nitrogen get returned to the environment?

The Nitrogen Cycle

Like carbon, nitrogen is a necessary building block in the matter that makes up living things. **In the nitrogen cycle, nitrogen moves from the air to the soil, into living things, and back into the air.** You can follow this process in Figure 8.

Since the air around you is about 78 percent nitrogen gas, you might think that it would be easy for living things to obtain nitrogen. However, most organisms cannot use nitrogen gas. Nitrogen gas is called "free" nitrogen because it is not combined with other kinds of atoms.

Nitrogen Fixation Most organisms can use nitrogen only once it has been "fixed," or combined with other elements to form nitrogen-containing compounds. The process of changing free nitrogen into a usable form of nitrogen is called **nitrogen fixation.** Most nitrogen fixation is performed by certain kinds of bacteria. Some of these bacteria live in bumps called nodules (NAHJ oolz) on the roots of certain plants. These plants, known as legumes, include clover, beans, peas, alfalfa, and peanuts.

The relationship between the bacteria and the legumes is an example of mutualism. Both the bacteria and the plant benefit from this relationship: The bacteria feed on the plant's sugars, and the plant is supplied with nitrogen in a usable form.

Return of Nitrogen to the Environment

Once nitrogen has been fixed, organisms can use it to build proteins and other complex compounds. Decomposers, in turn, break down these complex compounds in animal wastes and the bodies of dead organisms. Decomposition returns simple nitrogen compounds to the soil. Nitrogen can cycle from the soil to producers and consumers many times. At some point, however, bacteria break down the nitrogen compounds completely. These bacteria then release free nitrogen back into the air. The cycle continues from there.

 Reading Checkpoint Where do some nitrogen-fixing bacteria live?

FIGURE 9
Growth in Nitrogen-Poor Soil
Pitcher plants can grow in nitrogen-poor soil because they have another way of obtaining nitrogen. Insects become trapped in the plant's tube-shaped leaves. The plant then digests the insects and uses their nitrogen compounds for its functions.

Section 2 Assessment

Target Reading Skill **Sequencing** Refer to your cycle diagram about the water cycle as you answer Question 1.

Reviewing Key Concepts

1. a. **Defining** Name and define the three major processes that occur during the water cycle.
   b. **Making Generalizations** Defend this statement: The sun is the driving force behind the water cycle.
2. a. **Reviewing** Which two substances are linked in one recycling process?
   b. **Comparing and Contrasting** What role do producers play in the carbon and oxygen cycles? What role do consumers play in these cycles?
   c. **Developing Hypotheses** How might the removal of all of the producers in a community affect the carbon and oxygen cycles?

3. a. **Reviewing** Why do organisms need nitrogen?
   b. **Sequencing** Outline the major steps in the nitrogen cycle.
   c. **Predicting** What might happen in a community if all the nitrogen-fixing bacteria died?

Writing in Science

Comic Strip Choose one of the cycles discussed in this section. Then draw a comic strip with five panels that depicts the important events in the cycle. Remember that the last panel must end with the same event that begins the first panel.

Chapter 2 E ◆ 53

Section
3 Biogeography

Objectives

After completing the lesson, students will be able to

E.2.3.1 Explain how the movement of the continents has affected the distribution of species.

E.2.3.2 Name and describe three ways that dispersal of organisms occurs.

E.2.3.3 Name and describe factors that can limit the dispersal of a species.

Target Reading Skill ⟳

Relating Cause and Effect Explain that cause is the reason why something happens. The effect is what happens because of the cause. Relating cause and effect helps students relate the reason for what happens to what happens as a result.

Answers

Three causes of dispersal: Wind, water, and living things, including humans

All in One Teaching Resources

• Transparency E19

Preteach

Build Background Knowledge   L2

Identifying Why Organisms Disperse
Ask: **What are some reasons that animals move from one place to another?** (*Seasonal migrations, overpopulation or too much competition in the original area, need for food or water*)

Reading Preview

Key Concepts
• How has the movement of the continents affected the distribution of species?
• What are three ways that dispersal of organisms occurs?
• What factors can limit the dispersal of a species?

Key Terms
• biogeography
• continental drift • dispersal
• exotic species • climate

⟳ Target Reading Skill
Relating Cause and Effect As you read, identify three causes of dispersal. Write the information in a graphic organizer like the one below.

Causes

Wind	→	**Effect**
	→	Dispersal of species
	→	

Lab zone Discover **Activity**

How Can You Move a Seed?
1. Place a few corn kernels at one end of a shallow pan.
2. Make a list of ways you could move the kernels to the other side of the pan. You may use any of the simple materials your teacher has provided.
3. Now try each method. Record whether each was successful in moving the kernels across the pan.

Think It Over
Predicting How might seeds be moved from place to place?

Imagine how European explorers must have felt when they saw Australia for the first time. Instead of familiar grazing animals such as horses and deer, they saw animals that looked like giant rabbits with long tails. Peering into eucalyptus trees, the explorers saw bearlike koalas. And who could have dreamed up an egg-laying animal with a beaver's tail, a duck's bill, and thick fur? You can see why people who heard the first descriptions of the platypus accused the explorers of lying!

As the explorers had learned, different species live in different parts of the world. The study of where organisms live is called **biogeography.** The word *biogeography* is made up of three Greek word roots: *bio,* meaning "life"; *geo,* meaning "Earth"; and *graph,* meaning "description." Together, these root words tell what biogeographers do—they describe where living things are found on Earth.

Koala in a ▶ eucalyptus tree in Australia

Lab zone Discover **Activity**

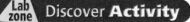

Skills Focus Predicting

Materials shallow pan; corn kernels; materials to move corn, such as water, straw, and tape

Time 15 minutes

Tips Students may have their own ideas about materials to use in addition to those you have provided.

Expected Outcome Students will find various ways to move the kernels—by pouring water next to them, blowing at them through a straw, picking them up with a piece of tape, and so forth.

Think It Over Based on the results of this activity, students might suggest that seeds are moved by wind, by moving water, and by being caught on an animal's fur or a person's clothing.

FIGURE 10
Continental Drift
The continents have drifted far from their positions 225 million years ago. Their movement is one factor affecting the distribution of organisms.
Interpreting Maps *How has Australia's location changed?*

Continental Drift

In addition to studying where species live, biogeographers also try to understand what led to the worldwide distribution of species that exists today. **One factor that has affected how species are distributed is the motion of Earth's continents.** The continents are parts of huge blocks of solid rock, called plates, that make up Earth's surface. Scientists have found that the plates have been moving very slowly for millions of years. As the plates move, the continents move with them in a process called **continental drift.**

Figure 10 shows how much the continents have moved over time. About 225 million years ago, all of today's continents were part of one large landmass now called Pangaea. But after millions of years of slow drifting, they have moved to their present locations.

Continental drift has had a great impact on the distribution of species. Consider Australia, for example. Millions of years ago Australia drifted away from the other landmasses. Organisms from other parts of the world could not reach the isolated island. Kangaroos, koalas, and other unique species developed in this isolation.

Reading Checkpoint What was Pangaea?

Means of Dispersal

The movement of organisms from one place to another is called **dispersal.** Organisms may be dispersed in several different ways. **Dispersal can be caused by wind, water, or living things, including humans.**

Wind and Water Many animals move into new areas on their own. But plants and small organisms need assistance to move from place to place. Wind can disperse seeds, the spores of fungi, tiny spiders, and other small, light organisms. Similarly, water transports objects that float, such as coconuts and leaves. Small animals may get a free ride to a new home on top of these floating rafts.

225 Million Years Ago

180–200 Million Years Ago

135 Million Years Ago

Earth Today

Go Online
active art
For: Continental Drift activity
Visit: PHSchool.com
Web Code: cfp-1015

Differentiated Instruction

Gifted and Talented **L3**
Explaining Continental Drift Ask students to research the geological processes driving continental drift *(plate tectonics)* and relate them to the occurrence of earthquakes and volcanoes. *(Earthquake and volcanic activity is concentrated near plate boundaries.)* Have students report their findings orally. **learning modality: verbal**

Special Needs **L1**
Identifying Dispersal Methods Connect the section's Discover activity to the section's content for students who need extra help by asking: **Which of the dispersal methods did you model when you moved the corn kernels?** *(Most students will have modeled all of the methods of dispersal mentioned in the text.)* **learning modality: logical/ mathematical**

Instruct

Continental Drift

Teach Key Concepts **L2**
Understanding Continents in Motion

Focus Tell students that Figure 10 shows a process that took hundreds of millions of years.

Teach Ask: **Why does Australia have so many unique organisms?** *(Australia drifted from the landmass and its species developed in isolation.)*

Apply Ask: **Have North and South America been connected ever since the breakup of Pangaea?** *(No)* **learning modality: visual**

All in One Teaching Resources
• Transparency E20

Go Online
active art
For: Continental Drift activity
Visit: PHSchool.com
Web Code: cfp-1015

Students explore the movement of continents from 225 million years ago to today.

Independent Practice **L2**

All in One Teaching Resources
• Guided Reading and Study Worksheet: *Biogeography*

Student Edition on Audio CD

Means of Dispersal

Teach Key Concepts **L2**
Describing How Species Disperse

Focus Have students study Figure 11.

Teach Ask: **What are three ways that organisms can be dispersed?** *(By wind, water, and other living things)*

Apply Ask: **When might seed dispersal not be beneficial?** *(When seeds are carried to an area where you do not want them to grow)*

Monitor Progress ___ **L2**

Answers
Figure 10 Australia moved away from Antarctica less than 135 million years ago.

Reading Checkpoint A landmass that contained all of today's continents about 225 million years ago

Limits to Dispersal

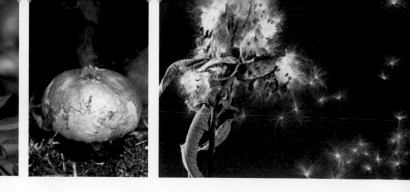

Teach Key Concepts   L2

Exploring Limits to Species Dispersal

Focus Tell students that species can be prevented from dispersing to new areas or from becoming successful there.

Teach Ask: **What are three factors limiting species dispersal?** *(Physical barriers, climate, and competition)* **If the seed of a tropical plant floated to Hawaii, would the species disperse successfully?** Have the class debate for or against this species' success. Ask students to give reasons for their opinions. *(For: seed overcame physical barriers, climate suits a tropical plant; against: existing plants can outcompete new species.)*

Apply Ask: **Which factors that limit dispersal also limit a population's size?** Students can refer to Populations and Communities. *(Competition and physical barrier)* Students should not equate weather and climate. **learning modality: logical/ mathematical**

Lab zone · Build Inquiry   L1

Relating Continental Drift to Dispersal

Materials world outline map, scissors

Time 15 minutes

Focus Review with students continental drift and species dispersal.

Teach Have students cut out the continents on a copy of a world map and arrange them as in the first map in Figure 10. Then have students move the continents into the positions of the third map, 135 million years ago. Ask: **Where would organisms still be able to move freely from one continent to another?** *(North America and Europe/Asia, Africa and South America, Antarctica and Australia)* Have students move the continents to their present location, in the fourth map. Ask: **What happened to India?** *(It joined Europe/Asia.)*

Apply Ask: **What do you think happened to organisms on the continents that remained separated?** *(They evolved into unique species found nowhere else in the world.)* **learning modality: kinesthetic**

FIGURE 11
Means of Dispersal
Berry seeds can be dispersed by animals, such as cedar waxwings (top left), that eat berries and leave seeds in their wastes. The spores of puffball mushrooms (top center) and the seeds of milkweed plants (top right) are usually dispersed by wind.
Inferring *What are two ways that seeds disperse?*

Other Living Things Organisms may also be dispersed by other living things. For example, a bird may eat berries in one area and deposit the seeds elsewhere in its wastes. And if your dog or cat has ever come home covered with sticky plant burs, you know another way seeds can get around.

Humans are also important to the dispersal of organisms. As people move around the world, they take organisms with them. Sometimes this dispersal is intentional, as when Europeans who explored Central and South America in the 1500s took corn and tomato plants back to Europe. Sometimes it is unintentional, as when insects are carried from one location to another by an airplane passenger. An organism that is carried into a new location by people is referred to as an **exotic species.**

Reading Checkpoint   How can humans disperse a species?

Limits to Dispersal

With all these means of dispersal, you might expect to find the same species everywhere in the world. Of course, that's not so. **Three factors that limit dispersal of a species are physical barriers, competition, and climate.**

Physical Barriers Barriers such as water, mountains, and deserts are hard to cross. These features can limit the movement of organisms. For example, once Australia became separated from the other continents, the ocean acted as a barrier to dispersal. Organisms could not easily move to or from Australia.

Competition When an organism enters a new area, it must compete for resources with the species already there. To survive, the organism must find a unique niche. Existing species may outcompete the new species. In this case, competition is a barrier to dispersal. Sometimes, however, new species outcompete the existing species. The existing species may be displaced.

Climate The typical weather pattern in an area over a long period of time is the area's **climate**. Climate differences can limit dispersal. For example, conditions at the top of the mountain shown in Figure 12 are very different from those at the base. The base of the mountain is warm and dry. Low shrubs and cactuses grow there. Higher up, the climate becomes cooler and wetter, and larger trees such as oaks and firs grow. Near the top of the mountain, it is very cold and windy. Only short plants can grow in this area.

Places with similar climates tend to have species that occupy similar niches. For example, most continents have a large area of flat, grassy plains. So these continents have organisms that occupy the niche of "large, grazing mammal." In North America, the large, grazing mammals of the grasslands are bison. In Africa, they are wildebeests and antelopes. And in Australia, they are kangaroos.

✔ **Reading Checkpoint** How does the climate at the base of a mountain differ from the climate at the top?

FIGURE 12
Climate Differences and Dispersal
The climate changes dramatically as you move up a tall mountain. Climate determines the distribution of species on different parts of the mountain.

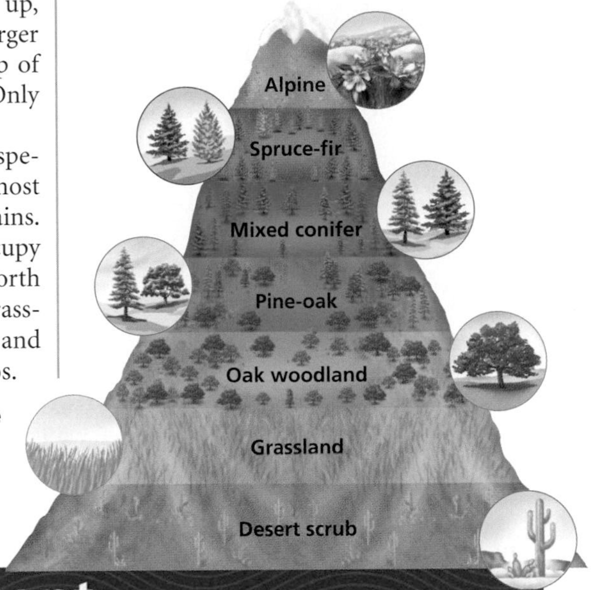

Alpine

Spruce-fir

Mixed conifer

Pine-oak

Oak woodland

Grassland

Desert scrub

Section 3 Assessment

◎ Target Reading Skill

Relating Cause and Effect Refer to your graphic organizer about means of dispersal to help you answer Question 2 below.

Reviewing Key Concepts

1. **a. Defining** What is continental drift?
   b. Explaining How has continental drift affected the dispersal of organisms?
   c. Relating Cause and Effect How can continental drift explain why unique species are often found on islands?

2. **a. Listing** What are three ways in which organisms can be dispersed?
   b. Explaining What role do humans play in the dispersal of species?
   c. Predicting Do you think the role of humans in the dispersal of species will increase or decrease in the next 50 years? Defend your answer.

3. **a. Identifying** What are three factors that can limit the dispersal of a species?
   b. Applying Concepts Suppose that a new species of insect were introduced to your area. How might competition limit its dispersal?

Lab zone **At-Home Activity**

Sock Walk Take an adult family member on a "sock walk" to learn about seed dispersal. Each person should wear a thick white sock over one shoe. Take a short walk through woods, a field, or a park. Back home, observe how many seeds you collected. Then plant the socks in pans of soil. Place the pans in a sunny spot and water them regularly. How many species did you successfully disperse?

Chapter 2 E ◆ 57

Lab zone **At Home Activity**

Sock Walk Before students plant their socks, remind them to tend to sprouting plants so that they can grow large enough to be identified as distinct species. Seek regular updates on the various outcomes.

Objectives

After completing the lesson, students will be able to

E.2.4.1 Name the six major biomes found on Earth.

E.2.4.2 Describe organisms that might be found in each biome and the adaptations they might possess.

E.2.4.3 Name and describe the factors that determine the type of biome found in an area.

Target Reading Skill 🔄

Comparing and Contrasting Explain that comparing and contrasting information shows how ideas, facts, and events are similar and different. The results of the comparison can have importance.

Answers

Tropical rain forest: warm all year; wet all year; orangutan. *Tundra:* cold all year; dry all year; mosses. *Temperate rain forest:* cool winters, warm in summer; rather wet all year; mule deer. *Desert:* usually hot with great daily extremes; dry all year; Gambel's quail. *Grassland:* temperatures vary throughout year; mostly dry with a wet season; grasses. *Deciduous forest:* warm in summer, cold in winter; moderate rainfall; red fox. *Boreal forest:* warm to cool in summer, cold in winter; abundant rain and snow; lynx.

All in One Teaching Resources

• Transparency E21

Preteach

Build Background Knowledge   L2

Predicting Effects of Climate

Ask: **What is the climate like in our area?** *(Students should describe conditions of temperature, precipitation, amount of sunlight during the seasons, and so forth.)* **How do you think our climate affects which organisms live here?** *(Answers will vary, depending on the climate of the area. For example, students may say that a warm, humid climate allows a great variety of organisms to live in the area.)*

Reading Preview

Key Concepts

• What are the six major biomes found on Earth?
• What factors determine the type of biome found in an area?

Key Terms

• biome • canopy • understory
• desert • grassland • savanna
• deciduous tree
• coniferous tree • tundra
• permafrost

🔄 Target Reading Skill

Comparing and Contrasting As you read, compare and contrast the different biomes by completing a table like the one below.

Characteristic	Tropical Rain Forest	Tundra
Temperature	Warm all year	
Precipitation		
Typical Organisms		

DISCOVERY CHANNEL SCHOOL

Ecosystems and Biomes

Video Preview
▶ Video Field Trip
Video Assessment

Lab zone — Discover Activity

How Much Rain Is That?

The table shows the typical amount of precipitation that falls each year in four locations. With your classmates, you will create a full-sized bar graph on a wall to represent these amounts.

Location	Precipitation (cm)
Mojave Desert	15
Illinois Prairie	70
Great Smoky Mountains	180
Costa Rican Rain Forest	350

1. Using a meter stick, measure a strip of adding-machine paper 15 centimeters long. Label this strip "Mojave Desert."
2. Repeat Step 1 for the other locations. Label each strip.
3. Follow your teacher's instructions on hanging your strips.

Think It Over

Developing Hypotheses What effect might the amount of precipitation have on the types of species that live in a location?

Congratulations! You and your classmates have been selected to take part in an around-the-world scientific expedition. On this expedition you will collect data on the climate and typical organisms of each of Earth's biomes. A **biome** is a group of land ecosystems with similar climates and organisms.

The ecologists leading your expedition have agreed to focus on six major biomes. **The six major biomes that most ecologists study are the rain forest, desert, grassland, deciduous forest, boreal forest, and tundra.**

Be sure to pack a variety of clothing for your expedition. You will visit places ranging from steamy tropical jungles to frozen Arctic plains. **It is mostly the climate—temperature and precipitation—in an area that determines its biome.** This is because climate limits the species of plants that can grow in an area. In turn, the species of plants determine the kinds of animals that live there.

Hurry up and pack—it's almost time to go!

Lab zone — Discover Activity

Skills Focus Developing hypotheses

Materials meter stick, adding-machine paper, scissors, marker, tape

Time 20 minutes

Tips CAUTION: Hanging the Costa Rican rain forest strip will require the use of a ladder. Choose three reliable students for this task, one to climb the ladder and two to hold the ladder securely. If you are not certain that students can do this task safely, have them hang the strips horizontally.

Expected Outcome Students should sequence the strips from least to most rainfall, as indicated in the table.

Think It Over The amount of rainfall affects what plant species can survive in a particular biome, and the plants in turn determine the consumer species found there.

Rain Forest Biomes

The first stop on your expedition is a rain forest. This biome is living up to its name—it's pouring! Fortunately, you remembered to pack a raincoat. After just a short shower, however, the sun reappears. Surprisingly, though, very little sunlight reaches you through the thick leaves above.

Plants are everywhere in the rain forest. Some plants, such as the ferns, flowers, and vines hanging from tree limbs, even grow on other plants! And animals are flying, creeping, and slithering all around you.

Temperate Rain Forests When you hear the term *rain forest*, you probably think of a warm, humid, "jungle" in the tropics. But there is another type of rain forest. The northwestern coast of the United States receives more than 300 centimeters of rain a year. Huge trees grow there, including cedars, redwoods, and Douglas firs. However, it is difficult to classify this region. Many ecologists refer to this ecosystem as a temperate rain forest. The term *temperate* means having moderate temperatures.

Rain Forest Biomes
- Tropical rain forest
- Temperate rain forest

FIGURE 13
Temperate Rain Forest
Temperate rain forests receive a great deal of rain and have moderate temperatures. Mule deer are commonly found in the Olympic Rain Forest in Washington State.
Interpreting Maps *Where is one temperate rain forest located?*

◄ Golden buprestid beetle

◄ Pileated woodpecker

E ◆ 59

Ecosystems and Biomes

Show the Video Field Trip to let students experience a desert biome and understand the adaptations and behaviors that help meerkats survive in a desert.

Instruct

Rain Forest Biomes

Teach Key Concepts   L2
Exploring the Rain Forests

Focus Tell students that tropical and temperate rain forests share many traits but differ in location and temperatures.

Teach Display a world map or globe and direct students to the biome map. Ask: **Where are the world's tropical rain forests located?** (*All are located at or near the equator.*) Locate the U. S. Pacific Northwest. Ask: **How do the location and climate of temperate rain forests differ from tropical rain forests?** (*Temperate rain forests are much farther north and much cooler.*)

Apply Ask: **How are temperate and tropical rain forests similar?** (*Both are humid, receive a lot of rain, and have a large variety of plant and animal species.*)
learning modality: visual

Independent Practice   L2

All in One **Teaching Resources**

- Guided Reading and Study Worksheet: *Biomes*

 **Student Edition on Audio CD**

Monitor Progress _____ L2

Answer
Figure 13 Along the U. S. northwestern coast

Desert Biomes

Teach Key Concepts   L2

Describing Desert Biomes

Focus Ask students who have visited a desert to describe it.

Teach Remind students that climate incorporates both temperature and precipitation. Ask: **What can you say about precipitation and evaporation in the desert?** *(Deserts receive less than 25 centimeters of precipitation each year; evaporation is greater than precipitation.)* **How might desert temperatures vary over a 24-hour day?** *(Deserts are very hot during the day but cool rapidly and can be very cold at night.)* Discuss the desert's hot, dry climate and the necessary adaptations organisms must possess to live under such harsh conditions.

Apply Ask: **How are desert animals adapted to the harsh climate?** *(Some animals burrow for long periods; others are active at night; some plants can store water.)*
learning modality: logical/mathematical

◄ Orangutan

▲ Bromeliad

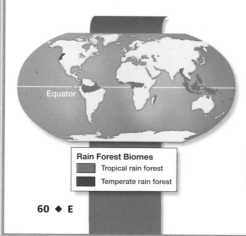

FIGURE 14
Tropical Rain Forest
Tropical rain forests are wet, warm biomes that contain an amazing variety of plants and other organisms. In the large photo, a river winds through the lush Indonesian rain forest.

Equator

Rain Forest Biomes
☐ Tropical rain forest
☐ Temperate rain forest

60 ◆ E

Tropical Rain Forests As you can see on the map, tropical rain forests are found in regions close to the equator. The climate is warm and humid all year long, and there is a lot of rain. Because of these climate conditions, an astounding variety of plants grow in tropical rain forests. In fact, scientists studying a 100-square-meter area of one rain forest identified 300 different kinds of trees!

Trees in the rainforest form several distinct layers. The tall trees form a leafy roof called the **canopy.** A few giant trees poke out above the canopy. Below the canopy, a second layer of shorter trees and vines form an **understory.** Understory plants grow well in the shade formed by the canopy. The forest floor is nearly dark, so only a few plants live there.

The abundant plant life in tropical rain forests provides habitats for many species of animals. Ecologists estimate that millions of species of insects live in tropical rain forests. These insects serve as a source of food for many reptiles, birds, and mammals. Many of these animals are, in turn, food sources for other animals. Although tropical rain forests cover only a small part of the planet, they probably contain more species of plants and animals than all the other biomes combined.

Reading Checkpoint What is the climate of the tropical rain forest?

Desert Biomes

The next stop on your expedition is a desert. It couldn't be more different from the tropical rain forest you just left. You step off the bus into the searing summer heat. At midday, you cannot even walk in the desert—the sand feels as hot as the hot water that comes from your faucets at home.

A **desert** is an area that receives less than 25 centimeters of rain per year. The amount of evaporation in a desert is greater than the amount of precipitation. Some of the driest deserts may not receive any precipitation in a year! Deserts often undergo large shifts in temperature during the course of a day. A scorching hot desert like the Namib Desert in Africa cools rapidly each night when the sun goes down. Other deserts, such as the Gobi in central Asia, are cooler, and even experience freezing temperatures in the winter.

Organisms that live in the desert must be adapted to the lack of rain and extreme temperatures. For example, the stem of a saguaro cactus has folds that work like the pleats in an accordion. The stem expands to store water when it is raining. Gila monsters can spend weeks at a time in their cool underground burrows. Many other desert animals are most active at night when the temperatures are cooler.

 Reading Checkpoint What are some adaptations that help organisms live in the desert?

Desert Biomes
Desert

FIGURE 15
Desert
The Mojave Desert in the southwestern United States is a typical hot desert.
Making Generalizations *Describe the climate conditions of a typical desert.*

Gambel's quail

E ◆ 61

Grassland Biomes

Teach Key Concepts `L2`

Exploring Grasslands

Focus Describe grasslands as widely distributed ecosystems that have moderate climates and are dominated by grasses.

Teach Have students locate Kenya on a world map or globe, as well as prairie areas in the midwestern United States. Ask: **What typical features of grassland biomes are visible in Figure 16?** *(Tall grass, large herbivores)* **Why do grasslands have so few trees?** *(They don't get enough rain to support trees.)*

Apply Ask: **How do savannas like that in Figure 16 differ from midwestern prairies?** *(Savannas are closer to the equator; they receive more rain.)* **learning modality: visual**

Deciduous Forest Biomes `L2`

Teach Key Concepts

Identifying Deciduous Forests

Focus Tell students that deciduous forests experience seasonal changes to which organisms are adapted.

Teach Ask: **What are climate patterns in a deciduous forest?** *(Temperatures that vary greatly during the year; sufficient rainfall to support trees)* **How are trees adapted to this seasonal biome?** *(They shed their leaves and grow new ones each year.)* **How are animals adapted?** *(Many birds migrate in winter; some mammals hibernate.)*

Apply Ask: **How does the variety of plant and animal species coexist in a deciduous forest?** *(The different plants create a mix of niches within the forest.)* **learning modality: logical/mathematical**

FIGURE 16
Savanna
Migrating wildebeest make their way across a vast Kenyan savanna. A savanna is one type of grassland biome—an area populated mostly by grasses and other non-woody plants.

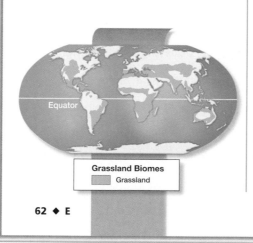

Equator

Grassland Biomes
Grassland

62 ◆ E

Grassland Biomes

The next stop on the expedition is a grassy plain called a prairie. Temperatures here are more comfortable than they were in the desert. The breeze carries the scent of soil warmed by the sun. This rich soil supports grasses as tall as you. Startled by your approach, sparrows dart into hiding places among the waving grass stems.

Although this prairie receives more rain than a desert, it does not get enough rain for trees to grow. Ecologists classify prairies, which are generally found in the middle latitudes, as grasslands. A **grassland** is an area that is populated mostly by grasses and other non-woody plants. Most grasslands receive 25 to 75 centimeters of rain each year. Fires and droughts are common in this biome. Grasslands that are located closer to the equator than prairies are known as savannas. A **savanna** receives as much as 120 centimeters of rain each year. Scattered shrubs and small trees grow on savannas along with grass.

Grasslands are home to many of the largest animals on Earth—herbivores such as elephants, bison, antelopes, zebras, rhinoceroses, giraffes, and kangaroos. Grazing by these large herbivores helps to maintain the grasslands. They keep young trees and bushes from sprouting and competing with the grass for water and sunlight.

Reading Checkpoint What type of grassland usually receives more rainfall, a prairie or a savanna?

Differentiated Instruction

English Learners/Beginning `L1`
Vocabulary: Prior Knowledge Write the word *grassland* on the board, say it aloud, and have students repeat it. Then draw boxes around *grass* and *land*. Ask students what each word means; if they do not know the English words, explain the definitions and clarify them with appropriate pictures. Ask students what they expect to find in a grassland biome. *(grass plants)* **learning modality: verbal**

English Learners/Intermediate `L2`
Vocabulary: Prior Knowledge Use the activity for Beginning students to discuss the meaning of the word *equator*. Indicate that the root word *equate* is associated with having equal amounts and that the equator divides Earth into two equal parts. **learning modality: verbal**

Deciduous Forest Biomes

Your trip to the next biome takes you to another forest. It is now late summer. Cool mornings here give way to warm days. Several members of the expedition are busy recording the numerous plant species. Others are looking through their binoculars, trying to identify the songbirds. You step carefully to avoid a small salamander.

You are now visiting a deciduous forest biome. Many of the trees in this forest are **deciduous trees** (dee SIJ oo us), trees that shed their leaves and grow new ones each year. Oaks and maples are examples of deciduous trees. Deciduous forests receive enough rain to support the growth of trees and other plants, at least 50 centimeters per year. Temperatures in the deciduous forest vary greatly during the year. The growing season usually lasts five to six months.

The variety of plants in a deciduous forest creates many different habitats. Different species of birds live in different parts of the forest, eating the insects and fruits in their specific areas. Mammals such as chipmunks and skunks live in deciduous forests. In a North American deciduous forest you might also see wood thrushes, white-tailed deer, and black bears.

If you were to return to this biome in the winter, you would not see much wildlife. Many of the bird species migrate to warmer areas. Some of the mammals hibernate, or enter a state of greatly reduced body activity similar to sleep. Animals that hibernate rely on fat stored in their bodies during the winter months.

Reading Checkpoint What are deciduous trees?

FIGURE 17
Deciduous Forest
This forest is a beautiful example of a deciduous forest in autumn. Most of the trees in a deciduous forest have leaves that change color and drop each autumn.
Comparing and Contrasting *How do deciduous forests differ from rain forests?*

▼ Southern flying squirrel

▼ Red fox

E ◆ 63

Lab zone **Build Inquiry** **L2**

Making Models of a Deciduous Forest

Materials none

Time 20 minutes

Focus Remind students that a habitat provides the things an organism needs to live, grow, and reproduce.

Teach Ask: **Suppose you want to model a rotting-log habitat on the forest floor. What abiotic materials would you need?** (*Soil, a source of filtered light, water, a rotting log, dead leaves or other dead plant material*) **What organisms would you place in the model habitat?** (*Mosses, ferns, fungi, earthworms, sowbugs, crickets, salamanders or toads*) Have students draw a model of a rotting-log habitat.

Apply: Ask: **What other deciduous forest habitats can you name?** (*Bird roosts and squirrel nests in trees, chipmunk burrows, bear dens, deer grazing areas, and the like*)
learning modality: logical/mathematical

Monitor Progress _____ L2

Skills Check Have each student create a compare/contrast table showing rainfall and temperature differences among the biomes described so far—rain forest, desert, grassland, and deciduous forest. Students can place their tables in their portfolios.

Portfolio

Answers
Figure 17 Rain forests get a lot of rain, and temperatures and sunlight there are fairly constant year-round. Deciduous forests receive less rainfall, and temperatures vary seasonally.

Reading Checkpoint A savanna

Reading Checkpoint Trees that shed their leaves and grow new ones each year

E ● 63

Boreal Forest Biomes

Teach Key Concepts L2

Exploring a Cold Climate

Focus Tell students that boreal forests are found in northern locations and have cold climates.

Teach Ask: **Why is water availability a challenge in boreal forests?** *(Temperatures are low enough that water is frozen much of the year.)* **How do plants adapt to lack of water?** *(Coniferous trees have thick, waxy needles that prevent water loss.)*

Apply Describe a boreal forest food chain. *(Producers—seeds and bark of coniferous trees; first-level consumers—red squirrel, insects, birds, snowshoe hare, moose, beaver; second-level consumers—wolf, bear, lynx, great horned owl)* **learning modality: logical/mathematical**

Lab zone Build Inquiry L2

Inferring Forest Climates

Materials globe, flashlight, masking tape
Time 10–15 minutes

Focus Allow students to visualize locations of deciduous forests and infer information on climate.

Teach Have pairs of students mark the locations of deciduous and boreal forests on a globe with strips of masking tape labeled *D* and *B*. With the room darkened, have one student shine a flashlight at the globe's equator as the other student slowly turns the globe on its axis. Ask: **Which of the two biomes gets stronger (more direct) light?** *(The deciduous forest)* **What do you think this has to do with the climate differences between the deciduous forest and the boreal forest?** *("Stronger" sunlight during the year makes the deciduous forests warmer than the boreal forests.)*

Apply Ask: **Which do you think gets stronger sunlight, the tropical rain forest or the temperate rain forest?** *(Tropical rain forest)* **learning modality: kinesthetic**

FIGURE 18
Boreal Forest
This boreal forest in Alaska's Denali National Park is home to coniferous trees and animals such as moose. The boreal forest is often called the "spruce-moose" forest.

Lynx

Boreal Forest Biomes

Now the expedition heads north into a colder climate. The expedition leaders claim they can identify the next biome, a boreal forest, by its smell. When you arrive, you catch a whiff of the spruce and fir trees that blanket the hillsides. Feeling the chilly early fall air, you pull a jacket and hat out of your bag.

Boreal Forest Plants Most of the trees in the boreal forest are **coniferous trees** (koh NIF ur us), trees that produce their seeds in cones and have leaves shaped like needles. The boreal forest is sometimes referred to by its Russian name, the *taiga* (TY guh). Winters in these forests are very cold. The snow can reach heights well over your head! Even so, the summers are rainy and warm enough to melt all the snow.

Tree species in the boreal forest are well-adapted to the cold climate. Since water is frozen for much of the year, trees in the boreal forest must have adaptations that prevent water loss. Fir, spruce, hemlock, and other coniferous trees all have thick, waxy needles that prevent water from evaporating.

Boreal Forest Animals Many of the animals of the boreal forest eat the seeds produced by the coniferous trees. These animals include red squirrels, insects, and birds such as finches and chickadees. Some herbivores, such as snowshoe hares, moose, and beavers, eat tree bark and new shoots. The variety of herbivores in the boreal forest supports many large predators, including wolves, bears, great horned owls, and lynxes.

Reading Checkpoint How are needles an advantage to trees in the boreal forest?

Lab zone Skills Activity

Inferring
Observe the map that shows the locations of boreal forests. Where are most boreal forests located? Why are there no boreal forests in the Southern Hemisphere?

Equator

Boreal Forest Biomes
■ Boreal forest

Lab zone Skills Activity

Skills Focus Inferring
Materials boreal forest biome map
Time 5 minutes
Tips Begin the activity by pointing out on a globe the equator and the Southern and Northern Hemispheres.
Expected Outcome Boreal forests grow in climates that are too cold for deciduous forests. Such climates typically occur in a band at latitudes far from the equator. There are no such areas in the Southern Hemisphere because that hemisphere does not have large continental land areas at the appropriate latitudes.
Extend Ask: **What type of habitat exists at the southernmost part of the Southern Hemisphere?** *(Ice, in Antarctica)* **learning modality: logical/mathematical**

Tundra Biomes

As you arrive at your next stop, the driving wind gives you an immediate feel for this biome. The **tundra** is an extremely cold and dry biome. Expecting deep snow, many are surprised to learn that the tundra may receive no more precipitation than a desert.

Most of the soil in the tundra is frozen all year. This frozen soil is called **permafrost.** During the short summer, the top layer of soil thaws, but the underlying soil remains frozen. Because rainwater cannot soak into the permafrost, there are many shallow ponds and marshy areas on the tundra in the summer.

Tundra Plants Plants of the tundra include mosses, grasses, shrubs, and dwarf forms of a few trees, such as willows. Most of the plant growth takes place during the long days of the short summer season. North of the Arctic Circle, the sun does not set during midsummer.

Tundra Animals In summer, the animals you might remember most are insects. Insect-eating birds take advantage of the plentiful food and long days by eating as much as they can. But when winter approaches, these birds migrate south. Mammals of the tundra include caribou, foxes, wolves, and Arctic hares. The mammals that remain on the tundra during the winter grow thick fur coats. What can these animals find to eat on the tundra in winter? The caribou scrape snow away to find lichens. Wolves follow the caribou and look for weak members of the herd to prey upon.

✓ Reading Checkpoint What is permafrost?

Tundra Biomes
■ Tundra

FIGURE 19
Tundra
Although it is frozen and seemingly barren in winter, the tundra in Alaska explodes with color in summer.
Relating Cause and Effect *Why are there no tall trees on the tundra?*

Musk ox ▲

E ◆ 65

Tundra Biomes

Teach Key Concepts L2
Investigating Tundra Biomes

Focus Tell students that the tundra biome has an extremely cold, dry climate and unique frozen soil called permafrost.

Teach Direct students' attention to Figure 19. Ask: **What does the land look like in this photograph of the tundra?** (*It is generally flat with low hills.*) Tell students that the term *tundra* comes from a Lapp word meaning "marshy plain." (Lapps are a group of people who live in Lapland.) Ask: **Do you think "marshy plain" is a good description of the tundra?** (*Students may be unsure about the "marshy" part of the description.*) Explain that because the permafrost does not allow water to drain from the soil and because the low temperatures slow evaporation, the tundra's soil is constantly saturated with water, even though the area receives little precipitation.

Apply Ask: **Why do you think insects are so common on the tundra in summer?** (*Many insects breed in standing water, such as in marshes.*) **learning modality: visual**

Monitor Progress L2

Skills Check Have students add the boreal forest and tundra biomes to the compare/contrast table they created.

Answers
Figure 19 The short, cool growing season does not allow tall trees to grow.

✓ Reading Checkpoint Needles prevent water from evaporating from the tree.

✓ Reading Checkpoint Permafrost is soil that stays frozen all year.

E ● 65

Mountains and Ice

Teach Key Concepts L2

Identifying High-Altitude Habitats

Focus Explain that mountains and ice do not fit into one biome classification, but they offer unique ecosystems.

Teach Ask: **Is the habitat the same at the bottom of a mountain as at the top?** (No, the habitats change with altitude.) **Can you name countries or continents that are covered with ice?** (Antarctica; most of Greenland)

Apply Ask: **Can ice sheets support organisms?** (Yes) **Name examples.** (Polar bears, emperor penguins, leopard seals) **learning modality: logical/mathematical**

L2

Drawing Mountain Habitats

Materials paper and pencils

Time 10 minutes

Focus Have students illustrate mountain habitats representing different biomes.

Teach Divide students into small groups. Have each group draw a side-view diagram of a mountain and label it with the biome names given in the text: grassland at the base, deciduous forest next, then boreal forest, and finally tundra at the top. Ask: **Why do the biomes vary at different locations on a mountain?** (Climate becomes colder from the base of a mountain to its top.) Students can add temperature information to their diagrams to see this pattern.

Apply Ask: **From what you know about this mountain's biomes, does the top of the mountain receive much rain?** (No, because it is tundra habitat, which is dry) **learning modality: visual**

Go Online
active art

For: Earth's Biomes activity
Visit: PHSchool.com
Web Code: cep-5024

Students compare and contrast the temperatures and rainfall levels of nine different biomes.

FIGURE 20
Mountains
Mountains, such as these in Banff National Park in Canada, are not part of any major biome. They do support ecosystems, however. **Classifying** Why can't a mountain be considered part of one specific biome?

▲ Dall sheep and lamb on a mountainside

Go Online
active art

For: Earth's Biomes activity
Visit: PHSchool.com
Web Code: cep-5024

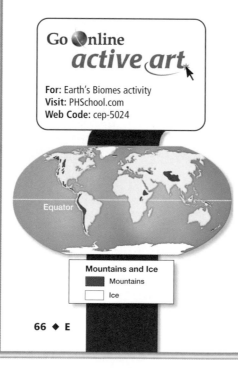

Equator

Mountains and Ice
◼ Mountains
◻ Ice

Mountains and Ice

Some areas of land are not part of any major biome. These areas include mountain ranges and land that is covered with thick sheets of ice.

You read in Section 3 that the climate of a mountain changes from its base to its summit. If you were to hike all the way up a tall mountain, you would pass through a series of biomes. At the base, you might find grasslands. As you climbed, you might pass through deciduous forest and then boreal forest. As you neared the top, your surroundings would resemble the treeless tundra.

Other places are covered year-round with thick ice sheets. Most of the island of Greenland and the continent of Antarctica fall into this category. Organisms that are adapted to life on ice include emperor penguins, polar bears, and leopard seals.

Reading Checkpoint What are two landmasses that are covered year-round with ice?

Differentiated Instruction

Gifted and Talented L3
Identifying Biome Composition Have students use biome maps and a world atlas or globe to locate biomes for a given continent. Provide each student or group an outline map of that continent. If possible, assign a different continent to each student or group. Students should refer to the map resources to sketch the locations of the various biomes found on their continent. (Example: North America has temperate deciduous forest in the East, rain forest in the U. S. Northwest, desert in the U. S. Southwest and northwestern Mexico, grassland through much of the center of the continent, and boreal forest and tundra in Canada and Alaska). Students should illustrate their maps as clearly and colorfully as possible and present them to the class. **learning modality: visual**

Biome Climates

An ecologist collected climate data from two locations. The graph shows the monthly average temperatures in the two locations. The total yearly precipitation in Location A is 250 cm. In Location B, the total yearly precipitation is 14 cm.

1. **Reading Graphs** What variable is plotted on the horizontal axis? On the vertical axis?

2. **Interpreting Data** Look over the graph. How would you describe the temperature over the course of a year in Location A? In Location B?

3. **Drawing Conclusions** Given the precipitation and temperature data for these locations, in which biome would you expect each to be located? Explain your answers.

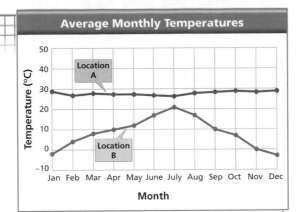

Average Monthly Temperatures

4. **Predicting** What would you expect a temperature graph for your biome to look like? Draw a temperature graph for the biome in which you live.

Section 4 Assessment

Target Reading Skill Comparing and Contrasting Use the information in your table about biomes to help you answer Question 1 below.

Reviewing Key Concepts

1. **a. Listing** What are the six major biomes found on Earth?
   b. Comparing and Contrasting How are the three forest biomes (rain forests, deciduous forests, and boreal forests) alike? How are they different?
   c. Inferring What biome might you be in if you were standing on a bitterly cold, dry plain with only a few, short plants scattered around?

2. **a. Reviewing** What two factors are most important in determining an area's biome?
   b. Relating Cause and Effect If deserts and tundras receive similar amounts of rainfall, why are these two biomes so different?
   c. Applying Concepts Why would hiking up a tall mountain be a good way to observe how climate determines an area's biome?

Writing in Science

Firsthand Account Choose one of the biomes and write a journal entry detailing the observations you made during your expedition. Include descriptions of sights, sounds, and smells you experienced as well as specific details about the organisms you observed. Conclude your journal entry with a surprising fact you learned about the biome while visiting.

Writing in Science

Writing Mode Description

Scoring Rubric

4 Includes sensory descriptions (sights, sounds, and smells), specific details about organisms, and a surprising fact; descriptions are vivid and well supported

3 Includes all descriptive components (sensory descriptions, organisms, surprising fact), but descriptions lack detail or clarity

2 Missing one descriptive component

1 Missing two descriptive components

Students can save their accounts in their portfolios.

Portfolio

Math Skill Interpreting graphs

Focus Have students study the graph. Point out that a line graph such as this one is a good way to show change over time.

Teach Remind students that each point on the graph represents a monthly average temperature for that location. Ask: **What temperature patterns will represent biomes?** (*High or low, steady or fluctuating*)

Answers

1. Month is plotted on the horizontal axis, temperature on the vertical axis.
2. Location A temperatures are steady; Location B temperatures fluctuate.
3. Location A: tropical rain forest; Location B: desert
4. Answers will vary but should reflect whether local climate is hot or cold, seasonal or steady.

Assess

Reviewing Key Concepts

1. a. Rain forest, desert, grassland, deciduous forest, boreal forest, and tundra
b. All have tall trees and many habitats for organisms. Students should cite differences in location (latitude), temperature, amount of sunlight, amount of precipitation, and specific types of plants and other organisms.
c. The tundra biome
2. a. Temperature and precipitation
b. They are found at very different latitudes, with tundra much farther north. **c.** Because climate conditions determined by altitude cause biomes to change from the base to the summit of a mountain

Reteach L1

Review the tables that students have made to compare and contrast the six biomes.

All in One Teaching Resources

- Section Summary: *Biomes*
- Review and Reinforce: *Biomes*
- Enrich: *Biomes*

Biomes in Miniature

Prepare for Inquiry

Key Concept
Differences in soil, light, and precipitation create different biomes.

Skills Objectives
After this lab, students will be able to
- observe and compare the growth of different plants in the model biomes
- make models of given biomes by varying abiotic factors

🕐 **Prep Time** 30 minutes
🕐 **Class Time** 30 minutes, then 5–10 minutes a day for at least one week

Advance Planning
- Ask students to bring in large milk or juice cartons that have been thoroughly washed.
- Obtain sufficient quantities of potting soil and sandy (cactus) soil from a nursery or gardening store.
- Allocate enough table space and lamps for students to expose each model biome to the amount of light required.

Safety
🔬 Make sure students wash their hands after they handle the soil and seeds, Review the safety guidelines in Appendix A.

All in One **Teaching Resources**
- Lab Worksheet: *Biomes in Miniature*

Guide Inquiry

Invitation
Ask students: **Why don't we see [name a non-native plant] growing in our area?** *(Students should describe climate conditions needed by the plant that are not met in your area.)* Review with students the major biomes discussed in the lesson. Tell students that in this activity they will make models of different biomes

---

Biomes in Miniature

Problem
What abiotic factors create different biomes around the world?

Skills Focus
observing, making models

Materials
- scissors
- clear plastic wrap
- index card
- lamp
- tape
- empty, clean cardboard milk carton
- stapler
- about 30 rye grass seeds
- 10 impatiens seeds
- 5 lima bean seeds
- sandy soil or potting soil

Procedure 🔬

1. Your teacher will assign your group a biome. You will also observe the other groups' biomes. Based on the chart below, predict how well you think each of the three kinds of seeds will grow in each set of conditions. Record these predictions in your notebook. Then copy the data table on the facing page four times, once for each biome.

2. Staple the spout of the milk carton closed. Completely cut away one of the four sides of the carton. Poke a few holes in the opposite side for drainage, and then place that side down.

3. Fill the carton to 3 centimeters from the top with the type of soil given in the table. Divide the surface of the soil into three sections by making two lines in it with a pencil.

4. In the section near the spout, plant the impatiens seeds. In the middle section, plant the lima bean seeds. In the third section, scatter the rye grass seeds on the surface.

5. Water all the seeds well. Then cover the open part of the carton with plastic wrap.

6. On an index card, write the name of your biome, the names of the three types of seeds in the order you planted them, and the names of your group members. Tape the card to the carton. Put the carton in a warm place where it will not be disturbed.

7. Once the seeds sprout, provide your biome with light and water as specified in the chart. Keep the carton covered with plastic wrap except when you add water.

8. Observe all the biomes daily for at least one week. Record your observations.

Growing Conditions			
Biome	**Soil Type**	**Hours of Light per Day**	**Watering Instructions**
Forest	Potting soil	1–2 hours of direct light	Let the surface dry; then add water.
Desert	Sandy soil	5–6 hours of direct light	Let the soil dry to a depth of 2.5 cm below the surface.
Grassland	Potting soil	5–6 hours of direct light	Let the surface dry; then add water.
Rain forest	Potting soil	No direct light; indirect light for 5–6 hours	Keep the surface of the soil moist.

Introducing the Procedure
- Invite students to read the entire lab procedure. Then ask: **What is the purpose of this lab?** *(To determine how well three kinds of plants grow in different biomes)*
- Direct students' attention to the Growing Conditions chart and ask: **What variables will you change to create models of four different biomes?** *(Soil type, amount of light, and amount of water)*

Troubleshooting the Experiment
- Observation criteria are not specified in Step 8 and could be determined as a class or by each group. Criteria could include the number of seeds that germinate successfully, plant height, the number and color of leaves, and yellowing (a sign of too much water) or wilting (a sign of not enough water).

Data Table

Name of Biome: _____

Day	Impatiens	Lima Beans	Rye Grass
1			
2			
3			
4			
5			
6			
7			

Analyze and Conclude

1. **Observing** In which biome did each type of seed grow best? In which biome did each type of seed grow least well?

2. **Making Models** In this experiment, how did you model the following abiotic factors: sunlight, water, and temperature?

3. **Inferring** How was each type of seed affected by the soil type, amount of light, and availability of water?

4. **Classifying** Why do you think that ecologists who study biomes often focus on identifying the key abiotic factors and typical plants in an area?

5. **Communicating** Write a paragraph explaining how your miniature biomes modeled real-life biomes. Which features of real-life biomes were you able to model well? Which features of real-life biomes were more difficult to model?

Design an Experiment

Write a plan for setting up a model rain forest or desert terrarium. Include typical plants found in that biome. *Obtain your teacher's approval before carrying out your investigation.*

E ◆ 69

E ● 69

Objectives

After completing the lesson, students will be able to

E.2.5.1 Name and describe the two major types of aquatic ecosystems.

E.2.5.2 Describe how organisms are adapted to each of the aquatic habitats.

Target Reading Skill

Outlining Explain that using an outline format helps organize information by main topic, subtopic, and details.

Answers

Aquatic Ecosystems
I. Freshwater ecosystems
   A. Streams and rivers
   B. Ponds and lakes
II. Marine ecosystems
   A. Intertidal zone
   B. Neritic zone
   C. Open ocean

All in One Teaching Resources

• Transparency E22

Preteach

Build Background Knowledge   L2

Identifying Aquatic Ecosystems

Ask: **Can you name any aquatic ecosystems in which organisms live in and around water?** (*Students will likely name ponds and lakes; rivers, creeks or streams; bays and sounds; and open oceans.*) **What is an important difference between marine ecosystems and ponds or rivers?** (*Marine ecosystems are saltwater ecosystems; ponds, lakes, and rivers are freshwater ecosystems.*)

Reading Preview

Key Concept

• What are the two major types of aquatic ecosystems?

Key Terms

• estuary   • intertidal zone
• neritic zone

Target Reading Skill

Outlining An outline shows the relationship between main ideas and supporting ideas. As you read, make an outline about the different types of aquatic ecosystems. Use the red headings for the main ideas and the blue headings for the supporting ideas.

Aquatic Ecosystems
I. Freshwater ecosystems
A. Streams and rivers
B.
II. Marine ecosystems
A.

FIGURE 21
A River Ecosystem
Streams and rivers are freshwater ecosystems in which the water flows in a current. These bears and gulls are enjoying the plentiful supply of fish in this river.

Lab zone **Discover Activity**

Where Does It Live?

1. The organism in the photo lives in a pond. Look carefully at its body.
2. Think about how the organism might move around and how it might eat.

Think It Over

Observing Make a list of the organism's features that might help it survive in its habitat. For each feature, describe how it is suited to its function.

No worldwide expedition could be complete without exploring Earth's waters. Since almost three quarters of Earth's surface is covered with water, don't be surprised at how much there is to see. Many living things make their homes in and near the water. **Your travels will take you to two types of aquatic, or water-based, ecosystems: freshwater ecosystems and marine (or saltwater) ecosystems.**

All aquatic ecosystems are affected by the same abiotic factors: sunlight, temperature, oxygen, and salt content. Sunlight is an especially important factor in aquatic ecosystems. Sunlight is necessary for photosynthesis in the water just as it is on land. However, because water absorbs sunlight, there is only enough light for photosynthesis near the surface or in shallow water. The most common producers in aquatic ecosystems are algae rather than plants.

Black bear with salmon ▶

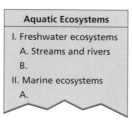

Lab zone **Discover Activity**

Skills Focus Observing

Materials none

Time 15 minutes

Tips Start the exercise as a class discussion, and then allow students to complete the activity in pairs.

Expected Outcome Students should describe how the duck feeds, floats, swims, and stays warm and dry.

Think It Over Likely answers: The bill is sturdy and shovel-shaped so that the bird can scoop up water and grab small water organisms; feathers resist water and keep the bird warm.

Freshwater Ecosystems

Even though most of Earth's surface is covered with water, only a tiny fraction is fresh water. Freshwater ecosystems include streams, rivers, ponds, and lakes. On this part of your expedition, you'll find that freshwater ecosystems provide habitats for an amazing variety of organisms, from microscopic algae to huge bears.

Streams and Rivers Your first stop is a mountain stream. Where the stream begins, the cold, clear water flows rapidly. Animals that live here are adapted to the strong current. For example, insects and other small animals have hooks or suckers that help them cling to rocks. Trout have streamlined bodies that allow them to swim despite the rushing water. Few plants or algae can grow in this fast-moving water. Instead, first-level consumers rely on leaves and seeds that fall into the stream.

As the stream flows along, other streams join it. The current slows, and the water becomes cloudy with soil. The slower-moving water is warmer and contains less oxygen. This larger stream might now be called a river. Different organisms are adapted to life in a river. Plants take root among the pebbles on the river bottom. These producers provide food for young insects and homes for frogs and their tadpoles. These consumers, in turn, provide food for many larger consumers.

Ponds and Lakes Your next stop is a pond. Ponds and lakes are bodies of standing, or still, fresh water. Lakes are generally larger and deeper than ponds. Ponds are often shallow enough that sunlight can reach the bottom even in the center of the pond, allowing plants to grow there. In large ponds and most lakes, however, algae floating at the surface are the major producers.

Many animals are adapted for life in the still water. Along the shore of the pond, you observe dragonflies, turtles, snails, and frogs. Sunfish live in the open water, feeding on insects and algae from the surface. Scavengers such as catfish live near the pond bottom. Bacteria and other decomposers also feed on the remains of other organisms.

 Reading Checkpoint What are two abiotic factors that affect organisms in a stream?

FIGURE 22
A Pond Ecosystem
Ponds and lakes are freshwater ecosystems characterized by still water. Pickerelweed and herons are typical pond organisms.
Interpreting Photographs *How is the heron well-suited to its aquatic environment?*

◄ Tricolored heron

E ◆ 71

Freshwater Ecosystems

Teach Key Concepts   L2
Classifying Freshwater Habitats

Focus Tell students that freshwater ecosystems are classified as lakes and ponds or rivers and streams, but these ecosystems include a variety of habitats.

Teach Have students describe the ecosystems shown in Figures 21 and 22. Ask: **Which habitats would you find in a lake ecosystem?** (*Shoreline, shallow water near shore, deep water away from shore, bottom of the lake, and water surface*) Remind students that organisms must be adapted to their habitat. Ask: **What adaptations does a fish have that allow it to live in lake water?** (*Gills for breathing oxygen in water; fins, a tail, and a streamlined body shape for swimming; scales for insulation and protection*)

Apply Ask: **What adaptations do animals have that live in fast-moving mountain streams?** (*Hooks or suckers to cling to rocks; streamlined body shapes*) **learning modality: verbal**

Independent Practice   L2

All in One Teaching Resources
• Guided Reading and Study Worksheet: *Aquatic Ecosystems*

Student Edition on Audio CD
Less Proficient Readers   L1

Monitor Progress   L2

Oral Presentation Call on various students to each choose one freshwater biome, identify one specific habitat in that biome, and name at least three organisms found in that habitat.

Answers
Figure 22 It has long legs for wading and a sharp beak and flexible neck for preying upon fish.

Reading Checkpoint Temperature and speed of the current

Differentiated Instruction

Identifying Main Ideas and Details
Students who need additional review of freshwater ecosystems can create their own game. Group students, have them reread page 71, and ask them to prepare two sketches, one of a pond or lake and one of a river or stream. Either provide cards with terms from this text passage, or allow groups to prepare the cards. Students should take turns picking a card and placing it on the appropriate drawing, the pond or lake or the river or stream. (*Terms for pond/lake: standing water, algae as producers, turtles, dragonflies, snails, frogs, catfish, sunfish; terms for river/lake: cold, clear, strong current, trout, hooks and suckers, streamlined bodies, few plants or algae*) **learning modality: kinesthetic**

Marine Ecosystems

Teach Key Concepts
Comparing Marine Habitats

Focus Remind students that a major difference between freshwater and marine ecosystems is that marine ecosystems are based on salt water.

Teach Use Figure 23 to describe the differences and similarities between marine habitats in location, water depth, amount of salt in water, organisms, and sunlight. Ask: **How are an estuary and the intertidal zone different?** *(Different organisms live in them; the water in the intertidal zone is saltier than the water in an estuary; the estuary does not have waves.)* **How are an estuary and the intertidal zone alike?** *(In both, the land is sometimes covered with water and at other times exposed to the air and sunlight.)*

Apply Ask: **Do you think estuaries are affected by ocean tides?** *(Yes; mudflats there are exposed during low tide and covered during high tide.)* **learning modality: verbal**

All in One Teaching Resources
• Transparency E23

Inferring Coral Structure

Materials coral

Time 10 minutes

Focus Ask students if a coral is a plant or animal. *(Animal)*

Teach Provide samples of different types of coral for students to examine. Visually impaired students can closely examine the coral by feeling it. Emphasize that these pieces of coral are not the coral animals, which are soft, but the structures they produced and left behind when they died. Ask: **Where do you think the coral animals lived?** *(Inside the tiny holes)*

Apply Ask: **How do you think this hard structure helps coral animals survive?** *(It provides protection for the animals' soft bodies and also anchors them to the ocean floor.)*
learning modality: visual

FIGURE 23
Marine Ecosystems

The ocean is home to a number of different ecosystems. Factors such as water temperature and the amount of sunlight determine what types of organisms can live in each zone.

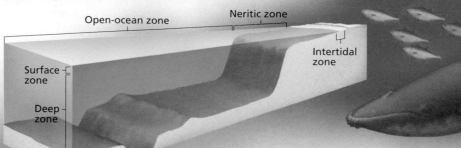

Marine Ecosystems

The expedition now heads to the coast to explore some marine ecosystems. On your way, you'll pass through an estuary. An **estuary** (ES choo ehr ee), is found where the fresh water of a river meets the salt water of the ocean. Algae and plants such as marsh grasses provide food and shelter for numerous animals, including crabs, worms, clams, and fish. Many animals use the calm waters of estuaries for breeding grounds.

Intertidal Zone Next, you take a walk along the rocky shoreline. Here, between the highest high-tide line and the lowest low-tide line, is the **intertidal zone.** Organisms here must be able to survive pounding waves and the sudden changes in water levels and temperature that occur with high and low tides. You observe animals such as barnacles and sea stars clinging to the rocks. Others, such as clams and crabs, burrow in the sand.

Neritic Zone Now it's time to set out to sea. The edge of a continent extends into the ocean for a short distance, like a shelf. Below the low-tide line is a region of shallow water called the **neritic zone** (nuh RIT ik), which extends over the continental shelf.

Because sunlight passes through the shallow water of the neritic zone, photosynthesis can occur. As a result, this zone is particularly rich in living things. Many large schools of fish, such as sardines, feed on algae. In warm ocean waters, coral reefs may form. Coral reefs provide living homes to a wide variety of other organisms.

Intertidal zone

Neritic zone

Go Online
SCiLINKS NSTA

For: Links on aquatic ecosystems
Visit: www.SciLinks.org
Web Code: scn-0525

Download a worksheet that will guide students' review of Internet resources on aquatic ecosystems.

The Open Ocean Out in the open ocean, light penetrates only to a depth of a few hundred meters. Algae carry out photosynthesis in this region of the open ocean, which is known as the surface zone. Marine animals, such as tuna, swordfish, and some whales, depend on the algae for food.

The deep zone is located below the surface zone. The deep zone is almost totally dark. Most animals in this zone feed on the remains of organisms that sink down from the surface zone. The deepest parts of the deep zone are home to bizarre-looking animals, such as giant squid that glow in the dark.

Go Online
SCiLINKS NSTA

For: Links on aquatic ecosystems
Visit: www.SciLinks.org
Web Code: scn-0525

Reading Checkpoint What two zones make up the open ocean?

Section 5 Assessment

Target Reading Skill **Outlining** Use the information in your outline about aquatic ecosystems to help you answer the questions below.

Reviewing Key Concepts
1. **a. Reviewing** Name two major types of aquatic ecosystems.
   b. Explaining Why is sunlight an important abiotic factor in all aquatic ecosystems?
   c. Predicting Would you expect to find many organisms living at the bottom of a deep lake? Explain.

Lab zone At-Home **Activity**

Aquatic Photos Find photos of two different aquatic ecosystems. Take notes on the similarities and differences between the ecosystems and the organisms that live in them. Then explain those characteristics to a family member.

Chapter 2 E ◆ 73

Monitor Progress — L2
Reading Checkpoint The surface zone and the deep zone

Assess

Reviewing Key Concepts
1. **a.** Freshwater and marine ecosystems
b. Whether or not an aquatic ecosystem receives sunlight determines if it can support producers. **c.** No, because no sunlight can reach the bottom, but there would be bacteria and scavengers

Reteach L1
Divide students into groups and assign each group one of the freshwater and marine ecosystems covered. Have the groups interact to review the topics, either by offering presentations or by preparing questions for a verbal quiz game.

Performance Assessment L2
Drawing Have each student draw a diagram showing the ocean's four zones and label each zone with its name, without referring to Figure 23. Students can save their drawings in their portfolios.

Portfolio

All in One Teaching Resources
• Section Summary: *Aquatic Ecosystems*
• Review and Reinforce: *Aquatic Ecosystems*
• Enrich: *Aquatic Ecosystems*

Lab zone At Home **Activity**

Remind students of the type of information to consider in comparing the ecosystems: salty water or fresh water, amount of available sunlight, still or moving water, affected or not affected by tides, common food resources, types of organisms, adaptations of organisms, and so on.

Lab zone Chapter **Project**

Keep Students on Track Monitor students as they analyze the data they have collected, compare results in the two chambers, and draw a conclusion about the effect of the variable they investigated. Remind students that the report can be in the form of a written summary, a poster, or some other product they can share with the class.

Change in a Tiny Community

Prepare for Inquiry

Key Concept
The types of organisms that predominate in a community change over time.

Skills Objectives
After this lab, students will be able to
- make and observe a model of a microscopic pond community
- compare and contrast the types of organisms and the sizes of the populations present in the community at intervals
- conclude that the predominance of various populations changed during the observation period

Prep Time 45 minutes

Class Time Day 1, set up community: 15 minutes; Days 3, 6, and 9, examine community: 20 minutes daily

Advance Planning
- The day before students will begin the lab, prepare a hay solution by adding a small amount of hay for each liter of hot water. Let the hay soak overnight, and then use a strainer to remove it from the solution.
- Collect a sample of pond water.
- Collect enough clean baby-food jars to provide one for each student or group.
- Collect field guides and other sources showing microscopic organisms found in ponds

Safety
Make sure students handle the slide and coverslip carefully and wash their hands each time they handle the jar and solution. Review the safety guidelines in Appendix A. Follow the guidelines for the recommended safe disposal of bacteria cultures.

All in One Teaching Resources
- Lab Worksheet: *Change in a Tiny Community*

Change in a Tiny Community

Problem
How does a pond community change over time?

Skills Focus
observing, classifying

Materials
- hay solution
- pond water
- small baby-food jar
- wax pencil
- plastic dropper
- microscope slide
- coverslip
- microscope

Procedure

1. Use a wax pencil to label a small jar with your name.
2. Fill the jar about three-fourths full with hay solution. Add pond water until the jar is nearly full. Examine the mixture, and record your observations in your notebook.
3. Place the jar in a safe location out of direct sunlight where it will remain undisturbed. Always wash your hands thoroughly with soap after handling the jar or its contents.
4. After two days, examine the contents of the jar, and record your observations.
5. Use a plastic dropper to collect a few drops from the surface of the solution in the jar. Make a slide following the procedures in the box at the right. **CAUTION:** *Slides and coverslips are fragile, and their edges are sharp. Handle them carefully.*
6. Examine the slide under a microscope, using both low and high power and following the procedures in the box at the right. Draw each type of organism you observe. Estimate the number of each type in your sample. The illustration below shows some of the organisms you might see.
7. Repeat Steps 5 and 6 with a drop of solution taken from the side of the jar beneath the surface.
8. Repeat Steps 5 and 6 with a drop of solution taken from the bottom of the jar. When you are finished, follow your teacher's directions about cleaning up.
9. After 3 days, repeat Steps 5 through 8.
10. After 3 more days, repeat Steps 5 through 8 again. Then follow your teacher's directions for returning the solution.

Paramecium   **Daphnia**   **Spirogyra**

Guide Inquiry

Invitation
Focus students' attention on the illustrations of microorganisms and ask: **Have you ever seen organisms like these before? Where?** (*Answers will depend on students' prior experience. If they have not observed living microorganisms, they may have at least seen photographs or drawings.*) Tell students that in this activity they will observe microscopic pond organisms.

Introducing the Procedure
- Review all procedures related to the correct and safe handling of slides, coverslips, and microscopes. If students have not prepared slides or used a microscope before, demonstrate these procedures.
- Introduce or review the guidelines for making scientific drawings: the drawings should be as realistic and accurate as possible, labeled appropriately, and drawn to scale.

Making and Viewing a Slide

A. Place one drop of the solution to be examined in the middle of a microscope slide. Place one edge of a coverslip at the edge of the drop, as shown in the photo. Gently lower the coverslip over the drop. Try not to trap any air bubbles.

B. Place the slide on the stage of a microscope so the drop is over the opening in the stage. Adjust the stage clips to hold the slide.

C. Look from the side of the microscope, and use the coarse adjustment knob to move the low-power objective close to, but not touching, the coverslip.

D. Look through the eyepiece, and use the coarse adjustment knob to raise the body tube and bring the slide into view. Use the fine adjustment knob to bring the slide into focus.

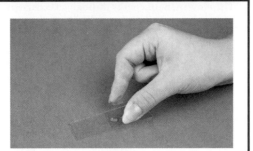

E. To view the slide under high power, look from the side of the microscope, and revolve the nosepiece until the high-power objective clicks into place just over, but not touching, the slide.

F. While you are looking through the eyepiece, use the fine adjustment knob to bring the slide into focus.

Analyze and Conclude

1. **Classifying** Identify as many of the organisms you observed as possible. Use the diagrams on the facing page and any other resources your teacher provides.

2. **Observing** How did the community change over the period of time that you made your observations?

3. **Inferring** What biotic and abiotic factors may have influenced the changes in this community? Explain.

4. **Developing Hypotheses** Where did the organisms you observed in the jar come from?

5. **Communicating** Based on what you have observed in this lab, write a paragraph that explains why ecosystems change gradually over time. Be sure to discuss the important factors that lead to changes in ecosystems.

Design an Experiment

Write a hypothesis about what would happen if you changed one biotic or abiotic factor in this activity. Design a plan to test your hypothesis. *Obtain your teacher's permission before carrying out your investigation.*

Analyze and Conclude

1. Students can usually expect to see a variety of microorganisms, including the three pictured.

2. The solution may have become cloudy. Small protists appeared, followed by larger protists, such as green algae, paramecia, and amoebas. Water fleas and rotifers were visible later.

3. Abiotic factors include amount of light, water temperature, and available space. Biotic factors include predation of some organisms by other organisms. As smaller organisms multiplied, they provided food for larger organisms, which then increased in numbers.

4. The organisms were already in the hay solution or pond water, are offspring of those original organisms, or developed from fertilized eggs in the hay solution or pond water.

5. Student answers might explain that adequate nutrients and abiotic conditions must first be present to support producers, then enough producers must multiply and produce enough food to support consumers, and so on. Students may also refer to succession.

Extend the Inquiry

Design an Experiment Possible changes in abiotic factors include keeping the jar in a slightly warmer or cooler place or exposing it to more or less light. Changes in biotic factors include varying the amounts of hay solution and pond water (the sources of organisms) or adding a specific population of producers or consumers to the community.

Expected Outcome

In general, large populations of smaller organisms such as bacteria and tiny protists will be present early in the exercise, whereas populations of larger protists and tiny animals will increase toward the end of the exercise.

Interactive Textbook

- Complete student edition
- Section and chapter self-assessments
- Assessment reports for teachers

Help Students Read

Building Vocabulary

Word Forms Before students read, have them write their own definitions of *drift* and *web*, using the dictionary for help. Then have students predict how the definitions relate to the terms *continental drift* and *food web*. After students study the section, have them discuss any differences between their predictions and the definitions in the text.

Paraphrasing Write sentences that feature key terms. Have students rewrite the sentences by paraphrasing the key terms. Example: The zoo animals are *herbivores*, *carnivores*, and *omnivores*; paraphrased: *The zoo animals are plant eaters, meat eaters, and animals that eat both plants and meat.*

Connecting Concepts

Concept Maps Help students develop one way to show how the information in this chapter is related. Earth's ecosystems, which are based on energy moving through food webs and food chains, and on the cycling of matter, cover a range of land and aquatic habitats. Have students brainstorm to identify the key concepts, key terms, details, and examples from this chapter, then write each one on a sticky note and attach it at random on chart paper or on the board. Tell students that this concept map will be organized in hierarchical order and to begin at the top with the key concepts. Ask students these questions to guide them to categorize the information on the stickies: **How does energy move through ecosystems? How is matter cycled? What are the various biomes and aquatic ecosystems?** Prompt students by using connecting words or phrases, such as "is affected by" and "moves up through" to indicate the basis for the organization of the

① Energy Flow in Ecosystems

Key Concepts

- Each organism in an ecosystem fills the energy role of producer, consumer, or decomposer.
- The movement of energy through an ecosystem can be shown in diagrams called food chains and food webs.
- The most energy is available at the producer level of the energy pyramid. As you move up the pyramid, each level has less energy available than the level below.

Key Terms

producer
consumer
herbivore
carnivore
omnivore
scavenger
decomposer
food chain
food web
energy pyramid

② Cycles of Matter

Key Concepts

- The processes of evaporation, condensation, and precipitation make up the water cycle.
- In ecosystems, the processes by which carbon and oxygen are recycled are linked. Producers, consumers, and decomposers play roles in recycling carbon and oxygen.
- In the nitrogen cycle, nitrogen moves from the air to the soil, into living things, and back into the air.

Key Terms

water cycle
evaporation
condensation
precipitation
nitrogen fixation

③ Biogeography

Key Concepts

- One factor that has affected how species are distributed is the motion of Earth's continents.
- Dispersal can be caused by wind, water, or living things, including humans.
- Three factors that limit dispersal of a species are physical barriers, competition, and climate.

Key Terms

biogeography   exotic species
continental drift   climate
dispersal

④ Biomes

Key Concepts

- The six major biomes that most ecologists study are the rain forest, desert, grassland, deciduous forest, boreal forest, and tundra.
- It is mostly the climate—temperature and precipitation—in an area that determines its biome.

Key Terms

biome   savanna
canopy   deciduous tree
understory   coniferous tree
desert   tundra
grassland   permafrost

⑤ Aquatic Ecosystems

Key Concept

- There are two types of aquatic, or water-based, ecosystems: freshwater ecosystems and marine (or saltwater) ecosystems.

Key Terms

estuary
intertidal zone
neritic zone

map. The phrases should form a sentence between or among a set of concepts.

Answer

Accept logical presentations by students.

All in One Teaching Resources

- Key Terms Review: *Ecosystems and Biomes*
- Transparency E24

Review and Assessment

Go Online
PHSchool.com
For: Self-Assessment
Visit: PHSchool.com
Web Code: cea-5020

Organizing Information

Sequencing Copy the cycle diagram about the nitrogen cycle onto a separate sheet of paper. Then complete it. (For more on Sequencing, see the Skills Handbook.)

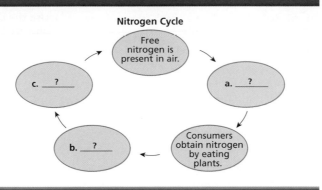

Nitrogen Cycle

Free nitrogen is present in air.

c. ___?___

a. ___?___

Consumers obtain nitrogen by eating plants.

b. ___?___

Reviewing Key Terms

Choose the letter of the best answer.

1. Which of the following organisms are typical decomposers?
   a. grasses and ferns
   b. mushrooms and bacteria
   c. mice and deer
   d. lions and snakes

2. A diagram that shows how much energy is available at each feeding level in an ecosystem is a(n)
   a. food chain.   b. food web.
   c. water cycle.   d. energy pyramid.

3. When drops of water in a cloud become heavy enough, they fall to Earth as
   a. condensation.   b. evaporation.
   c. permafrost.   d. precipitation.

4. Organisms may be dispersed in all the following ways *except* by
   a. wind.
   b. water.
   c. temperature.
   d. other organisms.

5. Much of Canada is covered in fir and spruce forests. The winter is cold and long. What is this biome?
   a. tundra
   b. boreal forest
   c. deciduous forest
   d. grassland

If the statement is true, write *true*. If it is false, change the underlined word or words to make the statement true.

6. An organism that eats the remains of dead organisms is called a(n) <u>herbivore</u>.

7. The study of where organisms live is called <u>continental drift</u>.

8. <u>Precipitation</u> and temperature are the two major abiotic factors that determine what types of plants can grow in an area.

Writing in Science

Encyclopedia Entry Write a half-page encyclopedia entry about life in the desert. Describe at least two plants and animals that live in the desert. Focus on the adaptations that allow these organisms to thrive in the harsh environment.

DISCOVERY CHANNEL SCHOOL

Ecosystems and Biomes
Video Preview
Video Field Trip
▶ Video Assessment

Chapter 2   E ◆ 77

Review and Assessment

Organizing Information

a. Bacteria in root nodules fix free nitrogen into compounds.
b. Decomposers break down wastes and remains of organisms.
c. Bacteria release some free nitrogen back into the air.

Reviewing Key Terms

   1. b **2.** d **3.** d **4.** c **5.** b
   6. false, scavenger
   7. false, biogeography
   8. true

Writing in Science

Writing Skill Description
Scoring Rubric
4 Includes detailed information about adaptations of more than two plants and animals
3 Includes all criteria
2 Includes brief descriptions or omits some criteria
1 Includes inaccurate information and omits some criteria

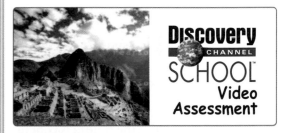

DISCOVERY CHANNEL SCHOOL Video Assessment

Ecosystems and Biomes

Show the Video Assessment to review chapter content and as a prompt for the writing assignment.

Go Online
PHSchool.com
For: Self-Assessment
Visit: PHSchool.com
Web Code: cea-5020

Students can take a practice test online that is automatically scored.

All in One Teaching Resources
- Transparency E25
- Chapter Test
- Performance Assessment Teacher Notes
- Performance Assessment Student Worksheet
- Performance Assessment Scoring Rubric

 ExamView® Computer Test Bank CD-ROM

Checking Concepts

9. Producers capture the energy of sunlight to make their own food. Consumers obtain energy by eating other organisms. Decomposers obtain energy by breaking down wastes and dead organisms.

10. A food chain is a single path of events in which one organism eats another. A food web is a combination of interconnected and overlapping food chains.

11. The sun or sunlight, because it provides energy for photosynthesis, which allows producers to make their food, and producers support consumers

12. Nitrogen-fixing bacteria convert free nitrogen in the atmosphere into nitrogen-containing molecules that other organisms can use.

13. Competition can be a barrier to dispersal when an existing species outcompetes a new one. Competition can also further dispersal when a new species outcompetes an existing one.

14. The abundant plant life provides a wide variety of habitats for organisms and an abundant supply of food.

15. Sunlight, temperature, oxygen, and salt content

Thinking Critically

16. Climate; polar bears' thick, insulating fur would make it difficult for them to live in a warmer environment; the white fur would make them stand out against land that was not covered with ice and snow.

17. Both the desert and the tundra are very dry and have extreme living conditions. The desert may be very hot during the day in summer, with large shifts in temperature between day and night; the tundra is cool in summer and bitterly cold in winter. Desert soil is sandy; most of the soil in the tundra is frozen all year long.

18. Killing off the algae would have a major impact on the food web, because algae are the major producers in the open ocean, and many marine animals depend on the algae for food.

19. Producers: algae; consumers: fish, snails

Performance Assessment Review students' written reports, posters, and other products. You may wish to have each student or group present their report to the rest of the class. Alternatively, you could have half the class present a "poster session" to the other half, then reverse roles.

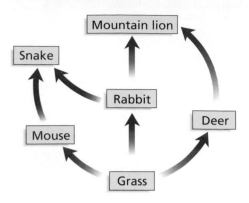

Review and Assessment

Checking Concepts

9. Name and describe each of the three energy roles organisms can play in an ecosystem.

10. How are food chains and food webs different?

11. What is the source of energy for most ecosystems? Explain.

12. Describe the role of nitrogen-fixing bacteria in the nitrogen cycle.

13. Explain how competition can affect the dispersal of species.

14. Why is the tropical rain forest able to support so many species?

15. Which abiotic factors are important to aquatic ecosystems?

Thinking Critically

16. Inferring Polar bears are very well adapted to life around the Arctic Ocean. Their white fur camouflages them in the snow. They can withstand freezing temperatures for a long time. They swim and hunt in very cold water. Is the distribution of polar bears limited by physical barriers, competition, or climate? Explain your answer.

17. Comparing and Contrasting How are the desert biome and the tundra biome similar? How are they different?

18. Predicting A chemical spill has just killed off all the algae in a part of the surface zone in the open ocean. How will this accident affect the food webs in that part of the surface zone?

19. Classifying Which organisms in the illustration are producers? Consumers?

Applying Skills

Use the diagram of a food web below to answer Questions 20–22.

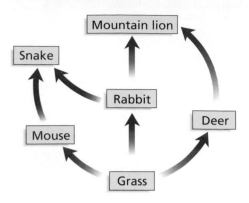

20. Classifying Identify the energy role of each organism in this food web. Specify whether each consumer is a first-level, second-level, or third-level consumer.

21. Inferring Which level of the food web contains the greatest amount of available energy?

22. Predicting If a disease were to kill most of the rabbits in this area, predict how the snakes, deer, and mountain lions would be affected.

Lab zone Chapter **Project**

Performance Assessment Create a report, poster, or other product that clearly presents your data and conclusions from your decomposition experiment. In your notebook, compare your results to your predictions about the different waste materials in the compost mixture. Were you surprised by any of your results? Based on what you have learned from your project and those of your classmates, make a list of the ideal conditions for decomposition.

Allow time for all students to compare their results so they can compile a list of "ideal" conditions. In general, compost will form most quickly when the compost is kept moist (molds grow better), well aerated (many decomposers are aerobic), and warm (metabolic activity is higher) and when soil organisms are added.

Standardized Test Prep

Choose the letter of the best answer.

1. You are in an area in Maryland where the fresh water of the Chesapeake Bay meets the Atlantic Ocean. What type of habitat are you in?
   A a neritic zone
   B an intertidal zone
   C an estuary
   D the tundra

2. Which pair of terms could apply to the same organism?
   F carnivore and producer
   G decomposer and consumer
   H scavenger and herbivore
   J carnivore and consumer

Use the energy pyramid diagram below and your knowledge of science to answer Questions 3 and 4.

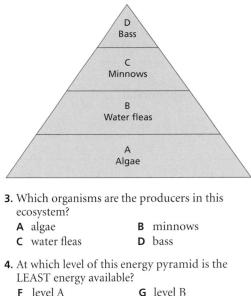

3. Which organisms are the producers in this ecosystem?
   A algae
   B minnows
   C water fleas
   D bass

4. At which level of this energy pyramid is the LEAST energy available?
   F level A
   G level B
   H level C
   J level D

5. You and your classmates have just set up a terrarium in a jar using gravel, moist soil, leafy plants, and mosses. The day after the jar was sealed, you noticed water droplets on the inside of the jar. What process caused the water droplets to form?
   A evaporation
   B condensation
   C precipitation
   D surface runoff

Constructed Response

6. Explain how the processes by which carbon and oxygen cycle through the atmosphere are interrelated.

Applying Skills

20. Grass: producer; mouse, rabbit, and deer: first-level consumers; snake and mountain lion: second-level consumers

21. The producers (grass)

22. The snake and mountain lion populations would decrease because there would be fewer prey organisms for them to eat. The deer populations would probably decrease at first as hungry lions preyed on deer. Later, as the lion populations decreased, the deer population would increase. Also, the deer would have less competition for grass.

Standardized Test Prep

1. C **2.** J **3.** A **4.** J **5.** B

6. Both are part of the processes of photosynthesis and cellular respiration. Carbon dioxide is used during photosynthesis, which produces oxygen. The oxygen is used during cellular respiration, which produces carbon dioxide.

Chapter at a Glance

PRENTICE HALL
Teacher**EXPRESS**™
Plan • Teach • Assess

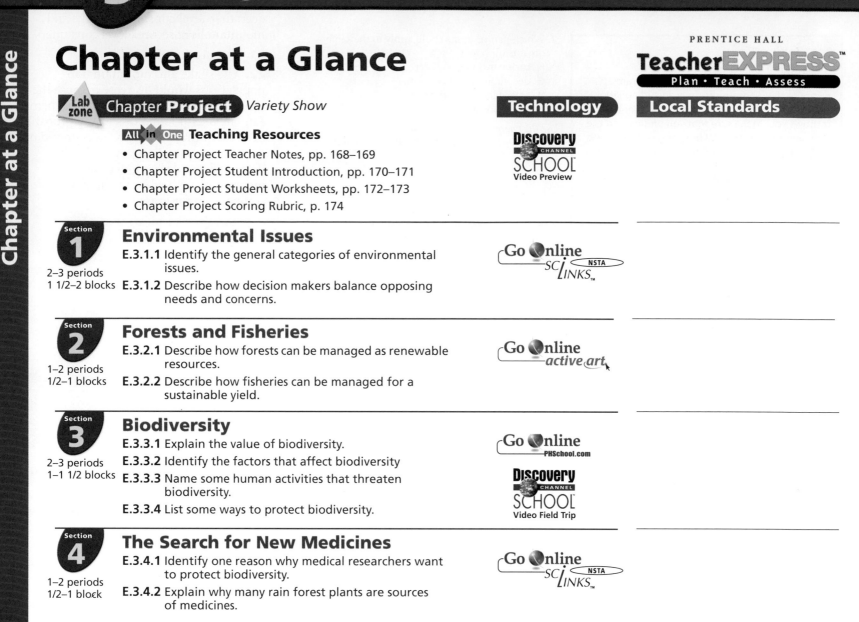

Lab zone Chapter **Project** *Variety Show*

Technology

Local Standards

All in One Teaching Resources
- Chapter Project Teacher Notes, pp. 168–169
- Chapter Project Student Introduction, pp. 170–171
- Chapter Project Student Worksheets, pp. 172–173
- Chapter Project Scoring Rubric, p. 174

Discovery CHANNEL SCHOOL Video Preview

Section 1 Environmental Issues

2–3 periods
1 1/2–2 blocks

E.3.1.1 Identify the general categories of environmental issues.
E.3.1.2 Describe how decision makers balance opposing needs and concerns.

Go Online SC*LINKS* NSTA

Section 2 Forests and Fisheries

1–2 periods
1/2–1 blocks

E.3.2.1 Describe how forests can be managed as renewable resources.
E.3.2.2 Describe how fisheries can be managed for a sustainable yield.

Go Online *active art*

Section 3 Biodiversity

2–3 periods
1–1 1/2 blocks

E.3.3.1 Explain the value of biodiversity.
E.3.3.2 Identify the factors that affect biodiversity
E.3.3.3 Name some human activities that threaten biodiversity.
E.3.3.4 List some ways to protect biodiversity.

Go Online PHSchool.com

Discovery CHANNEL SCHOOL Video Field Trip

Section 4 The Search for New Medicines

1–2 periods
1/2–1 block

E.3.4.1 Identify one reason why medical researchers want to protect biodiversity.
E.3.4.2 Explain why many rain forest plants are sources of medicines.

Go Online SC*LINKS* NSTA

Review and Assessment

All in One Teaching Resources
- Key Terms Review, p. 207
- Transparency E31
- Performance Assessment Teacher Notes, p. 214
- Performance Assessment Scoring Rubric p. 215
- Performance Assessment Student Worksheet, p. 216
- Chapter Test, pp. 217–220

Go Online PHSchool.com

Discovery CHANNEL SCHOOL Video Assessment

Test Preparation

Test Preparation Blackline Masters

Chapter Activities Planner

For more activities

LAB ZONE
Easy Planner
CD-ROM

Student Edition	Inquiry	Time	Materials	Skills	Resources
Chapter Project	Open-Ended	2 to 3 weeks	**All in One Teaching Resources** See p. 169	Classifying, making inferences, communicating	**Lab zone Easy Planner** **All in One Teaching Resources** Support pp. 169–174
Section 1					
Discover Activity, p. 82	Guided	15 minutes	None	Forming operational definitions	**Lab zone Easy Planner**
Skills Lab, p. 88	Directed	Prep: 15 minutes Class: 15 minutes on Day 1, 40 minutes on Day 2, 10 minutes on Day 3	Newspaper, microscope, water, eggbeater, square pan, screen, plastic wrap, mixing bowl, heavy book, microscope slide	Observing, predicting	**Lab zone Easy Planner** **Lab Activity Video** **All in One Teaching Resources** Skills Lab: *Recycling Paper,* pp. 182–183
Section 2					
Discover Activity, p. 89	Guided	15 minutes	Graph paper, ruler, pencil	Inferring	**Lab zone Easy Planner**
Skills Activity, p. 92	Guided	5 minutes	Calculator	Calculating	**Lab zone Easy Planner**
Skills Lab, p. 94	Guided	Prep: 15 minutes Class: 40 minutes	Tree cookie, metric ruler, hand lens, colored pencils, calculator (optional)	Observing, inferring, interpreting data	**Lab zone Easy Planner** **Lab Activity Video** **All in One Teaching Resources** Skills Lab: *Tree Cookie Tales,* pp. 192–193
Section 3					
Discover Activity, p. 95	Directed	20 minutes	Two labeled cups containing different seed mixtures, paper plate	Inferring	**Lab zone Easy Planner**
Try This, p. 99	Guided	20 minutes	None	Inferring	**Lab zone Easy Planner**
Section 4					
Discover Activity, p. 106	Directed	15 minutes	Black marking pen, strip of filter paper, water, clear plastic cup, tape, pencil	Observing	**Lab zone Easy Planner**

Section 1 Environmental Issues

⏱ *2–3 periods 1 1/2–2 blocks*

ABILITY LEVELS
L1 Basic to Average
L2 For All Students
L3 Average to Advanced

Objectives

E.3.1.1 Identify the general categories of environmental issues.
E.3.1.2 Describe how decision makers balance opposing needs and concerns.

Local Standards

Key Terms

• natural resource • renewable resource • nonrenewable resource • pollution
• environmental science

Preteach

Build Background Knowledge

Ask questions to help students understand the term *issue*.

Lab zone Discover Activity *How Do You Decide?*

Targeted Print and Technology Resources

All in One Teaching Resources

L2 Reading Strategy Transparency E26: Identifying Main Ideas

🔘 **Presentation-Pro CD-ROM**

Transparency E26

Instruct

Types of Environmental Issues Define and give examples of three types of environmental issues.

Making Environmental Decisions Ask leading questions for a discussion on the process of balancing needs by considering costs and benefits.

Lab zone Skills Lab *Recycling Paper*

Targeted Print and Technology Resources

All in One Teaching Resources

L2 Guided Reading, pp. 177–179
L2 Skills Lab: *Recycling Paper,* pp. 182–184

📼 **Lab Activity Video/DVD**
Skills Lab: *Recycling Paper*

www.SciLinks.org Web Code: scn-0531

🔘 **Student Edition on Audio CD**

Assess

Section Assessment Questions

🌀 Have students use their completed graphic organizers about types of environmental issues to help them answer questions.

Reteach

Brainstorm a list of the costs and benefits of damming a river and building a hydroelectric plant.

Targeted Print and Technology Resources

All in One Teaching Resources

• Section Summary, p. 176
L1 Review and Reinforce, p. 180
L3 Enrich, p. 181

Section 2 **Forests and Fisheries**

🕐 *1–2 periods 1/2–1 blocks*

ABILITY LEVELS
L1 Basic to Average
L2 For All Students
L3 Average to Advanced

Objectives

E.3.2.1 Describe how forests can be managed as renewable resources.

E.3.2.2 Describe how fisheries can be managed for a sustainable yield.

Key Terms

• clear-cutting • selective cutting • sustainable yield • fishery • aquaculture

Local Standards

Preteach

Build Background Knowledge

Help students identify classroom items made from trees.

Lab zone Discover Activity *What Happened to the Tuna?*

Targeted Print and Technology Resources

All in One Teaching Resources

L2 Reading Strategy Transparency E27: Using Prior Knowledge

💿 **Presentation-Pro CD-ROM**

Transparency E27

Instruct

Forest Resources Use photographs to help students classify products made from forest plants.

Managing Forests Use diagrams to determine which method of harvesting trees is the least disruptive.

Fisheries Study limits, changed methods, aquaculture, and new resources as ways to manage fisheries.

Lab zone Skills Lab *Tree Cookie Tales*

Targeted Print and Technology Resources

All in One Teaching Resources

L2 Guided Reading, pp. 187–189

L2 Transparency E28

L2 Skills Lab: *Tree Cookie Tales,* pp. 192–193

📼 **Lab Activity Video/DVD**
Skills Lab: *Tree Cookie Tales*

www.PHSchool.com Web Code: cep-5032

💿 **Student Edition on Audio CD**

Transparency E28

Assess

Section Assessment Questions

🔁 Have students use their Using Prior Knowledge graphic organizers as they answer the questions.

Reteach

Compare and contrast overfishing and clear-cutting.

Targeted Print and Technology Resources

All in One Teaching Resources

• Section Summary, p. 186

L1 Review and Reinforce, p. 190

L3 Enrich, p. 191

Section 3 **Biodiversity**

2–3 periods 1–1 1/2 blocks

ABILITY LEVELS
L1 Basic to Average
L2 For All Students
L3 Average to Advanced

Objectives

E.3.3.1 Explain the value of biodiversity.

E.3.3.2 Identify the factors that affect biodiversity.

E.3.3.3 Name some human activities that threaten biodiversity.

E.3.3.4 List some ways to protect biodiversity.

Local Standards

Key Terms

• biodiversity • keystone species • gene • extinction • endangered species
• threatened species • habitat destruction • habitat fragmentation • poaching
• captive breeding

Preteach

Build Background Knowledge

List the variety of organisms that live in the area and help students infer that there is a great diversity of species around them.

Lab zone Discover Activity *How Much Variety Is There?*

Targeted Print and Technology Resources

All in One Teaching Resources

L2 Reading Strategy: Building Vocabulary

⊙ Presentation-Pro CD-ROM

Instruct

The Value of Biodiversity Describe the economic and ecological values of biodiversity.

Factors Affecting Biodiversity Brainstorm a list of factors affecting biodiversity.

Gene Pool Diversity Discuss the usefulness of gene pool diversity to the survival of a species.

Extinction of Species Use photographs to show that some species, once prevalent on Earth, are no longer present or are endangered.

Causes of Extinction Describe agents causing extinction.

Protecting Biodiversity Define *captive breeding,* and discuss other methods that help protect biodiversity.

Targeted Print and Technology Resources

All in One Teaching Resources

L2 Guided Reading, pp. 196–198

www.PHSchool.com Web Code: ced-5033

⊙ Student Edition on Audio CD

Assess

Section Assessment Questions

 Have students use their definitions to answer the questions.

Reteach

List ways in which humans threaten biodiversity and ways to preserve biodiversity.

Targeted Print and Technology Resources

All in One Teaching Resources

• Section Summary, p. 195

L1 Review and Reinforce, p. 199

L3 Enrich, p. 200

Section 4 Integrating Health The Search for New Medicines

ABILITY LEVELS
L1 Basic to Average
L2 For All Students
L3 Average to Advanced

🕐 *1–2 periods, 1/2–1 block*

Objectives

E.3.4.1 Identify one reason why medical researchers want to protect biodiversity.

E.3.4.2 Explain why many rain forest plants are sources of medicines.

Local Standards

Key Term

• taxol

Preteach

Build Background Knowledge

Tap into prior knowledge to get descriptions of the locations of temperate rain forests.

Lab zone Discover Activity *How Are Plant Chemicals Separated?*

Targeted Print and Technology Resources

All in One Teaching Resources

L2 Reading Strategy Transparency E29: Asking Questions

🔘 **Presentation-Pro CD-ROM**

Transparency E29

Instruct

Biodiversity and Medicine Use leading questions to discuss organisms, some as yet undiscovered, that have medicinal value.

The Story of Taxol Describe the plant origins and medicinal applications of taxol.

Targeted Print and Technology Resources

All in One Teaching Resources

L2 Guided Reading, pp. 203–204

www.SciLinks.org Web Code: scn-0534

🔘 **Student Edition on Audio CD**

Assess

Section Assessment Questions

🎯 Have students refer to their graphic organizer about diversity and biodiversity to answer questions.

Reteach

Use a cause-and-effect graphic organizer to relate the causes and effects of declining diversity.

Targeted Print and Technology Resources

All in One Teaching Resources

• Section Summary, p. 202

L1 Review and Reinforce, p. 205

L3 Enrich, p. 206

Section 1 Environmental Issues

The environment and environmental issues are topics not limited to the twentieth and twenty-first centuries. In about 80 A.D., the Roman senate passed laws designed to protect the city's supply of clean water for drinking and bathing. Laws in fourteenth century England prohibited burning coal within the city limits of London. In the United States, William Penn decreed that Pennsylvania would set aside one acre of forest for every five acres cleared for settlement.

Today's environmental issues include pollution, resource use, and population growth. One example of today's environmental issues is the continuing discussion regarding oil exploration in the Arctic National Wildlife Refuge. Visitors to this vast preserve in northeastern Alaska can see wildlife ranging from polar bears to arctic foxes. Opponents worry that oil exploration would damage the fragile ecosystem. Proponents argue that the United States needs to produce more oil domestically, rather than to continue dependence on foreign oil.

In 2003, a plan to open the refuge to exploration was defeated when it was dropped from an energy bill proposed in Congress. However, it is likely that this decision will not end the discussion as energy needs increase and current supplies decrease. Decision-makers will have to balance opinions and facts as they weigh the costs and benefits of any proposals.

Section 2 Forests and Fisheries

Deforestation can have a profound effect on regional and global climates. During transpiration, a tree returns to the air about 97 percent of the water that the roots absorb from the ground. This water eventually returns to Earth through the water cycle. Deforestation can reduce rainfall in a region and increase the frequency of droughts.

Deforested tropical rain forests may contribute to an increase of global temperatures. For example, as felled trees are burned, they add carbon dioxide to the atmosphere, which increases the amount of heat the atmosphere retains rather than radiating it back into space.

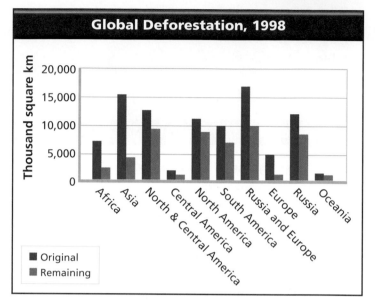

Global Deforestation, 1998

Today the most visible tenet of managed forestry is selective cutting. Several organizations, including the U.S. Forest Service, work to improve yield through their studies of tree physiology, entomology, and genetics.

Fisheries have only recently begun to moderate their catch in the hopes of maintaining a steady supply. Fishery management has expanded to aquaculture, commonly referred to as fish farming. Fish are reared under controlled conditions. They may be raised to maturity, or immature fish may be placed in open waters for catch when they are mature. This process has proved useful for lobster species, and indications are that it will work for other species as well.

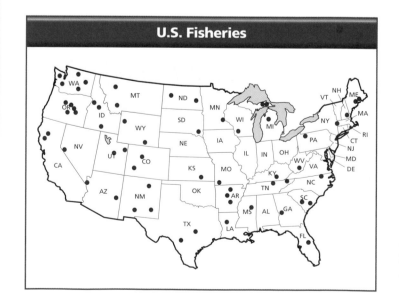

U.S. Fisheries

Section 3 Biodiversity

One benefit of biodiversity is the preservation of the gene pool. A diverse gene pool allows researchers to develop varieties of "new and improved" species that still exhibit the hardiness of unmodified species. In the past 100 years, researchers have greatly increased the yields of crops such as corn and wheat by creating highly productive, but genetically uniform, varieties. With genetic uniformity, however, comes decreased resistance to certain diseases and pests. To restore resistance to these crop varieties, scientists cross them with other, often wild, varieties. Scientists crossed genetically uniform varieties susceptible to blight with Mexican varieties that possessed the genes needed to be blight resistant. Because the cultivation of corn began in Mexico thousands of years ago, Mexican varieties are ancestral to modern varieties and have greater genetic diversity.

> ⚑ **Address Misconceptions**
>
> *All extinct animals lived long ago and became extinct under mysterious circumstances.* In the past few centuries, the number of species becoming extinct has increased dramatically. For example, the last passenger pigeon died in 1914. Whooping cranes, California condors, and Schaus swallowtail butterflies have low populations and are considered seriously endangered. For more on this misconception, see **Address Misconceptions** in Section 3.

Section 4 The Search for New Medicines

The potential to find medicines from organisms relies on preserving biodiversity. We do not know all the species on Earth, so we cannot know which of them might provide life-saving medicines. We benefit by preserving them. The search for these medicines is an environmental issue requiring sensitive cost-benefit comparison. Researchers hypothesize that one of the greatest sources of medicine-producing plants is the tropical rain forest. The medical benefits they can supply are undeniable. However, the rain forest continues to be destroyed, much of it burned by subsistence farmers clearing the forest to make way for crops. The economic needs of the farmer are undeniable. The challenge is to find a way to balance these competing benefits.

Help Students Read

Identifying Main Ideas

Strategy Help students become aware of text organization and help them identify key information. By identifying the main idea under each subhead, students will be able to distinguish important and unimportant information. Assign students the two paragraphs under the heading Population Growth.

Example

1. Main idea of a Paragraph Review with students the fact that most paragraphs have a topic sentence expressing the paragraph's main idea, while the other sentences provide supporting details.

2. Main Idea of a Subheading Guide students to make the connection that just as a paragraph has a main idea, the text under each subheading has a main idea carried within the paragraphs.

3. Inferring or Synthesizing a Main Idea State that it may be necessary to infer an unstated main idea by combining information carried in several paragraphs.

4. Practice Have students read through a section, noting each of the subheads as they read.

interactive Textbook
- Complete student edition
- Video and audio
- Simulations and activities
- Section and chapter activities

Chapter 3

Living Resources

Chapter Preview

1 Environmental Issues
Discover *How Do You Decide?*
Science and History *Making a Difference*
Skills Lab *Recycling Paper*

2 Forests and Fisheries
Discover *What Happened to the Tuna?*
Active Art *Logging Methods*
Skills Activity *Calculating*
At-Home Activity *Renewable Resource Survey*
Skills Lab *Tree Cookie Tales*

3 Biodiversity
Discover *How Much Variety Is There?*
Try This *Grocery Gene Pool*
Analyzing Data *California Peregrine Falcon Recovery*
At-Home Activity *Species Refuges*

4 The Search for New Medicines
Discover *How Are Plant Chemicals Separated?*

interactive Textbook

▶ Fish—including sharks—are an important source of food for people.

Lab zone   Chapter Project

Objectives
As this project progresses, students have a chance to apply methods and skills used by field biologists and environmental scientists. Students also develop an appreciation for the rich diversity of living things found in a small plot of land. After this Chapter Project, students will be able to
- observe, compare and contrast, and classify organisms
- infer relationships among organisms and between organisms and the abiotic factors in their environment
- create a data table for recording observations
- communicate observations and conclusions to others

Skills Focus
Observing, comparing and contrasting, classifying, inferring, creating data tables, communicating

Project Time Line 2 to 3 weeks

All in One Teaching Resources
- Chapter Project Teacher Notes
- Chapter Project Worksheet 1
- Chapter Project Worksheet 2
- Chapter Project Worksheet 3
- Chapter Project Scoring Rubric

Developing a Plan
Each small group of students should choose a location and secure teacher approval. Students proceed by staking the plot and preparing a notebook for recording observations. Advise students to make regular observations and record data carefully. At the conclusion of the observation period, students should prepare a presentation for the class that may include materials such as photographs, drawings, videos, or computer displays.

Possible Materials
- To mark the plot, each group will need a meter stick or metric tape measure, four small stakes, a hammer, sturdy string, and a directional compass.
- To observe plots, each group will need a thermometer, hand lenses, rulers, and trowels.
- Students will need a variety of field guides in order to identify and classify any unfamiliar organisms. A field guide to animal tracks will be helpful as well.

Lab zone Chapter **Project**

Variety Show

In this chapter's project, you will become an ecologist as you study the diversity of life in a small plot of land. Keep in mind that the area you will study has just a tiny sample of the huge variety of organisms that live on Earth.

Your Goal To observe the diversity of organisms in a plot of land

To complete this project, you must
● stake out a 1.5 meter-by-1.5 meter plot of ground
● keep a record of your observations of the abiotic conditions
● identify the species of organisms you observe
● follow the safety guidelines in Appendix A

Plan It! Look for a location for your plot. With your teacher's approval, stake out a square plot measuring 1.5 meters on each side. Prepare a notebook in which to record your observations, including the date, time, air temperature, and other weather conditions. Also include places for drawings or photographs of the organisms in your plot.

● Students will need art supplies to prepare their presentations. Cameras and videocassette recorders would be helpful, if available.

Advance Preparation

Before introducing the project, survey the grounds around your school so that you can guide students to areas where they are likely to find a good variety of organisms. If the school grounds are not appropriate, locate a nearby field, park, vacant lot, or other natural area to which you can take the class during school hours. Obtain permission to use the land, if necessary.

Living Resources

Show the Video Preview to introduce the Chapter Project and overview the chapter. Discussion questions: **What is overfishing?** *(Overfishing is killing more fish than can be replaced and thereby reducing the fish population in an area.)* **What is one negative effect of overfishing?** *(Few fish are left to reproduce.)*

Launching the Project

To introduce the project, draw a 1.5-by-1.5-meter square on the chalkboard. Ask: **How many different kinds of organisms do you think you can find in a plot of land this size?** *(Sample answer: Dozens; accept all responses at this time, and encourage creative thinking.)* Encourage discussion of the different kinds of living things students think they might find. Students could identify types of source materials they could use for their research. Answer any initial questions that students may have.

Performance Assessment

The Chapter Project Scoring Rubric will help you evaluate how well students complete the Chapter Project. You may want to share the scoring rubric with your students so they are clear about what will be expected of them. Students will be assessed on
● the completeness and accuracy of their observations and data
● their ability to use previous knowledge as well as reference sources to identify and classify organisms
● how well they communicate their findings to the rest of the class
● the extent of their participation in groups

Portfolio

E ● 81

Objectives

After this lesson, students will be able to

E.3.1.1 Identify the general categories of environmental issues.

E.3.1.2 Describe how decision makers balance opposing needs and concerns.

Target Reading Skill 🎯

Identifying Main Ideas Explain that identifying main ideas and details helps students sort the facts from the information into groups. Each group can have a main topic, subtopics, and details.

Answers

Three types of environmental issues are resource use, population growth, and pollution.

All in One Teaching Resources

• Transparency E26

Preteach

Build Background Knowledge   **L2**

Defining Issues

Ask: **What is an issue?** *(Students' responses should include the idea of a problem or question on which people have different viewpoints.)* **What are some examples of issues that you have heard about?** *(Possible responses: Should a run-down historic building in town be restored or demolished? Should owners of beachfront property be allowed to restrict public access to beaches?)*

Reading Preview

Key Concepts

• What are the general categories of environmental issues?

• How do decision makers balance different needs and concerns?

Key Terms

• natural resource
• renewable resource
• nonrenewable resource
• pollution
• environmental science

🎯 Target Reading Skill

Identifying Main Ideas As you read the Types of Environmental Issues section, write the main idea in a graphic organizer like the one below. Then write three supporting details that give examples of the main idea.

Main Idea

Three types of environmental issues are . . .

Detail | Detail | Detail

Lab zone Discover **Activity**

How Do You Decide?

1. On a sheet of paper, list the three environmental issues you think are most important today.

2. Next to each issue you have listed, write the reason you think it is important.

3. Form a group with three other classmates. Share your lists. Decide as a group which one of the issues on your lists is the most important.

Think It Over

Forming Operational Definitions Based on your group's discussion, how would you define *environmental issue?*

Here's a riddle for you: What is bigger than the United States and Mexico combined; is covered with two kilometers of ice; is a unique habitat for many animals; and is a source of oil, coal, and iron? The answer is Antarctica. Some people think of Antarctica as a useless, icy wasteland. But there are unique wildlife habitats in Antarctica. There are also valuable minerals beneath its thick ice.

Now the question is, What is the best use of Antarctica? Many people want access to its rich deposits of minerals and oil. Others worry that mining will harm its delicate ecosystems. Some people propose building hotels, parks, and ski resorts. But others feel that Antarctica should remain undeveloped. It is not even clear who should decide Antarctica's fate.

In 1998, 26 nations agreed to ban mining and oil exploration in Antarctica for at least 50 years. As resources become more scarce elsewhere in the world, the debate will surely continue.

1000 B.C.
About 50 million

A.D. 1
About 285 million

Lab zone Discover **Activity**

Skills Focus Forming operational definitions

Materials none

Time 15 minutes

Tips Encourage students to think of specific, *debatable* questions such as "Should people be rewarded for buying smaller, fuel-efficient cars?" "Should

companies be given tax credits for using less product packaging?" and "Should recycling be required?"

Expected Outcome Possible answers include pollution or declining resources.

Think It Over Definitions should allow for different viewpoints. Encourage students to apply their operational definitions to all of the environmental issues they listed. Have students explore any issues that do not lend themselves to the operational definition.

Types of Environmental Issues

The debate about Antarctica's future is just one environmental issue that people face today. **Environmental issues fall into three general categories: resource use, population growth, and pollution.** Because these three types of issues are interconnected, they are very difficult to study and solve.

Resource Use Anything in the environment that is used by people is called a **natural resource.** Some natural resources are renewable. **Renewable resources** are either always available or are naturally replaced in a relatively short time. Renewable resources include sunlight, wind, fresh water, and trees. Some people think that renewable resources can never be used up. This is not true for some renewable resources. For example, if people cut down trees faster than they can grow back, the supply of this resource will decrease and could possibly run out.

Natural resources that are not replaced in a useful time frame are called **nonrenewable resources.** As nonrenewable resources such as coal or oil are used, the supply decreases.

Population Growth Figure 1 shows how the human population has changed in the last 3,000 years. You can see that the population grew very slowly until about A.D. 1650. Around that time, improvements in medicine, agriculture, and waste disposal began to enable people to live longer. The human population has been growing faster and faster since then. However, scientists do not expect the population to grow as rapidly in the future.

When a population grows, the demand for resources also grows. Has your town ever experienced a water shortage? If so, you might have noticed that people have been asked to restrict their water use. This sometimes happens in areas with fast-growing populations. The water supplies in such areas were designed to serve fewer people than they now do, so shortages sometimes occur during unusually warm or dry weather.

A.D. 2000
About 6 billion

A.D. 1000
About 300 million

FIGURE 1
Population Growth
More than 6 billion people now live on Earth.
Making Generalizations
How has the human population changed over the past 1,000 years?

E ◆ 83

Types of Environmental Issues

Teach Key Concepts L2
Real-Life Application

Focus Ask: **What are some activities that would help protect the environment if a lot of people did them?** *(Sample answers: Recycling softdrink cans; putting on a sweater instead of turning up the heat)* List each action on the board.

Teach Refer to an action and ask: **How does this help solve environmental problems?** *(Sample answers: Recycling cans reduces the need to mine more aluminum ore, which is a nonrenewable resource. Putting on sweaters reduces our use of heating fuel, another nonrenewable resource.)*

Apply Tell students that every pound of recycled aluminum saves four pounds of ore. The energy saved from recycling one aluminum can is equivalent to the energy in one cup of gasoline. Ask: **How many recycled aluminum cans would save the energy equivalent of 10 gallons of gasoline?** *(2 cups/pint × 2 pints/quart × 4 quarts/ gallon × 10 gallons = 160)* **learning modality: logical/mathematical**

Independent Practice L2

 Teaching Resources

- Guided Reading and Study Worksheet: *Environmental Issues*

Student Edition on Audio CD

Differentiated Instruction

English Learners/Beginning L1
Vocabulary: Science Glossary
Pronounce and define vocabulary words aloud. Suggest that students start a personal glossary, with each term and its definition in English on one side of an index card and in the student's primary language on the other side. **learning modality: verbal**

English Learners/Intermediate L2
Vocabulary: Science Glossary Students can expand on the activity by adding other unfamiliar terms in this section: *shortage, impact, pollutants, refuge.* Have students write sentences that use each of these words. Call on individuals to read their sentences aloud. **learning modality: verbal**

Monitor Progress L2

Writing Have each student explain why the world's population has grown so dramatically in the past 350 years. Students can save their explanations in their portfolios.

Portfolio

Answers
Figure 1 It has increased by more than 5 billion people.

Build **Inquiry**

L2

Graphing

Materials graph paper, ruler, pencil, world map

Time 25 minutes

Focus Point out to students that Figure 1 shows population growth for the entire world. However, actual growth rates and population sizes vary among different regions and countries of the world.

Teach Give students the current populations of several countries listed below and have them construct bar graphs. Have students use their graphs to answer the following questions: **Which country has the largest population?** *(China)* **Which country has the next-largest population?** *(India)* **How many times larger than Japan's population is the U. S. population?** *(About twice as large)*

Apply Have students compare the United States' and Japan's land areas on a world map. Ask: **Which country has a greater population density? Explain.** *(Japan; if necessary, help students recall the term* population density *from Chapter 1.)*
learning modality: logical/mathematical

2002 Population of Selected Countries	
Brazil	179,914,212
China	1,279,160,885
Great Britain	59,912,431
India	1,034,172,547
Indonesia	231,326,092
Japan	127,065,841
Mexico	102,479,927
Nigeria	130,499,978
Russia	144,978,573
United States	287,675,526

Go Online
SciLINKS NSTA
For: Links on the environment
Visit: www.SciLinks.org
Web Code: scn-0531

Students can review environmental issues in an online activity.

Go Online
SciLINKS NSTA
For: Links on the environment
Visit: www.SciLinks.org
Web Code: scn-0531

Pollution The contamination of Earth's land, water, or air is called **pollution**. Pollution can be caused by a variety of factors, including chemicals, wastes, noise, heat, and light. Pollution can destroy wildlife and cause human health problems.

Pollution can be related to resource use. As you probably know, the burning of gasoline releases pollutants into the air. With more cars on the road, more gasoline is used, so more pollutants are released into the air.

Pollution can also be related to population growth. For example, as populations grow, and more people need to be fed, more fertilizers and other chemicals may be used to produce that food. As these chemicals run off the land, they can pollute bodies of water.

✓ **Reading Checkpoint** What are three factors that can cause pollution?

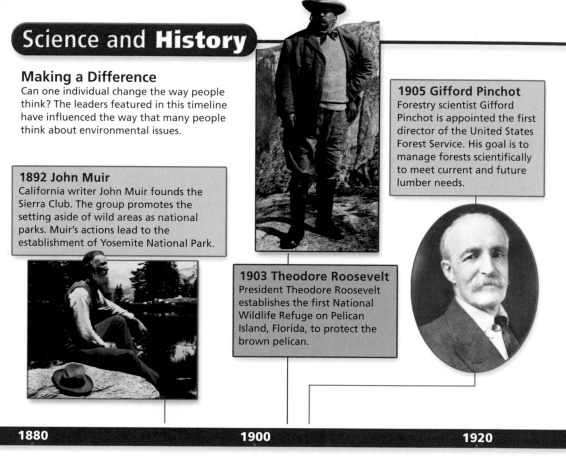

Science and **History**

Making a Difference
Can one individual change the way people think? The leaders featured in this timeline have influenced the way that many people think about environmental issues.

1892 John Muir
California writer John Muir founds the Sierra Club. The group promotes the setting aside of wild areas as national parks. Muir's actions lead to the establishment of Yosemite National Park.

1903 Theodore Roosevelt
President Theodore Roosevelt establishes the first National Wildlife Refuge on Pelican Island, Florida, to protect the brown pelican.

1905 Gifford Pinchot
Forestry scientist Gifford Pinchot is appointed the first director of the United States Forest Service. His goal is to manage forests scientifically to meet current and future lumber needs.

1880	1900	1920

84 ◆ E

Differentiated Instruction

Gifted and Talented L3
Research Report Invite pairs of students to research one of the following environmental activists.
- **Jacques Cousteau** introduced millions to ocean life and the importance of preserving it.
- **Dian Fossey** urged the preservation of the endangered mountain gorilla of east-central Africa.

- **Jane Goodall** increased our knowledge of the ecology of wild chimpanzees.
- **Chico Mendes** established reserves where rubber could be harvested without causing damage to the Brazilian rain forests.

Tell students to present their information in the form of an interview in which one student plays the role of the activist and the other student is the interviewer. **learning modality: verbal**

Making Environmental Decisions

Dealing with environmental issues means making decisions. These decisions can be made at personal, local, national, or global levels. Your decision to walk to your friend's house rather than ride in a car is made at a personal level. A town's decision about how to dispose of its trash is made at a local level. A decision about whether the United States should allow oil drilling in a wildlife refuge is a decision made on a national level. Decisions about how to protect Earth's atmosphere are made on a global level.

Every decision has some impact on the environment. Your personal decisions of what to eat or how to travel have a small impact. But when the personal decisions of millions of people are combined, they have a huge impact on the environment.

Focus Tell students that organized concern for the environment began to develop after the start of the Industrial Revolution.

Teach Focus attention on the timeline, a span of 100 years. As students read about the individuals featured, ask: **Which of these people would you like to learn more about?** *(Encourage students to explain their choices and how they would research.)*

Writing in Science

Writing Mode Persuasion
Scoring Rubric

4 Includes a complete and accurate description of the person and many interesting details
3 Includes a complete and accurate description of person
2 Includes only brief but accurate description of person
1 Includes inaccurate description

Portfolio

Making Environmental Decisions

Teach Key Concepts L2
Value-Based Decision Making

Focus Ask: **What is an example of something that is balanced?** (Sample answer: *A person on a tightrope.*)

Teach Draw students' attention to one of the environmental issues discussed in the text, such as the logging issue. Ask: **What needs must be balanced when making this decision?** *(Sample answer: The need to provide jobs, the demand for wood, the need to protect the ecosystem)*

Apply Invite students to consider other issues not discussed in the text. **learning modality: verbal**

Monitor Progress L2

Writing Have each student write a paragraph that explains how the actions of an individual can have a significant effect on environmental issues. Students can save their paragraphs in their portfolios.

Portfolio

Answer

✓ **Reading Checkpoint** Chemicals, wastes, noise, heat, light

Writing in Science

Research and Write Find out more about one of the people featured in this timeline. Write a short biography of the person's life that explains how he or she became involved in environmental issues. What obstacles did the person overcome to accomplish his or her goal?

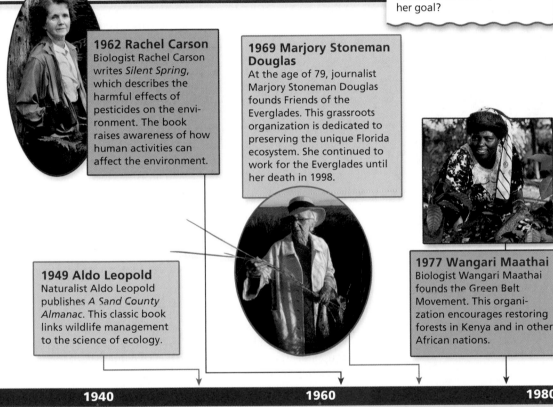

1962 Rachel Carson
Biologist Rachel Carson writes *Silent Spring,* which describes the harmful effects of pesticides on the environment. The book raises awareness of how human activities can affect the environment.

1969 Marjory Stoneman Douglas
At the age of 79, journalist Marjory Stoneman Douglas founds Friends of the Everglades. This grassroots organization is dedicated to preserving the unique Florida ecosystem. She continued to work for the Everglades until her death in 1998.

1977 Wangari Maathai
Biologist Wangari Maathai founds the Green Belt Movement. This organization encourages restoring forests in Kenya and in other African nations.

1949 Aldo Leopold
Naturalist Aldo Leopold publishes *A Sand County Almanac.* This classic book links wildlife management to the science of ecology.

1940   1960   1980

Differentiated Instruction

Gifted and Talented L3
Analyzing Issues Encourage students to research environmental issues in their community, state, or region. Have each group create a skit based on their research. Suggest that they describe different viewpoints and proposed solutions and include a photograph, graph, or other visual. **learning modality: verbal**

Comparing Costs and Benefits

Materials cost-benefit table

Time 20 minutes

Focus Suggest that the class develop a cost versus benefit table for one of the environmental issues mentioned in the text.

Teach Draw a two-column table on the board or overhead projector. Label the columns *Costs* and *Benefits*. Ask volunteers to suggest entries for the chart. Divide the entries into short-term costs and benefits and long-term ones. Have each volunteer explain why he or she chose the item. Ask volunteers to explain how they determined whether their suggestions were costs or benefits and whether they were short- or long-term.

Apply Suggest students listen to daily newscasts for a week or scan a week's worth of newspapers. Students can report on any discussions about the costs and/or benefits of a current environmental issue. **learning modality: logical/mathematical**

FIGURE 2

Resource Use

Decisions about undeveloped land must weigh the costs and benefits. Some benefits of parks are shown here.

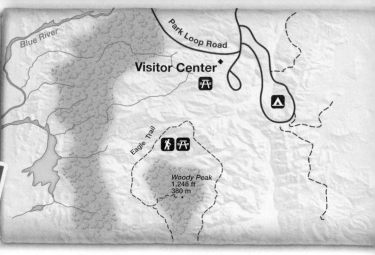

Scenic Benefit The park is a beautiful and peaceful place where we can hike and bird watch.

Economic Benefit The trees and other resources of the park provide jobs for loggers and builders.

Balancing Different Needs Lawmakers work with many groups to make environmental decisions. One such group is environmental scientists. **Environmental science** is the study of natural processes in the environment and how humans can affect them. But the data provided by environmental scientists are only part of the decision-making process.

Environmental decision making requires a delicate balance between the needs of the environment and the needs of people. **To help balance the different opinions on an environmental issue, decision makers weigh the costs and benefits of a proposal.**

Types of Costs and Benefits Costs and benefits are often economic. Will a proposal provide jobs? Will it cost too much money? But costs and benefits are not only measured in terms of money. For example, suppose a state must decide whether to allow logging in a park. Removing trees changes the ecosystem, which is an ecological cost. However, by providing jobs and needed wood, logging has an economic benefit.

It is also important to consider the short-term and long-term costs and benefits of an environmental decision. A plan's short-term costs might be outweighed by its long-term benefits.

Weighing Costs and Benefits Once you have identified the potential costs and benefits of a decision, you must analyze them. Consider the costs and benefits of drilling for oil in Antarctica. There would be many costs. It would be very expensive to set up a drilling operation in such a cold and distant place. Transporting the oil would also be difficult and costly. An oil spill in the seas around Antarctica could harm the fish, penguins, and seals there.

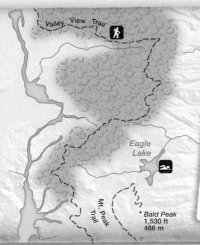

Valley View Trail

Eagle Lake

Mt. Peak Trail

Bald Peak
1,530 ft
466 m

Recreational Benefit The park rivers are great places for us to fish in.

On the other hand, there would be benefits to drilling for oil in Antarctica. Oil drilling would provide a new supply of oil for heat, electricity, and transportation. If the worldwide supply of oil were larger, the price might drop, making oil available to more people. The plan would also create many new jobs. Would the benefits of drilling for oil in Antarctica outweigh the costs? This is the kind of question lawmakers must ask before they make environmental decisions.

✓ Reading Checkpoint **What are two types of costs and benefits?**

Ecological Benefit The park contains habitats for many animals, plants, and other organisms.

Section 1 Assessment

⟳ **Target Reading Skill Identifying Main Ideas** Use your graphic organizer about types of environmental issues to help you answer Question 1 below.

Reviewing Key Concepts

1. a. **Identifying** What are the three main types of environmental issues?
   b. **Explaining** Why is population growth an environmental issue?
   c. **Relating Cause and Effect** How might a growing population affect the supply of trees, a renewable resource? Explain your answer.

2. a. **Reviewing** Why is weighing costs and benefits useful for decision makers?

b. **Classifying** Name one economic cost and one noneconomic cost of drilling for oil in Antarctica. List one benefit of drilling in Antarctica.
c. **Making Judgments** Suppose you were a world leader faced with the question of drilling in Antarctica. What decision would you make? Give reasons for your decision.

Writing in Science

Persuasive Letter Write a letter to the editor expressing your viewpoint on whether people should be allowed to use powerboats on a lake in your town. Your letter should clearly show how you weighed the costs and benefits to arrive at your viewpoint.

Chapter 3 E ◆ 87

Recycling Paper

Prepare for Inquiry

Key Concept
Paper is a renewable resource because it can be recycled.

Skills Objectives
After this lab, students will be able to
- observe and compare dry newspaper and recycled paper made from newspaper pulp
- predict how the structure of paper changes when it is recycled

Prep Time 15 minutes

Class Time 15 minutes on Day 1, 40 minutes on Day 2, 10 minutes on Day 3

Advance Planning
Gather an ample supply of old newspapers.

Safety
Students should handle the microscope slide carefully to avoid breakage. Review the safety guidelines in Appendix A.

All in One Teaching Resources
- Lab Worksheet: *Recycling Paper*

Guide Inquiry

Invitation
Ask: **What process do you think you can use to recycle newspapers?** (*Student answers should reflect an understanding of the procedure, including the making of paper pulp and drying the paper.*)

Introducing the Procedure
Emphasize to students that they will do the lab on three different days: Steps 1–2 on Day 1, Steps 3–6 on Day 2, and Step 7 on Day 3.

Troubleshooting the Experiment
- *Day 1*: In Step 1, ask: **What do you see in the paper?** (*Fibers*)
- *Day 2*: Have students reread Steps 3–6. Remind them to replace the newspaper under the screen each day if it is still wet.
- *Day 3*: Make certain the pulp is completely dry before students handle it.

Expected Outcome
The dried pulp will be rough, stiff, and grayish—like cardboard egg cartons. Cellulose fibers will be visible.

Skills Lab

Recycling Paper

Problem
Is paper a renewable resource?

Skills Focus
observing, predicting

Materials
- newspaper
- microscope
- water
- eggbeater
- square pan
- screen
- plastic wrap
- mixing bowl
- heavy book
- microscope slide

Procedure
1. Tear off a small piece of newspaper. Place it on a microscope slide and examine it under a microscope. Record your observations.
2. Tear a sheet of newspaper into pieces about the size of postage stamps. Place the pieces in the mixing bowl. Add enough water to cover the newspaper. Cover the bowl and let the mixture stand overnight.
3. The next day, add more water to cover the paper if necessary. Use the eggbeater to mix the wet paper until it is smooth. This thick liquid is called paper pulp.
4. Place the screen in the bottom of the pan. Pour the pulp onto the screen, spreading it out evenly. Then lift the screen above the pan, allowing most of the water to drip into the pan.
5. Place the screen and pulp on several layers of newspaper to absorb the rest of the water. Lay a sheet of plastic wrap over the pulp. Place a heavy book on top of the plastic wrap to press more water out of the pulp.
6. After 30 minutes, remove the book. Carefully turn over the screen, plastic wrap, and pulp. Remove the screen and plastic wrap. Let the pulp sit on the newspaper for one or two more days to dry. Replace the newspaper layers if necessary.
7. When the pulp is dry, observe it closely. Record your observations.

Analyze and Conclude
1. **Observing** What kind of structures did you observe when you examined torn newspaper under a microscope?
2. **Inferring** What are these structures made of? Where do they come from?
3. **Predicting** What do you think happens to the structures you observed when paper is recycled? How do you think this affects the number of times paper can be recycled?
4. **Communicating** Based on what you learned in this lab, do you think paper should be classified as a renewable or nonrenewable resource? Defend your answer with evidence and sound reasoning.

Design an Experiment
Using procedures like those in this lab, design an experiment to recycle three different types of paper, such as shiny magazine paper, paper towels, and cardboard. *Obtain your teacher's permission before carrying out your investigation.* How do the resulting papers differ?

Analyze and Conclude
1. Fibers

2. The fibers are made of plant material. They come from the plants used to make the paper.

3. When the paper is soaked and mashed, the fibers are broken. When the pulp is flattened and dried, the fibers intertwine. Each time the fibers are broken, the result is a weaker paper, which limits the number of times it can be recycled.

4. Paper is a renewable resource. It can be recycled, and new trees can be planted.

Extend the Inquiry

Design an Experiment Students' plans should be similar to the lab procedure. Paper towels make the weakest paper because the fibers are already somewhat broken down. Cardboard also makes a weak paper for the same reason. Magazine paper makes the strongest recycled paper because the fibers are still somewhat long.

Forests and Fisheries

Reading Preview

Key Concepts
- How can forests be managed as renewable resources?
- How can fisheries be managed for a sustainable yield?

Key Terms
- clear-cutting
- selective cutting
- sustainable yield • fishery
- aquaculture

Target Reading Skill
Using Prior Knowledge Before you read, write what you know about forests and fish resources in a graphic organizer like the one below. As you read, write what you learn.

What You Know
1. Forests provide people with lumber and paper.
2.

What You Learned
1.
2.

◀ Newspapers ready for recycling

Lab zone Discover **Activity**

What Happened to the Tuna?

1. Use the data in the table to make a line graph. Label the axes of the graph and add a title. (To review graphing, see the Skills Handbook.)
2. Mark the high and low points on the graph.

Think It Over

Inferring Describe the changes in the tuna population during this period. Can you suggest a reason for these changes?

Year	Western Atlantic Bluefin Tuna Population
1970	218,000
1975	370,000
1980	67,000
1985	58,000
1990	46,000
1995	63,000
2000	67,000

At first glance, an oak tree and a bluefin tuna may not seem to have much in common. One is a plant and the other is an animal. One lives on land and the other lives in the ocean. However, oak trees and tuna are both living resources. People use oak trees to make furniture, lumber, and cork. Tuna are a source of food for people.

Every day you use many different products that are made from living organisms. In this section, you will read about two major types of living resources: forests and fisheries.

Forest Resources

Forests contain many valuable resources. Many products are made from the fruits, seeds, and other parts of forest plants. Some of these products, such as maple syrup, rubber, and nuts, come from living trees. Other products, such as lumber and wood pulp for making paper, require cutting trees down. Coniferous trees, including pine and spruce, are used for construction and for making paper. Hardwoods, such as oak, cherry, and maple, are used for furniture because of their strength and beauty.

Trees and other plants produce oxygen that organisms need to survive. They also absorb carbon dioxide and many pollutants from the air. Trees help prevent flooding and control soil erosion. Their roots absorb rainwater and hold the soil together.

Chapter 3 E ◆ 89

Lab zone Discover **Activity**

Skills Focus Inferring

Materials graph paper, ruler, pencil

Time 15 minutes

Tips In Step 1, advise students to use *Population (in thousands)* as the vertical axis and *Year* as the horizontal axis.

Expected Outcome Students' graphs should reflect data in the table.

Think It Over The tuna population increased from 1970 to 1975, and then declined steadily from 1975 to 1980. From 1980 until today the population has remained about the same. The decline may have been due to overfishing of tuna. The increase may have resulted from limits on tuna fishing.

Objectives
After this lesson, students will be able to
E.3.2.1 Describe how forests can be managed as renewable resources.
E.3.2.2 Describe how fisheries can be managed for a sustainable yield.

Target Reading Skill

Using Prior Knowledge Explain that using prior knowledge helps students connect what they already know to what they are about to read.

Answers
Possible answers:

What You Know

1. Forests provide people with lumber and paper.

2. Commercial fishing boats harvest large amounts of fish.

What You Learned

1. Forests can be renewable resources.

2. Setting fishing limits, changing fishing methods, and developing aquaculture techniques are ways to manage fisheries for sustainable yields.

All in One Teaching Resources
- Transparency E27

Preteach

Build Background Knowledge   L1

Identifying Forest Products
Invite students to look around the classroom. Ask: **What are some of the things made from trees in this classroom?** *(Examples include writing paper, cardboard, poster board, paper towels, textbooks, wood furniture, pencils, and chairs.)*

Forest Resources

Teach Key Concepts   L2
Importance of Forests

Focus Remind students that forests are valuable resources.

Teach Ask: **What are some products that come from forests?** *(Possible answers: Nuts, lumber, rubber, fruits, pulp for paper)*

Apply Ask: **Why else are forests important?** *(Plants there produce oxygen, absorb pollutants, help prevent flooding, and control soil erosion.)* **learning modality: verbal**

Managing Forests

Teach Key Concepts   L2
Logging Methods

Focus Direct students' attention to Figure 3.

Teach Ask: **How can you describe the old-growth forest after clear-cutting?** *(No trees are left in the area that was clear-cut.)* **How can you describe the forest after selective cutting?** *(There is a mix of trees remaining.)*

Apply Ask: **Which final stage—replanted growth or diverse growth—is more like the original old-growth forest?** *(Diverse growth)*

Extend Ask: **Do you think you can replace an old-growth forest? Explain.** *(Students probably will recognize that they could replant trees, but not the original forest; the forest ecosystem will have been permanently altered even if selective cutting is used.)* **learning modality: visual**

All in One Teaching Resources

• Transparency E28

Independent Practice   L1

All in One Teaching Resources

• Guided Reading and Study Worksheet: *Forests and Fisheries*

💿 **Student Edition on Audio CD**

Go Online
active art
For: Logging Methods Activity
Visit: PHSchool.com
Web Code: cep-5032

Students can compare two methods of logging: clear-cutting and selective cutting.

Go Online
active art
For: Logging Methods activity
Visit: PHSchool.com
Web Code: cep-5032

FIGURE 3
Logging Methods
Clear-cutting involves cutting down all the trees in an area at once. Selective cutting involves cutting down only some trees.
Comparing and Contrasting *How does the growth of a forest after clear-cutting differ from the growth after selective cutting?*

Managing Forests

There are about 300 million hectares of forests in the United States. That's nearly a third of the nation's area! Many forests are located on publicly owned land. Others are owned by private timber and paper companies or by individuals. Forest industries in the United States provide jobs for 1.5 million people.

Because new trees can be planted to replace trees that are cut down, forests can be renewable resources. The United States Forest Service and environmental organizations work with forestry companies to conserve forest resources. They try to develop logging methods that maintain forests as renewable resources.

Logging Methods There are two major methods of logging: clear-cutting and selective cutting. **Clear-cutting** is the process of cutting down all the trees in an area at once. Cutting down only some trees in a forest and leaving a mix of tree sizes and species behind is called **selective cutting.**

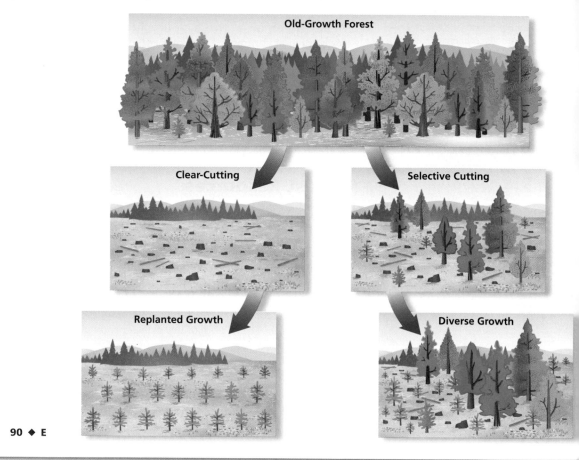

Old-Growth Forest

Clear-Cutting   Selective Cutting

Replanted Growth   Diverse Growth

Differentiated Instruction

Special Needs   L1
Three-Dimensional Models Students with visual impairments may have difficulty distinguishing the images in Figure 3. Prepare the following three-dimensional models. Insert wooden dowels of various lengths into clay to represent an old-growth forest. Prepare four other models with clay and dowels to represent the other images. Then pair students with visual impairments with sighted students to discuss the processes of clear-cutting and selective cutting. **learning modality: kinesthetic**

Each logging method has advantages and disadvantages. Clear-cutting is usually quicker and cheaper than selective cutting. It may also be safer for the loggers. In selective cutting, the loggers must move the heavy equipment and logs around the remaining trees in the forest. But selective cutting is usually less damaging to the forest environment than clear-cutting. When an area of forest is clear-cut, the ecosystem changes. After clear-cutting, the soil is exposed to wind and rain. Without the protection of the tree roots, the soil is more easily blown or washed away. Soil washed into streams may harm the fish and other organisms that live there.

Sustainable Forestry Forests can be managed to provide a sustainable yield. A **sustainable yield** is an amount of a renewable resource such as trees that can be harvested regularly without reducing the future supply. Sustainable forestry works sort of like a book swap: as long as you donate a book each time you borrow one, the total supply of books will not be affected. Planting a tree to replace one that was cut down is like donating a book to replace a borrowed one.

In sustainable forestry, after trees are harvested, young trees are planted. Trees must be planted frequently enough to keep a constant supply. Different species grow at different rates. Forests containing faster-growing trees, such as pines, can be harvested and replanted every 20 to 30 years. On the other hand, some forests containing hardwood trees, such as hickory, oak, and cherry, may be harvested only every 40 to 100 years. One sustainable approach is to log small patches of forest. This way, different sections of forest can be harvested every year.

Certified Wood The Forest Stewardship Council is an international organization dedicated to sustainable forest management. This organization oversees certification of forests that are well managed and provide good working conditions for workers. Once a forest is certified, its wood may carry a "well-managed" label. This label allows businesses and individuals to select wood from forests that are managed for sustainable yields.

Reading Checkpoint What is a sustainable yield?

FIGURE 4
Sustainable Forestry
Sustainable forestry practices include the planting of young trees after mature trees have been harvested.

Chapter 3   E ◆ 91

Lab zone Build Inquiry L2

Shelterwood Cutting

Materials 20 green, brown, red, and yellow plastic chips per group
Time 10 minutes

Focus Tell students that shelterwood cutting removes all the mature trees in an area at specified time intervals.

Teach Explain that shelterwood cutting occurs in three stages. At stage one, all unwanted trees are removed. Then remaining trees are allowed to grow and seedlings establish themselves. During stage two, many mature trees are removed and the forest is again left alone to grow. At stage three, the remaining mature trees are cut down. By this time, the seedlings have grown into young trees and more new seedlings are growing.

Apply Challenge small groups of students to develop a model of shelterwood cutting. (*Sample model: Use green plastic chips to represent mature trees and brown chips to represent unwanted trees. First stage: Remove all brown chips, leave green chips, add red chips (seedlings). Second stage: Remove some green chips, replace red chips with yellow chips (young trees), and add more red chips (seedlings). Third stage: Remove remaining green chips, replace yellow chips with green chips, replace red chips with yellow chips, and add more red chips.*) Ask: **How does the model illustrate that shelterwood cutting provides a sustainable yield?** (*The forest constantly replenishes itself.*) **learning modality: kinesthetic**

Monitor Progress _____ L2

Skills Check Have pairs of students construct a table comparing the advantages and disadvantages of clear-cutting and selective cutting.

Answer

Reading Checkpoint An amount of a renewable resource that can be regularly harvested without reducing the future supply

Fisheries

Teach Key Concepts L2

Managing Fish Populations

Focus Tell students that fisheries are renewable resources.

Teach Ask: **How can people manage fisheries for a sustainable yield?** *(Setting fishing limits, changing methods, developing aquaculture techniques, and finding new resources)* **How can setting limits on the size of fish that can be caught help maintain fish populations?** *(Young fish will be more likely to survive and reproduce.)* **What are some fishing methods that have been outlawed? Why?** *(Poisoning fish or exploding dynamite underwater are outlawed because they harm all the fish in the area.)*

Apply Ask: **What steps do you think scientists might take to convince the public to eat new species of fish?** *(Answers might include educating the public about the new species and the need to find new sources for food, and convincing chefs to introduce new species.)* **learning modality: logical/ mathematical**

Lab zone Skills Activity

Calculating

In a recent year, the total catch of fish in the world was 112.9 million metric tons. Based on the data below, calculate the percent of this total each country caught.

Country	Catch (millions of metric tons)
China	24.4
Japan	6.8
United States	5.6
Peru	8.9

Fisheries

An area with a large population of valuable ocean organisms is called a **fishery.** Some major fisheries include the Grand Banks off Newfoundland, Georges Bank off New England, and Monterey Canyon off California. Fisheries like these are valuable renewable resources.

Until recently, fisheries seemed like an unlimited resource. The waters held such huge schools of fish. And fish reproduce in incredible numbers. A single codfish can lay as many as 9 million eggs in a single year! But people have discovered that this resource has limits. After many years of big catches, the number of sardines off the California coast suddenly declined. The same thing happened to the huge schools of cod off the New England coast. What caused these changes?

The fish were caught at a faster rate than they could breed, so the population decreased. This situation is known as overfishing. Scientists estimate that 70 percent of the world's major fisheries have been overfished. But if fish populations recover, a sustainable yield of fish can again be harvested. **Managing fisheries for a sustainable yield includes strategies such as setting fishing limits, changing fishing methods, developing aquaculture techniques, and finding new resources.**

Fishing Limits Laws can ban the fishing of certain species. Laws may also limit the number or size of fish that can be caught or require that fish be within a certain range of sizes. This ensures that young fish survive long enough to reproduce and that all of the largest adult fish aren't caught. If a fishery has been severely overfished, however, the government may ban fishing completely until the populations recover.

FIGURE 5
Fisheries
Even though fisheries are renewable resources, they must be managed for sustainable yields, or the supply of fish may run out.

92 ◆ E

Lab zone Skills Activity

Skills Focus Calculating

Materials calculator

Time 5 minutes

Tips Review with students the steps needed to find percent and the conversion of a decimal value to a percent.

Expected Outcome China: 24.4 ÷ 112.9 = .216 or 21.6%; Japan: 6.0%; United States: 5.0%; Peru: 7.9%

Extend Challenge students to develop a way to compare the percentages visually. *(Students may produce a circle graph or bar graph.)* **learning modality: logical/ mathematical**

Fishing Methods Today many fishing crews use nets with a larger mesh size that allow small, young fish to escape. In addition, many other fishing practices are regulated by laws. Some fishing methods have been outlawed. These methods include poisoning fish with cyanide and stunning them by exploding dynamite underwater. These techniques harm all the fish in an area rather than targeting certain fish.

Aquaculture The practice of raising fish and other water-dwelling organisms for food is called **aquaculture.** The fish may be raised in artificial ponds or bays. Salmon, catfish, and shrimp are farmed in this way in the United States.

However, aquaculture is not a perfect solution. The artificial ponds and bays often replace natural habitats such as salt marshes. Maintaining the farms can cause pollution and spread diseases into wild fish populations.

New Resources Today about 9,000 different fish species are harvested for food. More than half the animal protein eaten by people throughout the world comes from fish. One way to help feed a growing human population is to fish for new species. Scientists and chefs are working together to introduce people to deep-water species such as monkfish and tile fish, as well as easy-to-farm freshwater fish such as tilapia.

 **Reading Checkpoint** What is aquaculture?

FIGURE 6
Aquaculture
Aquaculture is helping to meet the demand for fish. This fish farm in Hawaii raises tilapia.
Applying Concepts *What costs and benefits does aquaculture involve?*

Section 2 Assessment

Target Reading Skills **Using Prior Knowledge** Review your graphic organizer and revise it based on what you just learned in the section.

Reviewing Key Concepts

1. **a. Reviewing** Why are forests considered renewable resources?
   b. Comparing and Contrasting How does the clear-cutting logging method differ from selective cutting?
   c. Developing Hypotheses You are walking in a clear-cut section of forest a few days after a heavy rainstorm. A nearby stream is very muddy and has many dead fish. What might have happened?
2. **a. Listing** What are four ways fisheries can be managed for a sustainable yield?

   b. Explaining What are two kinds of laws that regulate fishing? How can they help ensure the health of a fishery?
   c. Predicting What might happen to a fish population over time if all the largest fish in the population were caught? Explain.

Lab zone **At-Home Activity**

Renewable Resource Survey With a family member, conduct a "Forest and Fishery" survey of your home. Make a list of all the things that are made from either forest or fishery products. Then ask other family members to predict how many items are on the list. Are they surprised by the answer?

Lab zone **At Home Activity**

Renewable Resource Survey
Encourage students to look beyond the most obvious products, such as wood and paper from forests, and salt and seafood from the ocean. Tell them to check labels closely to see if they can find the names of other items. Examples include nuts, spices, tree bark for mulch, and seaweeds.

Monitor Progress _____ **L2**

Answers
Figure 6 Aquaculture provides a much-needed food source. Artificial ponds and bays built for aquaculture often replace natural habitats, and maintaining the farms can cause pollution and spread diseases into natural populations.

Reading Checkpoint Aquaculture is the practice of raising fish and other water-dwelling organisms for food.

Assess

Reviewing Key Concepts

1. a. Because new trees can be replanted to replace cut-down trees, forests are considered renewable resources. **b.** During clear-cutting, the entire tree growth in an area is removed. During selective cutting, trees of a particular species and/or size are removed while other trees remain. **c.** Possible answer: Without tree roots to hold water and soil in place, large amounts of soil can be washed into a stream during a rainstorm. The soil in the water makes it more difficult for fish and other aquatic organisms to live.
2. a. Fishing limits can be imposed; fishing methods can be changed; aquaculture can replace fishing in natural areas; new resources can be found. **b.** Laws may limit the species, number, and size of fish that can be caught. Fishing methods can be regulated. This allows the fish population to reproduce and maintain its size. **c.** If all the largest fish in a region are caught, the average size of the fish may become smaller over time.

Reteach **L1**
Have students use Figure 3 to explain how overfishing and clear-cutting are similar and how they are different.

Performance Assessment **L2**
Oral Presentation Call on students at random to name a way to conserve forests or fisheries. Evaluate students' understanding of managing resources for sustainable yield.

All in One Teaching Resources
- Section Summary: *Forests and Fisheries*
- Review and Reinforcement: *Forests and Fisheries*
- Enrich: *Forests and Fisheries*

Tree Cookie Tales

Prepare for Inquiry

Skills Objectives
After this lab, students will be able to
- observe growth rings in a tree cookie
- infer a tree's age from the growth rings
- use their growth ring data to interpret why rings might be narrower some years than others

Prep Time 15 minutes

Class Time 40 minutes

All in One Teaching Resources
- Skills Lab: *Tree Cookie Tales*

Advance Planning
Purchase or prepare a tree cookie for each student group. Inexpensive classroom sets of tree cookies are available from biological supply houses. Tree cookies should come from trees that were more than 10 years old. You can make tree cookies by sawing a tree trunk into cross sections 1.5–2.5 cm thick. To preserve homemade tree cookies, spray or paint all surfaces with clear polyurethane or other clear sealant.

Guide Inquiry

Invitation
Point out the picture of the tree cookie and have students read its labels. Ask: **What can you learn from observing a tree cookie?** (*Sample answer: The age of the tree when it was cut down*)

Introducing the Procedure
Before students begin, clarify that a single year's growth is shown by a pair of rings— a light ring for spring and a dark ring for summer.

Troubleshooting the Experiment
When students have counted the number of annual rings, do a spot check to ensure that students have recognized that an annual ring is made up of a pair of rings, one light and one dark.

Expected Outcome
Results will vary depending on the particular tree cookie used.

Analyze and Conclude
1. Ages will vary. The tree's age is equal to the number of annual rings.

Tree Cookie Tales

Problem
What can tree cookies reveal about the past?

Skills Focus
observing, inferring, interpreting data

Materials
- tree cookie
- metric ruler
- hand lens
- colored pencils
- calculator (optional)

(Figure labels: Pith, Summer ring, Spring ring, Bark)

Procedure
1. Your teacher will give you a "tree cookie"—a slice of a tree trunk that contains clues about the tree's age, past weather conditions, and fires that occurred during its life. Use a hand lens to examine your tree cookie. Draw a simple diagram of your tree cookie. Label the bark, tree rings, and center, or pith.

2. Notice the light-colored and dark-colored rings. The light ring results from fast spring-time growth. The dark ring, where the cells are smaller, results from slower summertime growth. Each pair of light and dark rings represents one year's growth, so the pair is called an annual ring. Observe and count the annual rings.

3. Compare the spring and summer portions of the annual rings. Identify the thinnest and thickest rings.

4. Measure the distance from the center to the outermost edge of the last summer growth ring. This is the radius of your tree cookie. Record your measurement.

5. Measure the distance from the center to the outermost edge of the tenth summer growth ring. Record your measurement.

6. Examine your tree cookie for any other evidence of its history, such as damaged bark or burn marks. Record your observations.

Analyze and Conclude
1. **Inferring** How old was your tree? How do you know?

2. **Calculating** What percent of the tree's growth took place during the first ten years of its life? (*Hint:* Divide the distance from the center to the tenth growth ring by the radius. Then multiply by 100. This gives you the percent of growth that occurred during the tree's first ten years.)

3. **Observing** How did the spring rings compare to the summer rings for the same year? Suggest a reason.

4. **Interpreting Data** Why might the annual rings be narrower for some years than for others?

5. **Communicating** Using evidence from your tree cookie, write a paragraph that summarizes the history of the tree. Be sure to include as much detail as possible in your summary.

Design an Experiment
Suppose you had cookies from two other trees of the same species that grew near your tree. Write a plan for verifying the interpretations you made in this lab. *Obtain your teacher's permission before carrying out your investigation.*

---

2. The largest proportion of tree growth usually occurs during a tree's early years.

3. Observations may vary. Spring rings are usually wider because trees undergo a burst of new growth in the spring when it is usually wetter. This is followed by slower growth in summer, when it is usually drier.

4. Growth rings reflect weather conditions. Generally, rings are wider during warmer years and when rainfall is plentiful.

5. In addition to the tree's age and weather-related growth patterns, students may note holes made by insects or birds, blackening due to fire or lightning, a hollow pith due to disease, or cracks and gashes from tools.

Extend the Inquiry
Design an Experiment Students' plans should be similar to the lab procedure. Have students share their results.

Reading Preview

Key Concepts

- In what ways is biodiversity valuable?
- What factors affect an area's biodiversity?
- Which human activities threaten biodiversity?
- How can biodiversity be protected?

Key Terms

- biodiversity • keystone species
- gene • extinction
- endangered species
- threatened species
- habitat destruction
- habitat fragmentation
- poaching • captive breeding

Target Reading Skill

Building Vocabulary Using a word in a sentence helps you think about how best to explain the word. After you read this section, reread the paragraphs that contain definitions of Key Terms. Use all the information you have learned to write a meaningful sentence using each Key Term.

Lab zone Discover **Activity**

How Much Variety Is There?

1. You will be given two cups of seeds and two paper plates. The seeds in cup A represent the trees in a section of tropical rain forest. The seeds in cup B represent the trees in a section of deciduous forest.
2. Pour the seeds from cup A onto a plate. Sort the seeds by type. Count the different types of seeds. This number represents the number of different kinds of trees in that forest.
3. Repeat Step 2 with the seeds in cup B.
4. Share your results with your class. Use the class results to calculate the average number of different kinds of trees in each type of forest.

Think It Over

Inferring How do the variety of trees in the two forests differ? Can you suggest any advantages of having a wide variety of species?

No one knows exactly how many species live on Earth. As you can see in Figure 7, more than 1.5 million species have been identified so far. The number of different species in an area is called its **biodiversity.** It is difficult to estimate the total biodiversity on Earth because many areas of the planet have not been thoroughly studied. Some experts think that the deep oceans alone could contain 10 million new species! Protecting biodiversity is a major environmental issue today.

FIGURE 7
Diversity of Species
Organisms of many kinds are part of Earth's biodiversity.
Interpreting Data *Which group of organisms has the greatest number of species?*

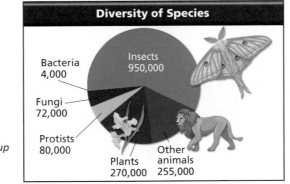

Diversity of Species

Bacteria 4,000
Insects 950,000
Fungi 72,000
Protists 80,000
Plants 270,000
Other animals 255,000

Chapter 3 E ◆ 95

Objectives

After this lesson, students will be able to
E.3.3.1 Explain the value of biodiversity.
E.3.3.2 Identify the factors that affect biodiversity.
E.3.3.3 Name some human activities that threaten biodiversity.
E.3.3.4 List some ways to protect biodiversity.

Target Reading Skill

Building Vocabulary Explain that knowing the definitions of key-concept words helps students understand what they read.

Answers

As students read each passage that contains a Key Term, remind them to write a sentence in their own words. Encourage students to write one or two descriptive phrases to help them remember the Key Term. Invite students to share their sentences and phrases.

Preteach

Build Background Knowledge   L1

Millions of Different Species
Ask: **What organisms thrive in our area?** *(Encourage students to consider a wide variety of organism types, including insects, worms, mosses, algae, and bacteria, as well as mammals, birds, fish, reptiles, and amphibians.)* After students have finished naming organisms, ask: **Would you say that there is a great deal of diversity among the species living here?** *(Answers may vary, but in most cases, students will say that there is.)*

Lab zone Discover **Activity**

Skills Focus Inferring

Materials 2 labeled cups containing different seed mixtures, paper plate

Time 20 minutes

Tips Use a mixture of at least ten types of seeds for Cup A and four or five types for Cup B. Advise students to record their observations in a table with headings "Number of Seeds in Rain Forest, Sample A" and "Number of Seeds in Deciduous Forest, Sample B."

Expected Outcome The average number of seed types will be greater for the tropical rain forest sample.

Think It Over The wider variety of tree species in a tropical rain forest supports a wider variety of other organisms that depend on the trees for habitat and food.

Monitor Progress   L2

Answer
Figure 7 Insects

The Value of Biodiversity

Teach Key Concepts `L2`

Economic Value of Biodiversity

Focus Have students describe the different organisms living in some of their favorite areas. Ask: **Would you enjoy this area as much if it didn't have as many different species?**

Teach Tell students that biodiversity is a source of beauty and economic value of any area. Ask: **How can entire ecosystems, such as rain forests, savannas, and mountain ranges, be used to generate sources of money?** *(They can be used for ecotourism, which creates jobs and brings in money from people who visit the sites.)*

Extend Ask: **What might happen if the biodiversity of some of these ecosystems is disrupted?** *(Possible answers: Other species might die out; the area might not be as attractive to tourists.)* **How might this effect the economy of the area?** *(Fewer people might visit the sites, resulting in loss of jobs and money.)* **learning modality: logical/ mathematical**

Independent Practice `L2`

 Teaching Resources

- Guided Reading and Study Worksheet: *Biodiversity*

⊙ **Student Edition on Audio CD**

The Value of Biodiversity

Perhaps you are wondering why biodiversity is important. Does it matter whether there are 50 or 5,000 fern species in some faraway rain forest? Is it necessary to protect every one of these species?

There are many reasons why preserving biodiversity is important. The simplest reason to preserve biodiversity is that wild organisms and ecosystems are a source of beauty and recreation. **In addition, biodiversity has both economic value and ecological value within an ecosystem.**

Economic Value Many plants, animals, and other organisms are economically valuable for humans. In addition to providing people with food, these organisms supply raw materials for clothing, medicine, and other products. No one knows how many other useful species have not yet been identified.

The ecosystems in which organisms live are economically valuable, too. For example, many companies now run wildlife tours in rain forests, savannas, mountain ranges, and other locations. This ecosystem tourism, or ecotourism, is an important source of jobs and money for such nations as Brazil, Costa Rica, and Kenya.

FIGURE 8
Economic Value of Biodiversity
The biodiversity in rainforests and other ecosystems can have great economic value. Rain forest organisms are a source of many products, including latex paints. Ecosystem tourism in countries such as Costa Rica provides many jobs for local people.

96 ◆ E

FIGURE 9
Ecological Value of Biodiversity
These sea stars in the Pacific Ocean near Washington and this sea otter near the California coast are both keystone species in their ecosystems. If the population of a keystone species drops too far, the entire ecosystem can be disrupted.
Relating Cause and Effect
How do sea otters help keep their ecosystem in balance?

Ecological Value All the species in an ecosystem are connected to one another. Species may depend on each other for food and shelter. A change that affects one species will surely affect all the others.

Some species play a particularly important role in their ecosystems. A **keystone species** is a species that influences the survival of many other species in an ecosystem. For example, the sea stars in Figure 9 prey mostly on the mussels that live in tide pools. When researchers removed the sea stars from an area, the mussels began to outcompete many of the other species in the tide pool. The sea star predators had kept the population of mussels in check, allowing other species to live. When the sea stars disappeared, the balance in the ecosystem was destroyed.

The sea otter in Figure 9 is another keystone species. In the 1800s, hunters killed most of the sea otters on the Pacific coast for fur. With the sea otters nearly extinct, the sea urchins they preyed on reproduced uncontrollably. The huge population of sea urchins ate all of the kelp. When sea otters were reintroduced into the ecosystem, they preyed on the sea urchins. With fewer sea urchins, the kelp population began to recover.

Reading Checkpoint What is a keystone species?

Go Online
PHSchool.com

For: More on biodiversity
Visit: PHSchool.com
Web Code: ced-5033

Lab zone Teacher **Demo**

Modeling Keystone Species

Materials model architectural building blocks or photograph of arch with keystone

Time 5–10 minutes

Focus Point out that an architectural keystone helps to maintain the structural integrity of an architectural feature.

Teach Use model architectural building blocks to construct an arch with a keystone. If such blocks are unavailable, use a photograph of an arch with a keystone. Point out the keystone, and ask: **What do you predict will happen if I remove this block?** *(Some may predict that the arch will fall.)* Remove the keystone to confirm students' predictions. Explain that the block you removed is called a keystone.

Apply Ask: **Why is a keystone a useful analogy for a keystone species?** *(When a keystone species is removed, the entire ecosystem may collapse.)* **learning modality: visual**

Go Online
PHSchool.com

For: More on biodiversity
Visit: PHSchool.com
Web Code: ced-5033

Students can review biodiversity in an online activity.

Monitor Progress _____ **L2**

Oral Presentation Have each student present reasons why biodiversity is important to plant and animal species.

Answers
Figure 9 Sea otters prey on and help control the population of sea urchins. If the number of sea otters decreases dramatically, the number of sea urchins increases. The sea urchins are then in a position to eat all the kelp in an area.

Reading Checkpoint A species that influences the survival of many other species in the same ecosystem

Factors Affecting Biodiversity

Teach Key Concepts L2
Identifying Factors

Focus Remind students that climate is the typical weather pattern—precipitation and temperature—of an area over a long period.

Teach Ask: **Which area is more likely to have greater biodiversity—a tropical rain forest or an area closer to Earth's poles?** *(A rain forest)* **Why?** *(Plants there can grow year-round, making food available all year to other organisms.)* **Why does a coral reef have such a diverse ecosystem?** *(A coral reef supports many different niches.)*

Apply Ask: **What might happen to the biodiversity of an area if its climate becomes colder?** *(Its biodiversity might decrease.)* **learning modality: verbal**

Help Students Read

Relate Text and Visuals After students have read about factors affecting biodiversity, call their attention to the circle graphs accompanying Figure 10. Ask: **How much of Earth's land area is made up of rain forests?** *(7 percent)* **What percentage of Earth's species are found there?** *(50 percent)* **What explanation can you give to explain how such a small percentage of Earth's land can be home to such a large percentage of species?** *(Rain forests have a climate that allows plants to grow all year and provide many different habitats.)* **learning modality: logical/mathematical**

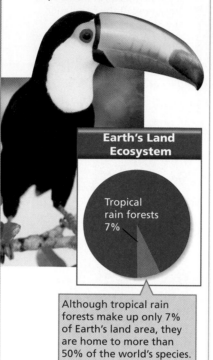

FIGURE 10
Factors Affecting Biodiversity
Three factors that affect the biodiversity of an ecosystem are area, climate, and niche diversity. **Making Generalizations** *Which factor is most likely responsible for the biodiversity of coral reefs? Of tropical rain forests?*

Earth's Land Ecosystem

Tropical rain forests 7%

Although tropical rain forests make up only 7% of Earth's land area, they are home to more than 50% of the world's species.

Earth's Ocean Ecosystems

Coral reefs 1%

Although coral reefs make up only 1% of Earth's oceans, they are home to about 20% of the world's saltwater fish species.

98 ◆ E

Factors Affecting Biodiversity

Biodiversity varies from place to place on Earth. **Factors that affect biodiversity in an ecosystem include area, climate, and diversity of niches.**

Area Within an ecosystem, a large area will contain more species than a small area. For example, suppose you were counting tree species in a forest. You would find far more tree species in a 100-square-meter area than in a 10-square-meter area.

Climate In general, the number of species increases from the poles toward the equator. The tropical rain forests of Latin America, southeast Asia, and central Africa are the most diverse ecosystems in the world. These forests cover only about 7 percent of Earth's land surface but contain more than half of the world's species.

The reason for the great biodiversity in the tropics is not fully understood. Many scientists hypothesize that it has to do with climate. For example, tropical rain forests have fairly constant temperatures and large amounts of rainfall throughout the year. Many plants in these regions grow year-round. This continuous growing season means that food is always available for other organisms.

Niche Diversity Coral reefs make up less than 1 percent of the oceans' area. But reefs are home to 20 percent of the world's saltwater fish species. Coral reefs are the second most diverse ecosystems in the world. Found only in shallow, warm waters, coral reefs are often called the rain forests of the sea. A reef supports many different niches for organisms that live under, on, and among the coral. This enables more species to live in the reef than in a more uniform habitat, such as a flat sandbar.

✓ **Reading Checkpoint** **What is the relationship between the size of an area and its biodiversity?**

Differentiated Instruction

Less Proficient Readers L1
Words in Context For students who need more help, review the meanings of the terms *area* (length times width), *climate* (the typical weather pattern in an area over a long period), and *niche* (an organism's unique position in an ecosystem). Students may wish to add these terms, and their definitions, to their own Science Glossaries.

FIGURE 11
Genetic Diversity
Diverse genes give these potatoes their rainbow of colors. Having a diverse gene pool helps a species fight disease and adapt to changes in its environment.

Gene Pool Diversity

Just as the diversity of species is important within an ecosystem, diversity is also important within a species. The organisms in a healthy population have a diversity of traits. Traits such as color, size, and ability to fight disease are determined by genes. **Genes** are the structures in an organism's cells that carry its hereditary information.

Organisms receive a combination of genes from their parents. Genes determine an organism's characteristics, from its size and appearance to its ability to fight disease.

The organisms in one species share many genes. But each organism also has some genes that differ from those of other individuals. These individual differences make up the total gene "pool" of that species.

Species that lack a diverse gene pool are less able to adapt to changes in the environment. For example, some food crops have little diversity. A fungus once wiped out much of the corn crop in the United States. Fortunately, some wild varieties of corn have genes that make them resistant to the fungus. Scientists were able to use some of those wild varieties to breed corn that could fight off the fungus. A species with a diverse gene pool is better able to survive such challenges.

Reading Checkpoint What do an organism's genes determine?

Lab zone | Try This **Activity**

Grocery Gene Pool
With a parent or other adult, visit a supermarket or produce market in your area. Choose one type of fruit or vegetable, such as apples or potatoes. Make a list of all the different varieties of that fruit or vegetable the store sells. Note any differences in appearance between the varieties.

Inferring Judging from the appearance of the different varieties, do you think your fruit or vegetable has a diverse gene pool? Explain.

Lab zone | Try This **Activity**

Skills Focus Inferring

Materials none

Time 20 minutes

Tips Each variety of fruit or vegetable will be labeled. Suggest that students take notes as they note differences in appearance.

Expected Outcome Generally, students will infer that the chosen produce has a diverse gene pool.

Extend Suggest students ask the produce manager why the store offers so many varieties. **learning modality: visual**

Gene Pool Diversity

Teach Key Concept   L2
Diversity and Survival of Species

Focus Ask students how dogs of the same breed might vary. (*Possible answers: Color, coarseness of fur, size*) Tell students that these are only some of the ways a species can vary.

Teach Tell students that genes determine some of an organism's characteristics. Ask: **What is the gene pool of a species?** (*The individual differences resulting from differences in genes between individuals in a species*)

Apply Ask: **How does having a diverse gene pool enable a species to survive changes in the environment?** (*It is likely to have members with characteristics needed in the changing environment.*) **learning modality: logical/mathematical**

Lab zone | Build **Inquiry**
                                          L2
Comparing Biodiversity

Materials photographs of ecosystems

Time 15 minutes

Focus Review with students factors that affect biodiversity: area, climate, niche diversity.

Teach Give each pair of students a picture of a different type of ecosystem. Have them analyze the pictures to determine the number and types of organisms shown. Then have students describe the abiotic factors in the ecosystem.

Apply Have students compare the ecosystems to determine which have the greatest biodiversity. Help students identify factors that most likely contribute to the diversity. **learning modality: logical/mathematical**

Monitor Progress _____ L2

Writing Have students write a paragraph explaining why gene pool diversity is so important to species' survival.

Answers
Figure 10 Coral reefs—niche diversity; tropical rain forests—climate

Reading Checkpoint Biodiversity increases as area increases.

Reading Checkpoint Characteristics, such as size, appearance, and ability to fight disease

Extinction of Species

Teach Key Concepts L2
Endangered Species

Focus Remind students that not all species of organisms that once lived are still living.

Teach Ask: **What is extinction?** *(The disappearance of all members of a species)* **How do threatened species differ from endangered species?** *(Endangered species are in danger of becoming extinct in the near future. Threatened species could become endangered in the near future.)*

Apply Ask: **What similar problem has caused the populations of California tiger salamanders and grizzly bears to decrease?** *(Destruction of natural habitat)* **learning modality: visual**

Help Students Read

Use Prior Knowledge Before students read "Extinction of Species," have them work in groups to brainstorm what they know about extinct species, including examples of extinct organisms and causes of extinction. After reading, have groups review their lists and determine how accurate their knowledge of extinction was.

FIGURE 12
Endangered Species
A broad range of species and habitats are represented on the endangered list in the United States.

▲ **Tennessee Purple Coneflower**
This daisy-like plant grows only in cedar forests in central Tennessee. It was once considered extinct, but today, five small populations are known to exist. Conservation organizations and landowners are working together to protect them.

Extinction of Species

The disappearance of all members of a species from Earth is called **extinction**. Extinction is a natural process. Many species that once lived on Earth, from dinosaurs to dodos, are now extinct. But in the last few centuries, the number of species becoming extinct has increased dramatically.

Once the size of a population drops below a certain level, the species may not be able to recover. For example, in the 1800s, there were millions of passenger pigeons in the United States. People hunted the birds for sport and food, killing many hundreds of thousands. This was only part of the total population. But the remaining birds could not reproduce enough to sustain the population. Only after 1914, when the species became extinct, did people realize that the species could not survive without its enormous numbers.

California Tiger Salamander ▶
Towns have replaced or fragmented most of this salamander's original habitat. The salamanders that remain are in danger of being run over by cars or washed down storm drains.

◀ **Grizzly Bear**
This omnivore needs a large area to obtain enough food. Shrinking wilderness areas have limited its numbers.

Species in danger of becoming extinct in the near future are called **endangered species**. Species that could become endangered in the near future are called **threatened species**. Threatened and endangered species are found on every continent and in every ocean. Some are well-known animals, such as China's giant panda. Others are little known, such as hutias, rodents that live on only a few Caribbean islands. Ensuring that these species survive is one way to protect Earth's biodiversity.

Reading Checkpoint How has the number of species becoming extinct changed in the last few centuries?

▲ **Piping Plover**
The population of this tiny, active coastal bird is recovering as a result of increased protection of its sand-dune nesting sites.

Whooping Crane ▶
Threatened by habitat destruction and disease, half of the remaining population of this wading bird is in zoos. The species seems to be recovering well since its lowest point in the 1940s.

◀ **Schaus Swallowtail Butterfly**
Threatened by habitat loss and pesticide pollution in the Florida Keys, this butterfly was nearly wiped out by Hurricane Andrew in 1992.

Steller's Sea Lion ▶
Overfishing has led to a decline in this mammal's sources of food. Other factors may also be threatening this species.

E ◆ 101

Address Misconceptions L2
Newly Extinct Species

Focus Students usually consider extinction as an event that occurred only in the distant past. Explain to students that many species have become extinct in relatively recent times.

Teach Provide students with a list of species that have become extinct within the past 300 years. Examples include the quagga, dodo, moa, Tasmanian wolf (thylacine), dusky seaside sparrow, Santa Barbara song sparrow, Greek auk, Hawaii oo, passenger pigeon, Abington tortoise, blue pike, Tecopa pupfish, and Sampson's pearly mussel. Invite pairs of students to research one of these species. Suggest that students find a description of the species and its habitat and the factors that researchers believe caused the extinction.

Apply Have students create an Extinction Timeline that contains information about all the species students have researched. Each entry in the timeline should show the year that each species became extinct and should include an illustration (or student-made drawing), as well as a short description of the species and an explanation of why it is now extinct.

Differentiated Instruction

English Learners/Beginning Comprehension: Ask Questions L1 Help students understand the difference between endangered and threatened species. Ask: **What does it mean to be "in danger"? What do you do when you are threatened?** Help students relate the answers to the questions to the meaning of the terms. **learning modality: verbal**

English Learners/Intermediate Comprehension: Ask Questions L2 Have students read the sentences containing the phrases *endangered species* and *threatened species*. Ask whether students can describe the difference between the two, and help them clarify the meanings. **learning modality: verbal**

Monitor Progress L2

Skills Check Have students explain how endangered species differ from threatened species.

Answer

Reading Checkpoint It increased in the last few centuries.

E ● 101

Causes of Extinction

Teach Key Concepts   L2

Human Causes of Extinction

Focus Tell students that extinction can result from natural causes and human causes.

Teach Ask: **How does habitat fragmentation contribute to extinction?** *(It can expose trees to wind damage; animals may not be able to find enough resources in a small area.)* **What is the illegal removal of wildlife species called?** *(Poaching)* **How does pollution contribute to species extinction?** *(Pollution can weaken individuals, kill them, or cause birth defects.)*

Apply Ask: **How does bringing exotic species into a country threaten biodiversity?** *(Some exotic species compete with native species for resources.)* **learning modality: logical/mathematical**

FIGURE 13
Poaching
These scarlet macaws at a zoo in Costa Rica were rescued from poachers who were exporting macaws illegally as pets. Zoo employees will help restore the birds to full health so they can be released back into their habitats.
Inferring *Why are there laws against removing endangered species from their habitats?*

Causes of Extinction

A natural event, such as an earthquake or a volcanic eruption, can damage an ecosystem, wiping out populations or even species. **Human activities can also threaten biodiversity. These activities include habitat destruction, poaching, pollution, and the introduction of exotic species.**

Habitat Destruction The major cause of extinction is **habitat destruction,** the loss of a natural habitat. This can occur when forests are cleared to build towns or create grazing land. Plowing grasslands or filling in wetlands greatly changes those ecosystems. Some species may not be able to survive such changes to their habitats.

Breaking larger habitats into smaller, isolated pieces, or fragments, is called **habitat fragmentation.** For example, building a road through a forest disrupts habitats. This makes trees more vulnerable to wind damage. Plants may be less likely to disperse their seeds successfully. Habitat fragmentation is also very harmful to large mammals. These animals usually need large areas of land to find enough food to survive. They may not be able to obtain enough resources in a small area. They may also be injured trying to cross to another area.

Poaching The illegal killing or removal of wildlife species from their habitats is called **poaching.** Many endangered animals are hunted for their skin, fur, teeth, horns, or claws. Hunters sell the animals they kill. The animal parts are then used for making medicines, jewelry, coats, belts, and shoes.

People illegally remove organisms from their habitats to sell them as exotic pets. Tropical fish, tortoises, and parrots are very popular pets, making them valuable to poachers. Endangered plants are sometimes illegally dug up and sold as houseplants or medicines.

102 ◆ E

California Peregrine Falcon Recovery

The peregrine falcon, the world's fastest bird of prey, was nearly extinct in the United States in 1970. The pesticide DDT was weakening peregrine eggshells, so the eggs rarely hatched. In 1972, the United States banned DDT. Use the graph to answer questions about the peregrine population in California.

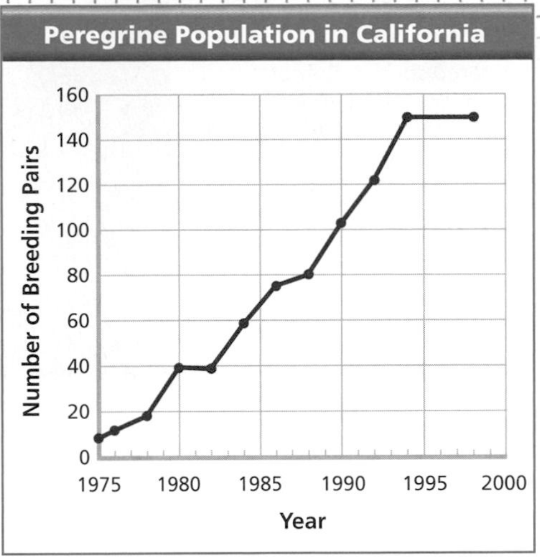

1. **Reading Graphs** What variable is plotted on the *x*-axis? What variable is plotted on the *y*-axis?

2. **Interpreting Data** How did California's peregrine population change from 1976 to 1998?

3. **Inferring** Why do you think the peregrine population grew fairly slowly at first?

Peregrine Population in California

4. **Predicting** What might this graph have looked like if DDT had not been banned?

Pollution Some species are endangered because of pollution. Substances that cause pollution, called pollutants, may reach animals through the water they drink or air they breathe. Pollutants may also settle in the soil. From there, they are absorbed by plants and build up in other organisms through the food chain. Pollutants may kill or weaken organisms or cause birth defects.

Exotic Species Introducing exotic species into an ecosystem can threaten biodiversity. When European sailors began visiting Hawaii hundreds of years ago, rats from their ships escaped onto the islands. Without any predators in Hawaii, the rats multiplied quickly. They ate the eggs of the nene goose. To protect the geese, people brought the rat-eating mongoose from India to help control the rat population. Unfortunately, the mongooses preferred eating eggs to rats. With both the rats and the mongoose eating its eggs, the nene goose is now endangered.

 Reading Checkpoint What is poaching?

FIGURE 14
Exotic Species
Kudzu is an exotic species that was introduced to the United States from Japan in 1876. It can grow up to 30 centimeters a day, so its vines can quickly strangle native trees and shrubs. It can also take over abandoned structures, such as this house in Georgia.

Chapter 3 E ◆ 103

Differentiated Instruction

Gifted and Talented L3
Species Competition Encourage students to research introduced species that compete with native species in the United States. Have them report on where competition is prevalent and consequences to the native species. Example species include purple loosestrife, kudzu, leafy spurge, flathead catfish, sea lamprey, zebra mussel, gypsy moth, fire ant, brown tree snake, and starling. Students can share their findings in a class discussion.
learning modality: verbal

Math Skill Making and interpreting graphs

Focus Tell students that the recovery of the peregrine falcon population is represented by a line graph, the most useful graph for showing change over an interval of time.

Teach Remind students what the axes represent and how the grid is structured. Ask: **What information do you have at any point along the graph?** (*The number of breeding pairs of birds in a particular year*) **How can you determine how many breeding pairs existed in 1990?** (*Follow the grid line for 1990 until it reaches the graph, then follow the grid line to the left. Read the number on the vertical axis: just over 100.*) **About how many breeding pairs existed in 1975?** (*About 10*)

Answers
1. Time interval in years is on the *x*-axis. Number of breeding pairs of peregrine falcons is on the *y*-axis.
2. The population grew steadily, except for a brief drop around 1980, until 1994, when the number of breading pairs remained the same for the four following years.
3. There were only a few breeding pairs at first, so they could produce only a few birds. These, in turn, had to grow up before they had a chance to breed. As more pairs grew to breeding age, more and more birds could be produced.
4. The graph probably would have sloped downward from left to right, possibly reaching zero breeding pairs.

Monitor Progress L2

Skills Check Call on students to identify and briefly explain the four causes of extinction presented in the text.

Answers
Figure 13 Removing an individual of an endangered species from its habitat subjects the individual to stress and risks, which may limit the individual's ability to thrive, thereby weakening the already endangered species.

Reading Checkpoint The illegal killing or removal of a wildlife species from its habitat

E ● 103

Protecting Biodiversity

Teach Key Concepts L2
Evaluating Approaches

Focus Remind students that biodiversity has both ecological and economic value within an ecosystem.

Teach Encourage students to share what they know about captive breeding programs in zoos and wildlife preserves. Then ask: **What are the advantages and disadvantages of this approach for protecting biodiversity?** *(Sometimes it is the only way to save a species. Captive breeding can be expensive.)* **What is one disadvantage of using laws and treaties to protect species?** *(The laws and treaties are sometimes difficult to enforce.)* **Why is setting aside wildlife habitats as parks an effective way to preserve biodiversity?** *(Protecting entire ecosystems ensures that many habitats are preserved, which contributes to diversity.)*

Apply How does setting aside large ecosystems as wildlife habitats protect species that live only in a small area of the ecosystem? *(Protecting whole ecosystems saves not only endangered species but also the species they depend on and those that depend on them.)* **learning modality: verbal**

Help Students Read
Identifying Main Ideas

Refer to the Content Refresher, which provides guidelines for identifying main idea. Have students read the main topic sentence in bold type under the heading Protecting Biodiversity. Ask: **Given this topic sentence, what are the main ideas that you should look for in the selection?** *(How captive breeding, laws and treaties, and habitat preservation protect biodiversity)* After students read the selection, have students work in groups to create index cards with a brief explanation of how each factor protects biodiversity.

FIGURE 15
Captive Breeding
Captive breeding programs use a scientific approach to protect endangered species. California condor chicks raised in captivity need to learn what adult condors look like. Here, a scientist uses a puppet to feed and groom a chick. **Predicting** *What sort of problems could animals raised by humans come upon when they are released into the wild?*

FIGURE 16
Laws and Treaties
Laws against selling products made from endangered species have helped protect animals such as these ocelots. These small cats were once hunted nearly to extinction for their fur.

Protecting Biodiversity

Some people who work to preserve biodiversity focus on protecting individual endangered species. Others try to protect entire ecosystems, such as the Great Barrier Reef in Australia. **Three successful approaches to protecting biodiversity are captive breeding, laws and treaties, and habitat preservation.**

Captive Breeding Captive breeding is the mating of animals in zoos or wildlife preserves. Scientists care for the young, and then release them into the wild when they are grown.

Captive breeding was the only hope for the California condor, the largest bird in North America. Condors became endangered due to habitat destruction, poaching, and pollution. By 1987, there were fewer than 30 California condors. Scientists captured all the condors and brought them to zoos to breed. Today, there are around 200 California condors. Though successful, this program has cost more than $20 million. You can see the drawback of captive breeding.

Laws and Treaties Laws can help protect individual species. In the United States, the Endangered Species Act prohibits trade in products made from threatened or endangered species. This law also requires the development of plans to save endangered species. American alligators and green sea turtles have begun to recover as a result of this law.

The most important international treaty protecting wildlife is the Convention on International Trade in Endangered Species. This treaty lists nearly 700 threatened and endangered species that cannot be traded for profit. Treaties like this are difficult to enforce. Even so, this treaty has helped to protect many endangered species, including African elephants.

Habitat Preservation The most effective way to preserve biodiversity is to protect whole ecosystems. Protecting whole ecosystems saves not only endangered species, but also the species they depend upon and those that depend upon them.

Beginning in 1872 with Yellowstone National Park, the world's first national park, many countries have set aside wildlife habitats as parks and refuges. In addition, private organizations have purchased millions of hectares of endangered habitats throughout the world. Today, there are about 7,000 nature parks, preserves, and refuges in the world.

To be most effective, reserves must have the characteristics of diverse ecosystems. For example, they must be large enough to support the populations that live there. The reserves must contain a variety of niches. And of course, it is still necessary to keep the air, land, and water clean, control poaching, and remove exotic species.

Reading Checkpoint What is the most effective way to preserve biodiversity?

FIGURE 17
Habitat Preservation
Preserving whole habitats is an effective way to protect biodiversity. Habitat preservation is the aim of national parks such as Yellowstone.

Section 3 Assessment

Target Reading Skill Building Vocabulary
Use your sentences to help answer the questions.

Reviewing Key Concepts

1. a. Listing What are two ways in which biodiversity is valuable?
  b. Problem Solving What economic reasons could you give people in the rain forest for preserving the ecosystem?

2. a. Identifying What are three factors that affect the biodiversity in an ecosystem?
  b. Explaining How does each of these factors affect biodiversity?
  c. Developing Hypotheses Would you expect to find great biodiversity in the tundra biome? Why or why not?

3. a. Listing Name four human activities that can threaten biodiversity.
  b. Applying Concepts Black bears are roaming through a new housing development in search of food, even though the housing development is still surrounded by forest. How can you account for the bears' behavior?

4. a. Reviewing What are three approaches to protecting biodiversity?
  b. Relating Cause and Effect For each approach to protecting biodiversity, list at least one factor that might limit its success.
  c. Making Judgments List some ways in which those limitations might be dealt with.

Lab zone At-Home Activity

Species Refuges Obtain a map of your community or state. With a family member, identify any city, state, or national parks, reserves, or refuges in your area. Choose one location and find out whether there are endangered or threatened species living there. Then prepare a five-minute presentation for your class on what you learned.

Chapter 3 E ◆ 105

Lab zone Chapter Project

Keep Students on Track Remind students that they need to make notes about abiotic factors as well as notes on organisms. Encourage students to draw or sketch the organisms they observe in detail so that they will be able to identify them using field guides. Students should be beginning to plan how they will present their findings.

Lab zone At Home Activity

Species Refuges Students can contact their state's EPA, local Audubon Society, or parks department. Remind students that refuges near bodies of water may be used primarily by migrating species. Students' presentations should describe the habitats of endangered or threatened species in the area.

Monitor Progress _____ L2

Skills Check Ask individual students to describe one way to protect biodiversity.

Answers
Figure 15 They may be unable to find food and feed themselves, they might be too trustful of humans, and they might not recognize their natural predators.

Reading Checkpoint Preserving entire ecosystems

Assess

Reviewing Key Concepts

1. a. Biodiversity has both an economic and ecological value. **b.** Using the rain forest for ecotourism brings in money. Certain organisms may provide food or medicines for humans.
2. a. area, climate, niche diversity
b. Greater area, greater niche diversity, and year-round growing seasons and abundant rainfall all yield greater biodiversity. **c.** No; the tundra growing season is too short to be able to provide a year-round food source for organisms.
3. a. Habitat destruction, poaching, pollution, and introduction of exotic species
b. Habitat fragmentation
4. a. Captive breeding, laws and treaties, habitat preservation **b.** Captive breeding is expensive. Laws and treaties are difficult to enforce. Preserved habitats must have characteristics of diverse ecosystems
c. Sample answer: Make certain exotic species are not accidentally introduced by visitors, campers, and boaters, limit travel by automobile to reduce pollution, and minimize the number of roads.

Reteach L1

As a class, list ways in which humans threaten biodiversity and ways humans preserve biodiversity.

All in One Teaching Resources
- Section Summary: *Biodiversity*
- Review and Reinforcement: *Biodiversity*
- Enrich: *Biodiversity*

Objectives

After this lesson, students will be able to

E.3.4.1 Identify one reason why medical researchers want to protect biodiversity.

E.3.4.2 Explain why many rain forest plants are sources of medicines.

Target Reading Skill

Asking Questions Explain that changing a head into a question helps students anticipate the ideas, facts, and events they are about to read.

Answers

Possible questions and answers are these:

Why is biodiversity important to medicine? *(Biodiversity is important because there may be undiscovered medicines that exist in nature.)* **What is the story of taxol?** *(Taxol is a cancer treatment drug that comes from the bark of the Pacific yew tree. As demand for the drug grew, scientists became concerned about the supply of Pacific yew trees.)* **How can we increase the supply of taxol?** *(Today taxol can be reproduced in the lab.)*

All in One Teaching Resources

• Transparency E29

Preteach

Build Background Knowledge L1

Temperate Rain Forests

Before students read the introductory text, ask: **Where are temperate rain forests located?** *(Along the northwest coast of the United States.)* If students have difficulty locating the temperate rain forests, direct their attention to the biome map in Ecosystems and Biomes. Then, have them match the legend with the location on the map.

Go Online
SciLINKS NSTA

For: Links on medicines from plants
Visit: www.SciLinks.org
Web Code: scn-0534

Download a worksheet that will guide students' review of Internet resources on medicines from plants.

Reading Preview

Key Concepts

• What is one reason why medical researchers want to protect biodiversity?

• Why are many rain forest plants sources of medicines?

Key Term

• taxol

Target Reading Skill

Asking Questions Before you read, preview the red headings. In a graphic organizer like the one below, ask a *what*, *how*, *who*, *when*, or *where* question for each heading. As you read, write the answers to your questions.

The Search for New Medicines

Question	Answer
Why is biodiversity important to medicine?	Biodiversity is important to medicine because . . .

Go Online
SciLINKS NSTA

For: Links on medicines from plants
Visit: www.SciLinks.org
Web Code: scn-0534

Lab zone Discover Activity

How Are Plant Chemicals Separated?

1. Using a black marking pen, draw a dot about 2 centimeters from the end of a strip of filter paper.
2. Pour a few centimeters of water into a clear plastic cup.
3. Tape the top edge of the filter paper strip to a pencil. Place the pencil across the top of the cup so that the ink dot hangs just below the water surface. If necessary, turn the pencil to adjust the length of the paper.
4. Observe what happens to the black dot.

Think It Over

Observing How many different colors of ink did you separate from the black ink? This process models one way of separating individual chemicals contained in plants.

You lace up your hiking boots and sling your collecting bag over your shoulder. It's time to head out for another day of searching in the cool, damp forest. Stepping carefully to avoid mud, you walk beneath giant evergreens. Their needle-covered branches form a thick roof above your head. Rotting logs covered with ferns, seedlings, and brightly colored fungi line your path. You scan the area for telltale signs of the object of your search. What are you searching for? A plant that can save lives!

This ancient forest is the temperate rain forest of the Pacific Northwest. Many of its giant trees are more than 200 years old. Like tropical rain forests, temperate rain forests are diverse ecosystems. They contain many species that are found nowhere else. Some of these species are threatened or endangered, including the bull trout, Olympic salamander, and the life-saving plant you are looking for—the Pacific yew tree.

Lab zone Discover Activity

Skills Focus Observing

Materials black marking pen, strip of filter paper, water, clear plastic cup, tape, pencil

Time 15 minutes

Tips If filter paper is not available, use white paper towels cut into strips.

Expected Outcome Water will carry the dissolved black ink up the strip, where the individual colors will separate out.

Think It Over The specific colors that separate from the black ink will depend on the marker used. Different colors will travel up the strip at different rates—blue the fastest, yellow slightly slower; and red much slower.

Biodiversity and Medicine

People have always studied plants for their ability to heal wounds, fight diseases, and ease pain. For example, aspirin was originally made from the bark of the willow tree. The active chemical in aspirin can now be made in a laboratory.

Almost half of all medicines sold today contain chemicals originally found in wild organisms. For example, digitalis, a medication used to treat certain heart problems, comes from the leaves of the foxglove, a common garden plant. The study of another plant, the Madagascar rosy periwinkle, has produced two effective cancer treatments. From this flowering plant, researchers have produced vincristine, a medication for childhood leukemia, and vinblastine, a medication for Hodgkin's disease.

What other medicines exist undiscovered in Earth's forests, oceans, and other locations? **In 1995, the American Medical Association called for the protection of Earth's biodiversity. Their goal was to preserve the undiscovered medicines that may exist in nature.** Governments, scientists, and private companies are working together to find new species and study known species all over the world. They are working hard to find new sources of disease-fighting drugs.

Reading Checkpoint From what plant was aspirin originally made?

▲ **Madagascar Rosy Periwinkle:** source of cancer treatments

▼ **Longsnout Seahorse:** possible source of painkillers and cancer treatments

Foxglove: ▶ source of heart medication

FIGURE 18
Biodiversity and Medicine
Scientists study organisms like the ones shown here to identify new sources of disease-fighting medicines. **Predicting** *How could the extinction of species affect the search for new medicines?*

E ◆ 107

The Story of Taxol

Teach Key Concepts

Taxol Today

Focus Tell students that the Pacific yew is a conifer that grows in temperate rain forests.

Teach Explain that scientists studied the Pacific yew because it is so resistant to many diseases and insects. Ask: **How is taxol used medically?** *(To treat cancer)* **How has the production of taxol changed since it was first discovered?** *(At first, it was made from the bark of the Pacific yew; now it is made in a laboratory.)*

Apply Tell students that thousands of people are treated with taxol each year. Ask: **How many Pacific yews would have to be cut down to treat a thousand people?** *(3,000)* Point out that making taxol in the laboratory has ensured a good supply of taxol and saved thousands of Pacific yews. **learning modality: logical/mathematical**

Integrating Health

Taxol was first tested in women with ovarian cancer that had not responded to chemotherapy and radiation. Ovarian tumors in 40 percent of the women shrank to half their original size. When taxol was later given to women with breast cancer, more than half the patients experienced partial remission. Ask: **Why do you think taxol was first tested on women whose cancer did not respond to traditional therapies?** *(There was no other choice available. Since traditional therapies had failed, this experimental drug was the only hope for these patients.)* **learning modality: verbal**

FIGURE 19
Pacific Yew Tree
Because the Pacific yew is so resistant to diseases and insects, scientists began to study it. Through this study, they discovered taxol, a cancer treatment.
Developing Hypotheses *Why might Pacific yew trees need such strong resistance?*

FIGURE 20
Treating Cancer With Taxol
These women are breast cancer survivors. Some of them probably received taxol as a treatment.

The Story of Taxol

Plants in many ecosystems can produce chemicals that protect them from predators, parasites, and diseases. This ability results from the plants' adaptations to their environment. In rain forests, where so many organisms eat plants, plants have many adaptations that protect them. **Some protective chemicals that rain forest plants produce can also be used to fight human diseases.**

The Pacific Yew The Pacific yew tree grows in the temperate rain forest. It is unusually resistant to the many diseases and insects found there. Scientists began to study the bark of the Pacific yew to find out why it was so hardy. When they separated the various chemicals found in the bark, they discovered unusual crystals. These crystals are made from a chemical called **taxol,** the substance that protects the Pacific yew tree.

Taxol as a Cancer Treatment Scientists conducted experiments with taxol in the laboratory. The experiments showed that taxol crystals affect cancer cells in an unusual way. Typically, cancer cells grow and divide very rapidly. This quick growth forms a mass of cells called a tumor. When cancer cells are exposed to taxol, the taxol forms structures that look like tiny cages around each cancer cell. These structures prevent the cancer cells from dividing. As a result, the cancer cannot grow and spread.

After more research, doctors were ready to test taxol on cancer patients. The taxol treatments often were able to shrink certain types of tumors. Sometimes they even stopped the cancer from spreading in the body. Taxol is now used to treat thousands of cancer patients each year.

The Supply of Taxol As the demand for taxol rapidly grew, many scientists became concerned about the supply of Pacific yew trees. The bark of three Pacific yew trees was required to produce enough pure taxol for just one cancer patient's treatment. Without its bark, a yew cannot survive. Also, by the time researchers discovered taxol's value as a cancer-fighting drug, large portions of the temperate rain forests where yew trees grow were gone.

Today, the bark of the Pacific yew is no longer used in the manufacture of taxol. Chemists worked for many years to reproduce taxol's complex chemical structure in the laboratory, and they finally succeeded in the mid-1990s. This discovery ensured a good supply of taxol for the future. It also helped protect the remaining Pacific yew trees for future generations.

✔ **Reading Checkpoint** Why was it important for scientists to find a way to make taxol in the laboratory?

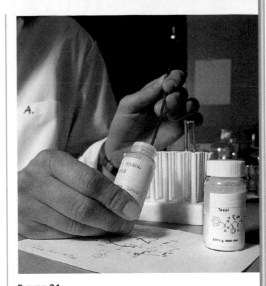

FIGURE 21
Supply of Taxol
Because of its complex chemical structure, it took scientists many years to create taxol in the laboratory.

Section 4 Assessment

🎯 **Target Reading Skill** Asking Questions Use the answers to the questions you wrote about the headings to help you answer the questions below.

Reviewing Key Concepts

1. a. **Reviewing** Why did the American Medical Association call for the protection of Earth's biodiversity?
   b. **Inferring** Do you think that scientists have identified all the wild plants that may have medical uses? Why or why not?
   c. **Predicting** Suppose many wild plants were to become extinct within a short time. What effect might this have on medical research? Explain your answer.
2. a. **Identifying** What adaptations of rain forest plants make them likely sources of medicines?
   b. **Explaining** What plant is the source of taxol, and what is the function of taxol in this plant?
   c. **Comparing and Contrasting** What is the effect of taxol on cancerous tumors? In what way is this effect similar to the function of taxol in the plant?

Writing in Science

News Report Suppose that you were a health news reporter at the time taxol became available as a cancer treatment. Write a two-paragraph news report about taxol. In the first paragraph, discuss the discovery of taxol. In the second paragraph, describe how taxol stops cancer from spreading.

Chapter 3 E ◆ 109

Monitor Progress _____ L2

Skills Check Ask students to summarize how taxol was developed as a cancer drug.

Answers
Figure 19 The Pacific yew tree grows in the temperate rain forest where many diseases and insects are found.

✔ **Reading Checkpoint** The demand for taxol from trees exceeded the yield, and harvesting the bark destroyed the trees.

Assess

Reviewing Key Concepts

1. a. The goal was to preserve undiscovered medicines that might exist in nature.
   b. No; many parts of the rain forest remain unexplored so it is likely that there are medicinal plants to be discovered. c. The extinction of wild plants provides medical researchers with fewer possible sources of medicine.
2. a. They produce chemicals that protect them from predators, parasites, and diseases. These same chemicals can be used to fight human diseases. b. The Pacific yew tree is the source of taxol, which protects the tree from diseases and insects in its environment. c. Taxol forms structures around cancer cells that prevent the cancer cells from dividing. In both cancer patients and the yew tree, taxol protects against disease.

Reteach L1
Have students place the phrases *logging and development of temperate rain forest, declining biodiversity,* and *lower possibility of finding plant-based medicines* in a cause-and-effect graphic organizer.

Performance Assessment L2
Oral Presentation Have students tell the taxol story.

All in One Teaching Resources
• Section Summary: *The Search for New Medicines*
• Review and Reinforcement: *The Search for New Medicines*
• Enrich: *The Search for New Medicines*

Lab zone **Chapter Project**

Keep Students on Track As students observe their plots, encourage them to draw the organisms in detail so that they can identify them later using field guides. Remind students to make notes about abiotic factors as well. Check each group's notebook occasionally to make sure students are recording data.

Writing in Science

Writing Skill News Report
Scoring Rubric
4 Includes detailed and accurate information with engaging and newsy style
3 Includes complete and accurate information
2 Includes incomplete information and some inaccuracies
1 Includes incomplete or inaccurate information

interactive Textbook

- Complete student edition
- Section and chapter self-assessments
- Assessment reports for teachers

Help Students Read

Building Vocabulary

Word-Part Analysis List on the board the following word parts and meanings: *bio,* meaning "life"; *aqua,* meaning "water"; *non,* meaning "not"; and *micro,* meaning "very small." Have students identify these word parts in the vocabulary terms. Discuss the terms' meanings with students.

Vocabulary Knowledge Rating Chart

Have students construct a chart with four columns: *Term, Can Define or Use It, Have Heard or Seen It,* and *Don't Know.* Have students copy the Key Terms for this chapter under the first column and then rate their knowledge of each.

Connecting Concepts

Concept Maps Help students develop one way to show how the information in this chapter is related. When making environmental decisions, the issues—the impact of resource use, population growth, and pollution—are debated to help balance the needs of the environment and the needs of people. Have students brainstorm to identify the Key Concepts, Key Terms, details, and examples. Then write each one on a sticky note and attach it at random on chart paper or on the board.

Tell students that this concept map will be organized in hierarchical order and to begin at the top with the Key Concepts. Ask students these questions to guide them to categorize the information on the stickies: **How can environmental decisions affect resources? How can environmental decisions affect biodiversity? What must be considered when making environmental decisions?**

① Environmental Issues

Key Concepts

- Environmental issues fall into three general categories: resource use, population growth, and pollution.
- To help balance the different opinions on an environmental issue, decision makers weigh the costs and benefits of a proposal.

Key Terms

natural resource   pollution
renewable resource   environmental science
nonrenewable
  resource

② Forests and Fisheries

Key Concepts

- Because new trees can be planted to replace trees that are cut down, forests can be renewable resources.
- Managing fisheries for a sustainable yield includes setting fishing limits, changing fishing methods, developing aquaculture techniques, and finding new resources.

Key Terms

clear-cutting
selective cutting
sustainable yield
fishery
aquaculture

③ Biodiversity

Key Concepts

- Biodiversity has both economic value and ecological value within an ecosystem.
- Factors that affect biodiversity in an ecosystem include area, climate, and diversity of niches.
- Human activities can threaten biodiversity. These activities include habitat destruction, poaching, pollution, and the introduction of exotic species.
- Three successful approaches to protecting biodiversity are captive breeding, laws and treaties, and habitat preservation.

Key Terms

biodiversity
keystone species
gene
extinction
endangered species
threatened species
habitat destruction
habitat fragmentation
poaching
captive breeding

④ The Search for New Medicines

Key Concepts

- In 1995, the American Medical Association called for the protection of Earth's biodiversity. Their goal was to preserve the undiscovered medicines that may exist in nature.
- Some protective chemicals that rain forest plants produce can also be used to fight human diseases.

Key Term

taxol

Prompt students by using connecting words or phrases such as "affected by" or "managed by" to indicate the basis for the organization of the map. The phrases should form a sentence between or among a set of concepts.

Answers

Accept logical presentations by students.

All in One Teaching Resources

- Key Terms Review: *Living Resources*

Review and Assessment

Organizing Information

Concept Mapping Copy the concept map about biodiversity onto a separate sheet of paper. Then complete it and add a title. (For more on Concept Mapping, see the Skills Handbook.)

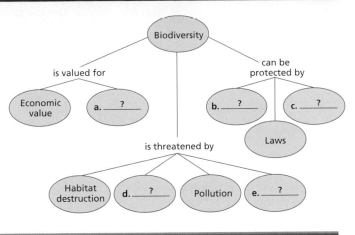

Reviewing Key Terms

Choose the letter of the best answer.

1. The contamination of Earth's air, land, or water is called
   a. extinction.
   b. aquaculture.
   c. pollution.
   d. habitat destruction.

2. The practice of raising fish for food is called
   a. aquaculture.
   b. overfishing.
   c. poaching.
   d. captive breeding.

3. The most diverse ecosystems in the world are
   a. coral reefs.
   b. deserts.
   c. grasslands.
   d. tropical rain forests.

4. If all members of a species disappear from Earth, that species is
   a. extinct.
   b. endangered.
   c. nonrenewable.
   d. threatened.

5. The most effective way to preserve biodiversity is through
   a. habitat fragmentation.
   b. habitat destruction.
   c. habitat preservation.
   d. captive breeding.

6. Taxol, which originally came from Pacific yew trees, is a medicine that is used to fight
   a. heart disease.   b. cancer.
   c. lung disease.   d. diabetes.

Writing in Science

Dialogue The salmon population in an area of the ocean has declined significantly. Fishers depend on catching salmon to make a living. Write a dialogue in which an environmental scientist and a fisher try to find a solution to the problem.

Living Resources
Video Preview
Video Field Trip
▶ Video Assessment

Organizing Information
a. Ecological value
b. Captive Breeding
c. Habitat preservation
d. Poaching
e. Exotic species

Reviewing Key Terms
1. c **2.** a **3.** d **4.** a **5.** c **6.** b

Writing in Science

Writing Mode Persuasion
Scoring Rubric
4 Includes opinions and detailed reasons for both sides of the issue
3 Includes all criteria
2 Includes brief details or omits some criteria
1 Includes inaccurate information and omits some criteria

Living Resources

Show the Video Assessment to review chapter content and as a prompt for the writing assignment. Discussion questions: **Why is it important for fishers to throw back the younger, smaller fish and crabs that they catch?** *(The smaller fish and crabs will mature and reproduce.)* **What is aquaculture? Describe one advantage and one disadvantage of aquaculture.** *(A type of fish farming in which managers control the environment, and supply food and protection from predators; aquaculture allows for less fish to be taken from the ocean, but disease can spread easily in the close quarters and runoff can pollute natural waterways and spread disease.)*

Go Online
PHSchool.com
For: Self-assessment
Visit: PHSchool.com
Web Code: cea-5030

Students can take a practice online test that is automatically scored.

All in One Teaching Resources
- Transparency E31
- Chapter Test
- Performance Assessment Teacher Notes
- Performance Assessment Student Worksheet
- Performance Assessment Scoring Rubric

💿 **ExamView® Computer Test Bank CD-ROM**

Checking Concepts

7. A renewable resource is either always available or is naturally replaced in a relatively short time. A nonrenewable resource is not replaced in a useful time frame.

8. By considering the viewpoints of many different people and weighing the costs and benefits of different solutions

9. In a sustainable forest after trees are harvested, young trees are planted. In fisheries yields can be sustained by using strategies such as setting limits, changing fishing methods, developing aquaculture, and finding new resources.

10. Any one: Set limits on the amount or size of fish that can be caught; use nets with larger mesh size; outlaw fishing methods that kill all the fish in an area rather than selected species; aquaculture harvest new species

11. Species with gene pool diversity are better able to adapt to changes in the environment.

12. Species lose the places where they feed, breed, and nest. If they cannot find a substitute niche, they must move to a new location to survive. If they cannot relocate, they will not survive.

13. Almost half of all medicines sold today contain chemicals originally found in wild organisms. Many organisms have potential medical uses that have not been discovered yet. The more diversity that exists, the more potential for sources of disease-fighting drugs.

Thinking Critically

14. As the number of humans increase, they use more resources, which can reduce resource availability and contribute to pollution, such as air pollution that is produced when fossil fuels are burned.

15. Clear-cutting is shown. Clear-cutting is usually quicker and cheaper, but it changes the ecosystem. It exposes soil to wind and rain, which can result in erosion. Selective cutting is usually less damaging to the environment.

16. An exotic species may prey on native species or compete with them for limited resources. If the exotic species has no natural predators in its new habitat, it may outcompete the native species.

17. Sample answer: The species might have been the source of a medicine or had another use that is unknown today. The species might have been important to the survival of another species.

Review and Assessment

Checking Concepts

7. What is a renewable resource? What is a nonrenewable resource?

8. Describe how environmental decisions are made.

9. How does the idea of a sustainable yield pertain to forestry? How does it apply to fisheries?

10. Describe one way that overfishing can be prevented.

11. Why is gene pool diversity important to survival of a species?

12. Explain how habitat destruction affects species.

13. Describe the importance of biodiversity to drug research.

Thinking Critically

14. Relating Cause and Effect Explain how human population growth affects resource use and pollution.

15. Comparing and Contrasting Which logging method is shown below? Compare the effects of this method with those of selective cutting.

16. Making Generalizations Describe how an exotic species can threaten other species in an ecosystem.

17. Predicting How could the extinction of a species today affect your life in 20 years?

Applying Skills

Use the table to answer Questions 18–21.

A study was done to identify the reasons why mammal and bird species become endangered or threatened. The data are shown in the table below.

Threats to Biodiversity		
Reason	**Mammals**	**Birds**
Poaching	31%	20%
Habitat loss	32%	60%
Exotic species	17%	12%
Other causes	20%	8%

18. Graphing Make a bar graph comparing the reasons why mammals and birds become endangered or threatened. Show reasons on the horizontal axis and percentages of animal groups on the vertical axis.

19. Interpreting Data What is the major reason that mammals become endangered or threatened? What is the main threat to birds?

20. Predicting Would stricter laws against poaching be likely to benefit mammal species or bird species more? Explain.

21. Developing Hypotheses Suggest two explanations for the differences between the data for mammals and birds.

Chapter **Project**

Performance Assessment In your presentation, clearly describe the biodiversity you observed in your plot. You can use drawings, video, photos, or a computer for your presentation. Be sure to include the data you collected on abiotic factors as well.

Chapter **Project**

Performance Assessment Before groups give their presentations to the entire class, meet with each group briefly to review students' plans. Suggest any questions that may not have occurred to them.

Let each group reconvene to discuss their answers to these questions. Then encourage all groups to share their ideas in a class discussion.

Standardized Test Prep

Choose the letter of the best answer.

1. A disease kills most members of a plant species in an ecosystem. Several animal species feed on that plant species. After a time, the populations of those animal species decline. Which of the following inferences is valid?
   A The ecosystem will soon recover.
   B The plant species will become extinct.
   C The plant species is a keystone species in that ecosystem.
   D Several animal species in the ecosystem will eventually become extinct.

2. In some areas, foresters plant one tree for every tree they cut. This activity is an example of
   F a nonsustainable approach to a nonrenewable natural resource
   G a sustainable approach to a nonrenewable natural resource
   H a nonsustainable approach to a renewable natural resource
   J a sustainable approach to a renewable natural resource

The graph below shows how the population of one kind of fish, haddock, changed in Georges Bank between 1980 and 2000. Use the graph below and your knowledge of science to answer Questions 3 and 4.

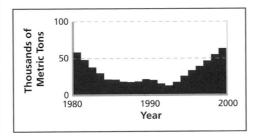

3. Which of the following statements is a valid interpretation of the graphed data?
   A Overfishing of haddock began in 1990 and stopped in 2000.
   B By 2000, the haddock population had begun to recover.
   C The haddock population from 1980 to 1990 demonstrates the idea of sustainable use.
   D The haddock population is decreasing and will probably continue to decrease.

4. Which of the following probably accounts for the trend shown between 1992 and 2000?
   F laws regulating haddock fishing
   G overfishing
   H niche diversity
   J habitat fragmentation

Constructed Response

5. Explain how people benefit when biodiversity is maintained and worldwide ecosystems contain a wide variety of organisms.

18.

Applying Skills

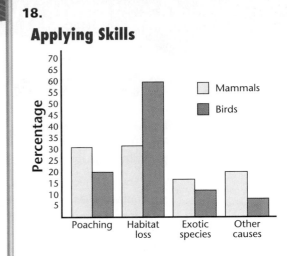

19. Habitat loss is the major cause for both birds and mammals. Poaching is almost as significant for mammals.

20. Student responses will vary but should be supported with information from the chapter.

21. Sample answer: Areas where birds tend to nest and breed, such as wetlands, are particularly threatened by habitat destruction.

Standardized Test Prep

1. C **2.** J **3.** B **4.** F
5. Sample answer: People benefit both economically and ecologically when biodiversity is maintained. Biodiversity enables a supply of diverse foods and raw materials for clothing, medicine, and other products. Ecotourism is an important source of jobs and money in many nations.

Chapter at a Glance

PRENTICE HALL
TeacherEXPRESS™
Plan · Teach · Assess

Lab zone Chapter **Project** *Design and Build a Product Package*

Technology

Local Standards

All in One Teaching Resources
- Chapter Project Teacher Notes, pp. 228–229
- Chapter Project Student Overview, pp. 230–231
- Chapter Project Student Worksheets, pp. 232–233
- Chapter Project Scoring Rubric, p. 234

Discovery CHANNEL SCHOOL
Video Preview

Section 1 **Conserving Land and Soil**

2–3 periods
1–1 1/2 blocks

E.4.1.1 Tell how people use land.
E.4.1.2 Describe the structure of fertile soil.
E.4.1.3 Identify problems that occur when soil is not properly managed.

Go Online PHSchool.com

Section 2 **Waste Disposal and Recycling**

2–3 periods
1–1 1/2 blocks

E.4.2.1 Name three methods of solid waste disposal.
E.4.2.2 Identify ways people can help control the solid waste problem.
E.4.2.3 Explain how hazardous wastes can be safely disposed of.

Go Online *active art*

Section 3 **Water Pollution and Solutions**

1–2 periods
1/2–1 blocks

E.4.3.1 Explain why fresh water is a limited resource.
E.4.3.2 Identify the major sources of water pollution.
E.4.3.3 Describe how water pollution can be reduced.

Discovery CHANNEL SCHOOL
Video Field Trip

Go Online PHSchool.com

Section 4 **Air Pollution and Solutions**

2–3 periods
1–1 1/2 blocks

E.4.4.1 Identify the causes of smog and acid rain.
E.4.4.2 Describe the causes of indoor air pollution.
E.4.4.3 Explain the key to reducing air pollution.

Go Online PHSchool.com

Section 5 **Global Changes in the Atmosphere**

2–3 periods
1–1 1/2 blocks

E.4.5.1 Describe how human activities have damaged the ozone layer.
E.4.5.2 Identify ways that human activities might be linked to global climate changes.

Go Online SCI LINKS™ NSTA

Review and Assessment

All in One Teaching Resources
- Key Terms Review, p. 279
- Transparency E44
- Performance Assessment Teacher Notes, p. 286
- Performance Assessment Scoring Rubric, p. 287
- Performance Assessment Student Worksheet, p. 288
- Chapter Test, pp. 289–293

Go Online PHSchool.com

Discovery CHANNEL SCHOOL
Video Assessment

Test Preparation

Test Preparation Blackline Masters

Lab zone

Chapter Activities Planner

For more activities

 **LAB ZONE Easy Planner CD-ROM**

Student Edition	Inquiry	Time	Materials	Skills	Resources
Chapter Project	Open-Ended	1 to 2 weeks	**All in One** Teaching Resources See p. 222	Classifying, inferring, making models, communicating	**Lab zone Easy Planner** **All in One** Teaching Resources Support pp. 222–228
Section 1					
Discover Activity, p. 116	Guided	10 minutes	Pan, mixture of sand and soil, 10–15 sunflower seeds, pencil, tweezers, spoon, paper towel	Predicting	**Lab zone Easy Planner**
Section 2					
Discover Activity, p. 122	Guided	20 minutes	Trash bag containing common household wastes, plastic gloves, graph paper, ruler	Interpreting data	**Lab zone Easy Planner**
Skills Activity, p. 125	Guided	15 minutes	Protractor, drawing compass	Graphing	**Lab zone Easy Planner**
Try This, p. 126	Guided	10 minutes	Pieces of plastic products	Classifying	**Lab zone Easy Planner**
Skills Lab, pp. 130–131	Directed	Prep: 20 minutes Day 1: 40 minutes; Day 2: 20 minutes	measuring cup, metric ruler, soil, small pebbles, cheesecloth, scissors, plastic wrap, water, newspaper, 5 rubber bands, red food coloring, tweezers, heavy-duty plastic bag, 12 small sponge cubes, 3 transparent wide-mouthed jars	Observing, making models	**Lab zone Easy Planner Lab Activity Video** **All in One** Teaching Resources Skills Lab: *Waste, Away!*, pp. 253–255
Section 3					
Discover Activity, p. 132	Directed	5 minutes	Flashlight, clear plastic cup, water, plastic dropper, milk	Observing	**Lab zone Easy Planner**
Try This, p. 134	Directed	10 minutes	Cooled herbal tea, 2 clear plastic cups, paper filter, funnel, crushed charcoal	Observing	**Lab zone Easy Planner**
Try This, p. 136	Directed	10 minutes plus 5 minutes for follow-up observations on several days	15 mL water, plastic cup, spoon, graduated cylinder, food coloring, half-teaspoon sugar	Making models	**Lab zone Easy Planner**
Section 4					
Discover Activity, p. 138	Guided	5 minutes	Spray bottle with perfume	Inferring	**Lab zone Easy Planner**
Try This, p. 140	Directed	10 minutes	Rainwater, 2 plastic cups, pH paper, pH chart, lemon juice	Measuring	**Lab zone Easy Planner**
Design Your Own Lab, pp. 144–145	Open-Ended	Prep: 30 minutes Class: Day 1, 30 minutes; Days 2–6, 5 minutes each	2 plastic petri dishes with lids, wax pencil, potting soil, acid solution, 20 radish seeds, oil solution, detergent solution, salt solution, day-old tap water, masking tape, 10 mL graduated cylinder, metric ruler	Controlling variables, interpreting data, designing experiments	**Lab zone Easy Planner Lab Activity Video** **All in One** Teaching Resources Skills Lab: *How Does the Garden Grow?*, pp. 270–271
Section 5					
Discover Activity, p. 146	Directed	20 minutes	UV-sensitive beads, pipe cleaners, pieces of T-shirt fabric	Developing hypotheses	**Lab zone Easy Planner**

Section 1 Conserving Land and Soil

⏱ *2–3 periods, 1–1 1/2 blocks*

Objectives

E.4.1.1 Tell how people use land.
E.4.1.2 Describe the structure of fertile soil.
E.4.1.3 Identify problems that occur when soil is not properly managed.

Local Standards

Key Terms

- development • litter • topsoil • subsoil • bedrock • erosion • nutrient depletion
- fertilizer • desertification • drought • land reclamation

Preteach

Build Background Knowledge

Share observations about soil and what it might be made of.

Lab zone **Discover Activity** *How Does Mining Affect the Land?*

Targeted Print and Technology Resources

All in One Teaching Resources

L2 Reading Strategy Transparency E32: Identifying Main Ideas

💿 **Presentation-Pro CD-ROM**

Transparency E32

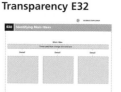

Instruct

Types of Land Use Use photos to describe how land is used in agriculture, development, and mining and how each use changes the land.

The Structure of the Soil Use a diagram to identify the components of fertile soil.

Soil Management Use photos and maps to discuss soil management problems and possible solutions.

Targeted Print and Technology Resources

All in One Teaching Resources

L2 Guided Reading, pp. 237–241
L2 Transparency E33

www.SciLinks.org Web Code: scn-0541

💿 **Student Edition on Audio CD**

Transparency E33

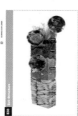

Assess

Section Assessment Questions

↻ Have students use their Identifying Main Ideas graphic organizers to answer the questions.

Reteach

Call on students to name Key Terms as you provide the definitions.

Targeted Print and Technology Resources

All in One Teaching Resources

- Section Summary, p. 236
L1 Review and Reinforce, p. 242
L3 Enrich, p. 243

Section 2 Waste Disposal and Recycling

🕐 *2–3 periods, 1–1 1/2 blocks*

ABILITY LEVELS KEY
L1 Basic to Average
L2 For All Students
L3 Average to Advanced

Objectives

E.4.2.1 Name three methods of solid waste disposal.
E.4.2.2 Identify ways people can help control the solid waste problem.
E.4.2.3 Explain how hazardous wastes can be safely disposed of.

Key Terms

• municipal solid waste • incineration • leachate • sanitary landfill • recycling
• biodegradable • composting • hazardous waste

Local Standards

Preteach

Build Background Knowledge

Lead a discussion about what kinds of things students' families throw away and how these things are disposed of.

Lab zone **Discover Activity** *What's in the Trash?*

Targeted Print and Technology Resources

All in One Teaching Resources
L2 Reading Strategy Transparency E34: Asking Questions

⊙ **Presentation-Pro CD-ROM**

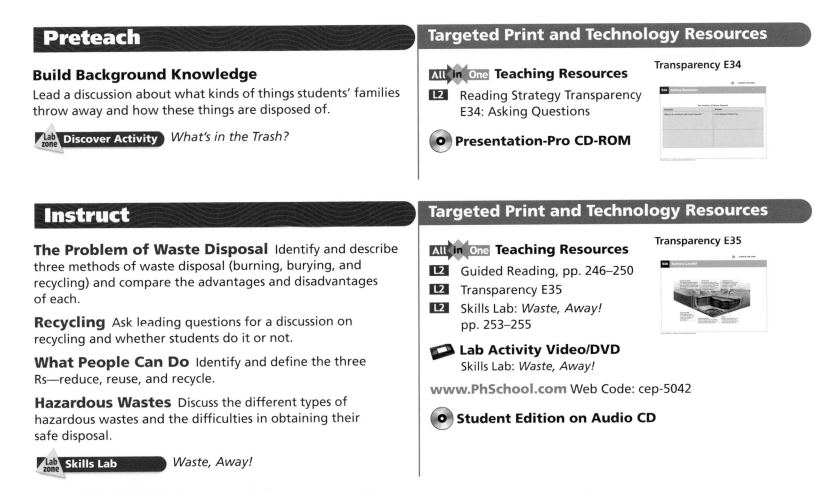

Transparency E34

Instruct

The Problem of Waste Disposal Identify and describe three methods of waste disposal (burning, burying, and recycling) and compare the advantages and disadvantages of each.

Recycling Ask leading questions for a discussion on recycling and whether students do it or not.

What People Can Do Identify and define the three Rs—reduce, reuse, and recycle.

Hazardous Wastes Discuss the different types of hazardous wastes and the difficulties in obtaining their safe disposal.

Lab zone **Skills Lab** *Waste, Away!*

Targeted Print and Technology Resources

All in One Teaching Resources
L2 Guided Reading, pp. 246–250
L2 Transparency E35
L2 Skills Lab: *Waste, Away!* pp. 253–255

📼 **Lab Activity Video/DVD**
Skills Lab: *Waste, Away!*

www.PhSchool.com Web Code: cep-5042

⊙ **Student Edition on Audio CD**

Transparency E35

Assess

Section Assessment Questions

↻ Have students use their completed Asking Questions graphic organizers to answer the questions.

Reteach

Discuss how wastes can be reduced, reused, or recycled.

Targeted Print and Technology Resources

All in One Teaching Resources
• Section Summary, p. 245
L1 Review and Reinforce, p. 251
L3 Enrich, p. 252

Section 3 **Water Pollution and Solutions**

ABILITY LEVELS KEY
L1 Basic to Average
L2 For All Students
L3 Average to Advanced

1–2 periods, 1/2–1 block

Objectives

E.4.3.1 Explain why fresh water is a limited resource.

E.4.3.2 Identify the major sources of water pollution.

E.4.3.3 Describe how water pollution can be reduced.

Local Standards

Key Terms

• groundwater • pollutant • sewage • pesticide • sediment

Preteach

Build Background Knowledge

Use a world map or globe to estimate how much of Earth's surface is covered by oceans, and to discover where other forms of water exist.

Lab zone Discover Activity *How Does the Water Change?*

Targeted Print and Technology Resources

All in One Teaching Resources

L2 Reading Strategy Transparency E36: Previewing Visuals

Presentation-Pro CD-ROM

Transparency E36

Instruct

Water—A Limited Supply Use an analogy to demonstrate that most of the water on Earth is scarce.

Water Pollution Identify forms of water pollutants, and explain why wastes produced by human activities often end up in water.

Keeping Water Clean Introduce the keys to keeping water clean—proper sewage treatment, reduction of pollutants, and effective cleanup of oil and gasoline spills.

Targeted Print and Technology Resources

All in One Teaching Resources

L2 Guided Reading, pp. 258–260

L2 Transparency E37

www.PHSchool.com Web Code: ced-5043

Student Edition on Audio CD

Transparency E37

Assess

Section Assessment Questions

Have students use their completed Previewing Visuals graphic organizers to answer the questions.

Reteach

Demonstrate how to use the headings of the section to create an outline of the information including details.

Targeted Print and Technology Resources

All in One Teaching Resources

• Section Summary, p. 257

L1 Review and Reinforce, p. 261

L3 Enrich, p. 262

Section 4 Air Pollution and Solutions

Objectives

E.4.4.1 Identify the causes of smog and acid rain.
E.4.4.2 Describe the causes of indoor air pollution.
E.4.4.3 Explain the key to reducing air pollution.

Local Standards

Key Terms

• emissions • photochemical smog • ozone • temperature inversion
• acid rain • radon

Preteach

Build Background Knowledge

Discuss students' observations about the kinds of pollution they have seen and which kinds might be controlled.

Lab zone Discover Activity *How Does the Scent Spread?*

Targeted Print and Technology Resources

All in One Teaching Resources
L2 Reading Strategy Transparency E38: Relating Cause and Effect

○ **Presentation-Pro CD-ROM**

Transparency E38

Instruct

Smog Use photographs to encourage a discussion about the sources of smog and its health effects.

Acid Rain Use photographs to define and to show the effects of acid rain.

Indoor Air Pollution Identify the sources of indoor air pollution and discuss how it affects people.

Reducing Air Pollution Brainstorm a list of key ways to reduce air pollution.

Lab zone Design Your Lab *How Does the Garden Grow?*

Targeted Print and Technology Resources

All in One Teaching Resources
L2 Guided Reading, pp. 265–267
L2 Transparency E39
L2 Design Your Own Lab: *How Does the Garden Grow?* pp. 270–271

📼 **Lab Activity Video/DVD**
Skills Lab: *Design Your Own Lab: How Does the Garden Grow?*

www.PHSchool.com Web Code: ced-5044

○ **Student Edition Audio CD**

Transparency E39

Assess

Section Assessment Questions

↻ Have students use their completed Relating Cause and Effect graphic organizers to answer the questions.

Reteach

List types of air pollution, their causes, and ways to control them.

Targeted Print and Technology Resources

All in One Teaching Resources
• Section Summary, p. 264
L1 Review and Reinforce, p. 268
L3 Enrich, p. 269

Section 5 Global Changes in the Atmosphere

ABILTIY LEVELS KEY
L1 Basic to Average
L2 For All Students
L3 Average to Advanced

🕐 *2–3 periods, 1–1 1/2 blocks*

Objectives

E.4.5.1 Describe how human activities have damaged the ozone layer.

E.4.5.2 Identify ways that human activities might be linked to global climate changes.

Local Standards

Key Terms

• ozone layer • chlorofluorocarbon • greenhouse effect • global warming

Preteach

Build Background Knowledge

Share experiences with sunburn and discuss the causes of sunburn.

Lab zone Discover Activity *What Happens to the Beads?*

Targeted Print and Technology Resources

All in One Teaching Resources

L2 Reading Strategy Transparency E40: Outlining

⊙ **Presentation-Pro CD-ROM**

Transparency E40

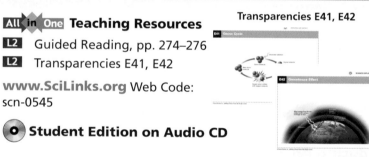

Instruct

The Thinning of the Ozone Layer Determine the causes for the ozone hole, and describe CFCs as human-made gases.

Global Climate Change Use a diagram to study the greenhouse effect and to explain that increased levels of carbon dioxide may be intensifying the effect.

Targeted Print and Technology Resources

All in One Teaching Resources

L2 Guided Reading, pp. 274–276

L2 Transparencies E41, E42

www.SciLinks.org Web Code: scn-0545

⊙ **Student Edition on Audio CD**

Transparencies E41, E42

Assess

Section Assessment Questions

↻ Have students use their completed Outlining graphic organizer to answer the questions.

Reteach

Use a figure to review the greenhouse effect.

Targeted Print and Technology Resources

All in One Teaching Resources

• Section Summary, p. 273

L1 Review and Reinforce, p. 277

L3 Enrich, p. 278

Go Online

NSTA-PDi*Links*

For: Professional Development Support
Visit: www.SciLinks.org/PDLinks
Web Code: scf-0540

Professional Development

Section 1 Conserving Land and Soil

The Dust Bowl and Conservation Districts Along with the Great Depression in the 1930s came the ecological disaster known as the Dust Bowl. A long and severe drought on the Great Plains, coupled with overgrazing and poor soil management, resulted in the windblown erosion of the region's soil.

In 1935, Congress declared soil conservation a national priority in response to the blackened skies of the Dust Bowl. Congress realized that only active support from landowners would guarantee success of conservation on private land, because about three fourths of the land in the United States is privately owned. Today there are about 3,000 conservation districts formed to educate and help local citizens conserve land, water, forests, wildlife, and other natural resources. The National Association of Conservation Districts (NACD), formed in 1946, develops national conservation policies, influences lawmakers, and provides services to districts to help them serve their communities.

More than 15,000 volunteers serve on conservation districts' governing boards. They work with more than 2.3 million land managers and influence conservation on more than 778 million acres of private land. To further soil conservation efforts, conservation districts help implement practices to keep soil in the fields and out of waterways, plant trees and other ground cover to keep soil in place, help developers and homeowners manage the land in an environmentally sound manner, and work with schools to teach the value of conservation efforts.

The weather still challenges farmers, but the Dust Bowl taught everyone a valuable lesson. It also brought about the formation of conservation districts that help citizens respond to ecological challenges.

⚑ Address Misconceptions

Many people believe that droughts cause desertification, and that once the land has begun the process, it can't be stopped. In reality, desertification is revealed by drought, but if the process has not gone too far, it can be reversed. For a strategy for overcoming this misconception, see **Address Misconceptions** on page 120.

Section 2 Waste Disposal and Recycling

Municipal Solid Waste Disposal Reduction, reuse, recycling, and composting can considerably lessen the amount of solid waste that has to be disposed of. However, what remains is an enormous burden to landfills. In 2001, U.S. residents and businesses produced more than 229 million tons of waste. That is about 4.4 lbs of waste per person per day.

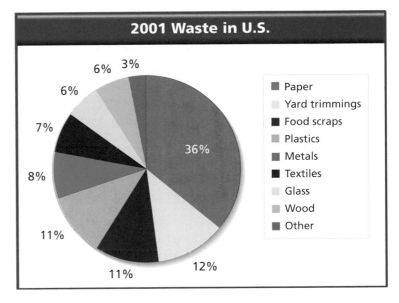

2001 Waste in U.S.

- Paper
- Yard trimmings
- Food scraps
- Plastics
- Metals
- Textiles
- Glass
- Wood
- Other

36%, 12%, 11%, 11%, 8%, 7%, 6%, 6%, 3%

To reduce waste volume, some local governments have implemented a controlled incineration system that can drastically reduce volume and can also convert water to steam to fuel heating systems or generate electricity. These approved incinerators utilize scrubbers to reduce toxic emissions, and can reduce the volume of waste up to 90 percent. Incineration has the added benefit of destroying harmful chemical compounds and disease-causing bacteria.

Section 3 Water Pollution and Solutions

Nonpoint Source Pollution Nonpoint source pollution can be thought of as a source of pollution you can't "point to" directly. Effluent pouring from a pipe coming out of a factory is, on the other hand, a point source because it is coming from a specific point.

Nonpoint source pollution is the leading cause of water pollution in the United States. It comes from scattered sources in the environment. As water moves across and through the land it picks up pollutants and carries them into waterways and groundwater. These pollutants include fertilizers and pesticides from agriculture, oil and toxic chemicals from urban runoff, sediment from construction sites and eroding stream banks, bacteria and nutrients from livestock, and even atmospheric particles.

Nonpoint source pollution is difficult to control because there is no one source against which to levy a fine, enforce regulations, or mandate a cleanup. It is, in fact, the responsibility of individuals to be aware of their own contributions to nonpoint source pollution. Every person can contribute to the problem without even realizing it. No one would think of pouring oil into the sewer from their car, but the person whose car drips oil on the driveway contributes to nonpoint source pollution.

Section 4 Air Pollution and Solutions

Acid Rain Acid rain is a general term to describe precipitation that has a pH lower than 5.6, which is that of normal rain. (Pure water has a pH of 7.) As of the year 2000, the most acidic rain falling in the U. S. had a pH of about 4.3. The Environmental Protection Agency uses a more specific term—acid deposition.

Acid deposition has two parts: wet and dry. Wet deposition refers to acidic rain, fog, and snow. This acidic precipitation flows over the ground and affects plants, animals, and structures.

Dry deposition refers to acidic gases and particles. Half of the acidity in the atmosphere falls back to Earth through dry deposition and is blown onto cars, buildings, homes, and trees. Often, dry deposition is washed off these surfaces by rain, making the combination more acidic than the acid rain alone.

The National Atmospheric Deposition Program measures wet deposition and maintains maps of rainfall pH and other precipitation chemistry measurements. The Clean Air Status and Trends Network is responsible for measurements of dry deposition.

Acid deposition has a variety of effects including reducing visibility in the air. An additional effect is the deteriorating

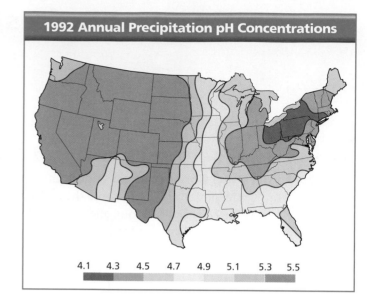

1992 Annual Precipitation pH Concentrations

4.1 4.3 4.5 4.7 4.9 5.1 5.3 5.5

effect acid deposition has on buildings and monuments. Because of air pollution, some of our nation's buildings and sculptures of historic or cultural value may be lost prematurely.

⚑ Address Misconceptions

Many students think that oxygen is the most common gas in the air we breathe. In reality, nitrogen gas composes 78 percent of the air we breathe. For a strategy for overcoming this misconception, see **Address Misconceptions** on page 139.

Section 5 Global Changes in the Atmosphere

Global Warming New evidence supports the idea that most of the global warming over the last 50 years is due to human activities. According to the National Academy of Sciences, Earth's surface temperature has risen by about 17 degrees Celsius (1 degree Fahrenheit) in the last century, with accelerated warming during the last 20 years. Human activities have contributed to the buildup of greenhouse gases in the atmosphere, primarily carbon dioxide, methane, and nitrous oxide.

Since the beginning of the industrial revolution, atmospheric concentrations of carbon dioxide have increased nearly 30 percent, methane concentrations have doubled, and nitrous oxide concentrations have risen by about 15 percent.

Plant respiration and the decomposition of organic matter release more than 10 times the carbon dioxide released by human activities, but these releases are natural. Carbon dioxide is absorbed by terrestrial vegetation and the oceans, and the release and uptake of this greenhouse gas has been in balance up until the industrial revolution.

How did the industrial revolution tip the balance? By signaling the beginning of the widespread use of fossil fuels. Fossil fuels burned to run cars and trucks and for heat and power are responsible for about 98 percent of the carbon dioxide emissions in the U. S., 24 percent of methane emissions, and 18 percent of nitrous oxide emissions. The twentieth century's ten warmest years all occurred in the last 15 years of the century, with 1998 the warmest year on record. Globally, sea level has risen four to eight inches over the past 100 years. Increasing concentrations of greenhouse gases are likely to accelerate the rate of climate change.

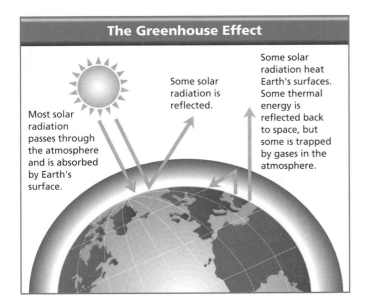

The Greenhouse Effect

Most solar radiation passes through the atmosphere and is absorbed by Earth's surface.

Some solar radiation is reflected.

Some solar radiation heat Earth's surfaces. Some thermal energy is reflected back to space, but some is trapped by gases in the atmosphere.

Help Students Read

KWL (Know-Want-Learned)
What I Know/Want to Know/Learned

Strategy To help students access prior knowledge, set a purpose for reading, recall what has been read, and link new information to prior knowledge. The KWL strategy has students create ad complete a three-column chart similar to the one below.

Know	Want to Know	Learned

Finally students categorize information they learned in a box like the one below.

Information I Expect to Use

Assign a section in chapter 4, such as Conserving Land and Soil, for students to read. Before they begin, have them create and complete the first two columns of the KWL chart.

Example
1. Draw a three-column KWL chart of the board.
2. Have students complete the Know column with facts, examples, and other information they already know about the topic.
3. Tell students to complete the Want to Know column with questions about the topic that they want answers to. Students may scan the section to help them generate questions.
4. Have students read the section to learn more about the topic and determine answers to their questions. As they read, have them note answers in the Learned column, along with other facts, examples, and details they learned.
5. Below their KWL chart, have students draw an Information I Expect to Use box. Have them review the information in the Learned column and use it to complete the box with useful categories of information.

interactive Textbook
- Complete student edition
- Video and audio
- Simulations and activities
- Section and chapter activities

Chapter Project

Objectives

This project will provide an opportunity for students to examine and identify materials used in product packaging and to investigate what happens to these materials when they are discarded. After this Chapter Project, students will be able to

- classify the types of materials used in product packages
- infer the purpose of each material
- make a model of a product package
- communicate the features of their model to the class

Skills Focus

Classifying, inferring, making models, communicating

Project Time Line 1 to 2 weeks

All in One Teaching Resources

- Chapter Project Teacher Notes
- Chapter Project Worksheet 1
- Chapter Project Worksheet 2
- Chapter Project Worksheet 3
- Chapter Project Scoring Rubric

Safety

Tell students to make sure the packages are empty before they bring them to school. Advise them to wash cans, bottles, and plastic containers with hot, soapy water before bringing them to class. Do not allow students to use packaging from raw meat. Be aware of your school's policy about students' bringing medicine or vitamin containers to school. Review the Safety Guidelines in Appendix A.

Chapter 4

Land, Water, and Air Resources

Chapter Preview

❶ **Conserving Land and Soil**
Discover *How Does Mining Affect the Land?*

❷ **Waste Disposal and Recycling**
Discover *What's in the Trash?*
Active Art *Sanitary Landfill*
Skills Activity *Graphing*
Try This *It's in the Numbers*
Skills Lab *Waste, Away!*

❸ **Water Pollution and Solutions**
Discover *How Does the Water Change?*
Try This *Is There Tea There?*
Try This *Getting Clean*

❹ **Air Pollution and Solutions**
Discover *How Does the Scent Spread?*
Try This *How Acid Is Your Rain?*
Design Your Own Lab *How Does the Garden Grow?*

❺ **Global Changes in the Atmosphere**
Discover *What Happens to the Beads?*
Math Skills *Calculating a Concentration*
Analyzing Data *Chlorine Levels*

The curved rows made by contour plowing help to conserve soil on hilly farms. ▶

Developing a Plan

This project is most appropriate as an individual activity, though students could work cooperatively. As the class studies Section 1, each student can choose a product package and begin analyzing the materials used in it. Most of the time needed for this project involves creating and testing a package model.

Possible Materials

- Students will need scissors to take apart their packages.
- Provide poster board, tape, colored markers, plastic wrap, aluminum foil and other materials for making the models.

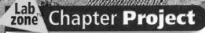

Chapter **Project**

Design and Build a Product Package

The next time you're in the supermarket, look at all the different kinds of packages. There are plastic bottles, metal cans, cardboard boxes, paper wrappers, and more! Most of this packaging is eventually thrown away. In this chapter, you will learn what happens to wastes after they are discarded. In this project, you will be creating a less wasteful product package.

Your Goal To design and build a new package for an existing product that has the least possible packaging waste, but that protects the product

To complete this project, you must

- include a cutaway portion of the product's current package with each material labeled
- create a model of your new package
- test how well your new package protects the product and redesign it if necessary
- follow the safety guidelines in Appendix A

Plan It! Select a product package to study. Empty the package and clean it out if necessary. Then cut the package open and identify the materials from which it is made. Determine how each of these materials protects the product. Decide whether each material could be eliminated or replaced without losing the package's protective function. Then start to sketch some ideas for your new product package.

Chapter 4 E ◆ 115

Launching the Project

To introduce the project, have students brainstorm types of packaging materials they know of, and list their ideas on the board.

Ask: **How might the materials be grouped?** (*Accept all reasonable responses.*)

Discuss some purposes of packaging materials; for example, to prevent spoilage or breakage, or for convenience in using and storing. Ask: **Which packaging materials might be best for each purpose?** (*Accept all reasonable responses.*)

Land, Water, and Air Resources

Show the Video Preview to introduce the Chapter Project and present an overview of the chapter content. Discussion question: **How has the beluga whale population at the mouth of the Saint Lawrence River changed in recent years?** (*It has dwindled from over 5,000 to 650.*)

Performance Assessment

The Chapter Project Scoring Rubric will help you evaluate how well students complete the Chapter Project. Share the rubric with students at the beginning of the project so they will know what is expected. Students will be assessed on

- their completeness and accuracy in classifying the types of materials used in a product package
- their ability to infer the purpose of each packaging material
- how well their models product the product
- the thoroughness and organization of their presentation

Portfolio

E ● 115

Objectives

After this lesson, students will be able to

E.4.1.1 Tell how people use land.

E.4.1.2 Describe the structure of fertile soil.

E.4.1.3 Identify problems that occur when soil is not properly managed.

Target Reading Skill

Identifying Main Ideas Explain that identifying main ideas and details helps students sort the facts from the information into groups. Each group can have a main topic, subtopics, and details.

Answers

Possible answers include the following:

- **Detail:** Agriculture—new farmland is created by clearing forests, draining wetlands, and irrigating deserts.
- **Detail:** Mining—strip mines expose the soil, which can then be blown or washed away more easily.
- **Detail:** Development—as populations grow, people build more houses and paved roads.

All in One Teaching Resources

- Transparency E32

Preteach

Build Background Knowledge L2

Soil Components

Ask: **What is soil made of?** (*Rock that was broken down into very small pieces over time; accept other reasonable responses without comment at this time.*) **What else does soil contain?** (*Students may mention minerals, nutrients, dead and living organisms.*)

Reading Preview

Key Concepts

- How do people use land?
- What is the structure of fertile soil?
- What kinds of problems occur when soil is not properly managed?

Key Terms

- development • litter
- topsoil • subsoil • bedrock
- erosion • nutrient depletion
- fertilizer • desertification
- drought • land reclamation

Target Reading Skill

Identifying Main Ideas As you read the "Types of Land Use" section, write the main idea in a graphic organizer like the one below. Then write three supporting details that give examples of the main idea.

Main Idea

Three uses that change the land are . . .

Detail	Detail	Detail

Lab zone Discover **Activity**

How Does Mining Affect the Land?

1. You will be given a pan filled with sand and soil that represents a mining site. There are at least ten deposits of "ore" (sunflower seeds) buried in your mining site.

2. Your goal is to locate and remove the ore from your site. You may use a pencil, a pair of tweezers, and a spoon as mining tools.

3. After you have extracted the chunks of ore, break them open to remove the "minerals" inside.
   CAUTION: *Do not eat the sunflower seeds.*

4. Observe your mining site and the surrounding area after your mining operations are finished.

Think It Over

Predicting How did mining change the land at your mining site? Predict whether it would be easy or difficult to restore the land to its original state. Explain.

Less than a quarter of Earth's surface is dry land. Except for a small amount that forms when volcanoes erupt, new land cannot be created. All the people on Earth must share this limited amount of land to produce their food, build shelter, and obtain other resources. Land is a precious resource. As the American author Mark Twain once said about land, "They don't make it anymore."

Lab zone Discover **Activity**

Skills Focus Predicting

Materials pan, mixture of sand and soil, sunflower seeds, pencil, tweezers, spoon, paper towel. For each student or small group, fill a pan about half full with a mixture of sand and soil. Bury 10–15 sunflower seeds in the mixture, and then smooth the surface to hide the seeds.

CAUTION: *Make sure students wash their hands when they finish.*

Time 10 minutes

Tips Allow students to use any method they wish to locate and extract the seeds.

Expected Outcome The site will have many holes and mounds of dirt.

Think It Over The land is changed significantly when a site is mined. Restoring it is difficult; holes must be filled, the excavated soil replaced and regraded, and the land replanted.

Types of Land Use

People use land in many ways. **Three uses that change the land are agriculture, mining, and development.** Some examples of land use are shown in Figure 1.

Agriculture Land is the source of most of the food that people eat. Crops such as wheat, rice, and potatoes require large areas of fertile land. But less than a third of Earth's land can be farmed. The rest is too dry, too wet, too salty, or too mountainous. To provide food for the growing population, new farmland is created by clearing forests, draining wetlands, and irrigating deserts. When people make these changes, organisms that depend on the natural ecosystem must find new homes.

Not all agricultural land is used to grow food for people. Some land is used to grow food for livestock. Some animals, such as cows and horses, also require pasture or rangeland for grazing.

Mining Mining is the removal of nonrenewable resources from the land. Resources just below the surface are strip mined. Strip mining involves removing a strip of land to obtain minerals and then replacing the strip. Strip mines expose the soil, which can then be blown or washed away more easily. Strip-mined areas may remain barren for years before the soil becomes rich enough to support plant growth again.

For resources located deep underground, it is necessary to dig a tunnel, or shaft. The minerals are carried up through the shafts. This process is called underground mining.

Development People settled first in areas that had good soil and were near a source of fresh water. As populations grew, these settlements became towns and cities. People built more houses and paved roads. The construction of buildings, roads, bridges, dams, and other structures is called **development.**

In the United States, about a million hectares of farmland (an area half the size of New Jersey) are developed each year. Development not only reduces the amount of farmland, but can also destroy wildlife habitats.

Reading Checkpoint Why isn't all land suitable for farming?

FIGURE 1
Land Uses
Much of the land on Earth is used for agriculture and development. Dairy farms (far left) require large areas of land for grazing animals. The construction of houses (below) is one example of development.

E ◆ 117

The Structure of Soil

Teach Key Concepts L2
Soil Layers

Focus Remind students that good soil is necessary for one of the uses of land—agriculture.

Teach Ask: **What does soil contain that plants need to grow?** (*Minerals and nutrients*) **How does soil help break down waste?** (*It contains bacteria, fungi, and other organisms that help break down waste.*) **What natural processes break up bedrock?** (*Freezing, thawing, acids in rainwater and chemically released by lichens, and plant roots that wedge between rocks*) Have students look at Figure 2, and ask a student volunteer to read the definition of each layer of soil.

Apply Ask students to identify the layer of soil where each of the following is most likely to be found: **Rock fragments but only a small amount of animal and plant matter** (*Subsoil*), **water and nutrients absorbed by many plant roots** (*Topsoil*), **dead leaves and grass** (*Litter*), **rock** (*Bedrock*). **learning modality: visual**

All in One **Teaching Resources**
• Transparency E33

Help Students Read

KWL Refer to the Content Refresher, which provides the guidelines for KWL.

Before students read *The Structure of Soil*, have them construct a KWL chart with three columns: *What I Know, What I Want to Know,* and *What I Learned.* Tell them to fill out the first two columns. After they have read pages 118–120, have them fill out the final column.

Go Online
SciLINKS NSTA

For: Links on erosion
Visit: www.SciLinks.org
Web Code: scn-0541

Download a worksheet that will guide students' review of Internet resources on erosion.

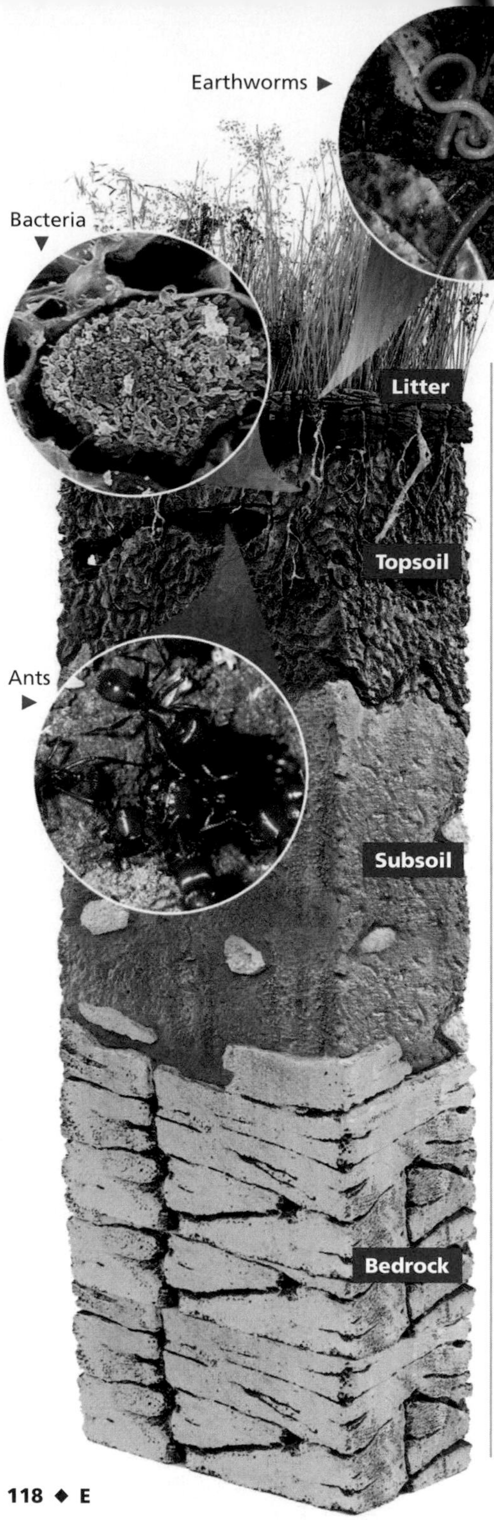

Earthworms ▶

Bacteria ▼

Ants ▶

Litter

Topsoil

Subsoil

Bedrock

FIGURE 2
Soil Structure
Soil consists of several layers. Organisms such as ants, earthworms, and bacteria live mostly in the topsoil. **Applying Concepts** *In which layer are most plant roots located? What do the roots absorb there?*

The Structure of Soil

Have you ever thought about how much you depend on soil? You probably haven't. But soil contains the minerals and nutrients that plants need to grow. Soil also absorbs, stores, and filters water. Living in soil are the bacteria, fungi, and other organisms that break down the wastes and remains of living things. (Recall the nitrogen cycle from Chapter 2.) Without soil, most life on land could not exist.

Figure 2 shows the structure of fertile soil. **Fertile soil is made up of several layers, including litter, topsoil, and subsoil.** The very top layer of dead leaves and grass is called **litter.** The next layer, **topsoil,** is a mixture of rock fragments, nutrients, water, air, and decaying animal and plant matter. The water and nutrients are absorbed by the many plant roots located in this layer. Below the topsoil is the **subsoil.** The subsoil also contains rock fragments, water, and air, but has less animal and plant matter than the topsoil.

It can take hundreds of years to form just a few centimeters of new soil. All soil begins as **bedrock,** the rock that makes up Earth's crust. Natural processes such as freezing and thawing gradually break apart the bedrock. Plant roots wedge between rocks and break them into smaller pieces. Acids in rainwater and chemicals released by lichens slowly break the rock into smaller particles. Animals such as earthworms and moles help grind rocks into even smaller particles. As dead organisms break down, their remains also contribute to the mixture.

Reading Checkpoint *What is the first step in the process of soil creation?*

Terracing ▲

Windbreaks ▲

Soil Management

Because rich topsoil takes so long to form, it is important to protect Earth's soil. **Poor soil management can result in three problems: erosion, nutrient depletion, and desertification.** Fortunately, damaged soil can sometimes be restored.

Erosion The process by which water, wind, or ice moves particles of rocks or soil is called **erosion.** Normally, plant roots hold soil in place. But when plants are removed during logging, mining, or farming, the soil is exposed, and erosion occurs more easily. Some farming methods that help reduce erosion are shown in Figure 3.

Nutrient Depletion Plants make their own food through photosynthesis. But plants also need nutrients found in soil. Decomposers supply these nutrients to the soil as they break down the wastes and remains of organisms. But if a farmer plants the same crops in a field every year, the crops may use more nutrients than the decomposers can supply. The soil becomes less fertile, a situation called **nutrient depletion.**

When soil becomes depleted, farmers usually apply **fertilizers,** which include nutrients that help crops grow better. Farmers may choose other methods of soil management, however. Fields can be periodically left fallow, or unplanted. The unused parts of crops, such as cornstalks, can be left in the fields to decompose, adding nutrients to the soil. Farmers can also rotate crops. The first year, a farmer might plant corn, a crop that uses many nutrients. The next year, the farmer might plant oats, which use fewer nutrients. The year after that, the farmer might sow alfalfa to help restore nutrients.

FIGURE 3
Reducing Erosion
Terracing and the use of windbreaks are two methods of preventing erosion. In terracing, hillsides are built up into a series of flat "terraces." The ridges of soil at the edges slow runoff and catch eroding soil. Windbreaks such as rows of trees block wind and help keep soil from eroding.

For: Links on erosion
Visit: www.SciLinks.org
Web Code: scn-0541

Chapter 4   E ◆ 119

Soil Management

Teach Key Concepts   L2
Protecting Earth's Soil

Focus Remind students that soil can take hundreds of years to form.

Teach Ask: **What happens when soil is exposed?** (*Erosion occurs more easily.*) **What farming practice contributes to nutrient depletion?** (*Planting the same crops in a field every year*) **How can farmers prevent this?** (*Apply fertilizers, leave fields unplanted periodically, and rotate the crops*) **What are some causes of desertification?** (*Climate, overgrazing of grasslands, and cutting down trees*)

Apply Ask students to discuss the time and expense of managing soil. **learning modality: logical/mathematical**

Lab zone   Build Inquiry   L2

Observing Soil Layers

Materials glass jars with screw-on lids, water, soil samples, hand lens

Time 20 minutes over 2 days

Focus Review the layers of soil.

Teach Ask students to bring in about 500 mL of soil (removing any visible living organisms and leaving them at the location). Have students put their soil in jars, add water to cover it, screw on the lid, and then shake the jar gently to mix the soil and water. Remind students to wash their hands. Leave the jars undisturbed overnight and examine them the next day.

Apply Ask: **What do you see in the jar now?** (*The largest and most dense particles will have settled in the bottom and finest particles at the top.*) Ask students to identify any layers of soil in their samples. **learning modality: kinesthetic**

Differentiated Instruction

Special Needs   L1
Understanding Land Reclamation Ask students to relate the text's description of erosion to their own direct experience. If students did the Discover Activity at the beginning of the section, ask: **What did your mining site look like when you finished?** (*The site was full of holes and*

piles of soil.) Have students recall their predictions about how easy or difficult it would be to restore the land. Ask: **Now that you have read about erosion, do you think it would be difficult to restore eroded croplands?** (*Yes; the subsoil and topsoil would have to be replaced after continued erosion.*) **learning modality: verbal**

Monitor Progress   L2

Drawing Have students draw a labeled diagram of soil layers.

Answers
Figure 2 Topsoil; water and minerals

Reading Checkpoint The breakup of bedrock into smaller pieces of rock

Use Visuals: Figure 4 L2

Areas of Desertification

Focus Review the meaning of the key term *desertification*.

Teach Ask students to name areas of existing deserts. *(Southwestern U.S., the southern part of South America, the northern part of Africa, a small part of central Asia, and much of Australia)* Have students compare this map with the maps of the desert and grassland biomes in Chapter 2. Ask: **Which type of biome is most threatened by desertification? Why?** *(Grasslands; these areas tend to be dry, so wind erodes exposed soil.)*

Apply Ask students to identify methods to slow or reduce desertification based on what they have learned in this section. *(Possible answer: Terracing, windbreaks, not allowing livestock to overgraze, not cutting down trees)*
learning modality: visual

Modeling Soil Conservation

Materials mixture of sand and soil, spray bottle, 2 deep pans, water, small handheld rake or large fork

Time 15 minutes

Focus Tell students that runoff of water is the main cause of erosion.

Teach Pile up sand and soil in a mound in each pan. Spray one mound with water to show how easily the soil flows downhill. On the other mound, use the rake to make small grooves that encircle the pile, and then gently spray the mound. Explain that farmers plow grooves such as these to follow the contour of the land.

Apply Ask: **How did the grooves help prevent erosion?** *(The water collected in the grooves before running downhill and carrying away the soil.)* **learning modality: visual**

FIGURE 4
Desertification
Large areas of the world are at risk of desertification. One cause is overgrazing. Without grass to hold the soil in place, grasslands can become deserts.
Interpreting Maps *In which biome are most of the areas at risk of desertification located?* (*Hint:* Refer to *Chapter 2.*)

Desertification If the soil in a once-fertile area becomes depleted of moisture and nutrients, the area can become desert-like. The advance of desert-like conditions into areas that previously were fertile is called **desertification** (dih zurt uh fih KAY shun). In the past 50 years, desertification has occurred on about 5 billion hectares of land.

One cause of desertification is climate. For example, a **drought** is a period when less rain than normal falls in an area. During droughts, crops fail. Without plant cover, the exposed soil easily blows away. Overgrazing of grasslands by cattle and sheep also exposes the soil. In addition, cutting down trees for firewood can expose soil and cause desertification.

Desertification is a very serious problem. People cannot grow crops and graze livestock where desertification has occurred. As a result, people may face famine and starvation. In central Africa, where desertification is severe, millions of rural people are moving to the cities because they can no longer support themselves on the land.

Reading Checkpoint What are three causes of desertification?

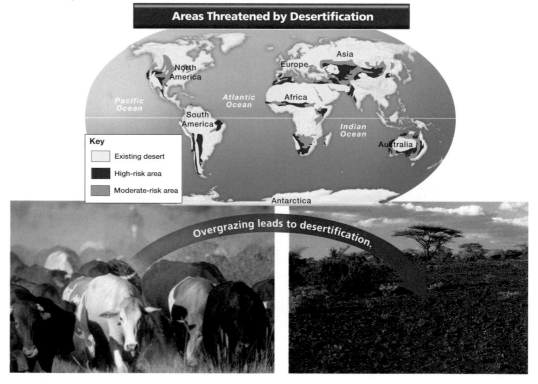

Areas Threatened by Desertification

Key
Existing desert
High-risk area
Moderate-risk area

Overgrazing leads to desertification.

Before

After

Land Reclamation Fortunately, it is often possible to restore land damaged by erosion or mining. The process of restoring an area of land to a more natural, productive state is called **land reclamation.** In addition to restoring land for agriculture, land reclamation can restore habitats for wildlife. Many different types of land reclamation projects are currently underway all over the world. But it is generally more difficult and expensive to restore damaged land and soil than it is to protect them in the first place.

Figure 5 shows an example of land reclamation. When the mining operation in the first scene was completed, the mine operators smoothed out the sides of the mining cuts. Then they carefully replaced the subsoil and topsoil that had been removed before mining. Finally, they planted grass and trees. The former mine is now becoming a wooded area.

FIGURE 5
Land Reclamation
It's hard to believe that this wooded area used to be an open mine. Thanks to land reclamation practices, many mining areas are being restored for other uses.

Section 1 Assessment

Target Reading Skill Identifying Main Ideas Use the graphic organizer you created to help you answer Question 1 below.

Reviewing Key Concepts

1. a. Identifying What are three ways that people use land?
  b. Explaining For each land use, describe how it changes the land.
  c. Predicting How would you expect each type of land use to change if the world's population were to continue to increase?
2. a. Reviewing Describe the different layers of fertile soil in order, from the surface downward.
  b. Relating Cause and Effect If large amounts of pesticides are applied to soil, the process of soil creation may be negatively affected. Why might this be the case?

3. a. Listing List three problems that can occur when soil is not properly managed.
  b. Comparing and Contrasting How are the causes of desertification related to erosion?
  c. Developing Hypotheses Suppose that a farmer's field is on a slight hill. How might this farmer reduce erosion of his field?

Writing in Science

Description Imagine that you are holding a lump of fertile soil in your hand. Write a paragraph describing its texture, appearance, smell, and anything else you would observe. Be sure to use a variety of adjectives in your paragraph.

Assess

Reviewing Key Concepts

1. a. Agriculture, development, mining **b.** Farmland is created by clearing forests, draining wetlands, and irrigating deserts; development destroys wildlife habitats; mining removes the land and exposes the soil. **c.** All types of land use would increase and change the land further to meet the needs of a growing population.
2. a. Litter is a layer of dead leaves and grass. Topsoil is a mixture of rocks, nutrients, water, air, and decaying organic matter. The subsoil has rocks, nutrients, water, and air, but less decaying matter. Bedrock is the rock that makes up Earth's crust. **b.** Pesticides could destroy animals, such as earthworms, that grind rocks into smaller particles as part of soil formation.
3. a. Erosion, nutrient depletion, desertification **b.** Overgrazing of grasslands or tree cutting during drought conditions exposes the bare soil. Wind and water can erode soil that has no plant cover. **c.** The farmer could build up the soil into terraces, which slow runoff and catch eroding soil.

Reteach L1

Call on students to name key terms as you provide the definitions. Then have students describe how each word relates to land use, structure of soil, or to soil management.

Performance Assessment L2

Writing Have students briefly explain the major problems and prevention of poor soil management.

All in One Teaching Resources
- Section Summary: *Conserving Land and Soil*
- Review and Reinforce: *Conserving Land and Soil*
- Enrich: *Conserving Land and Soil*

Lab zone Chapter **Project**

Keep Students on Track

✂ CAUTION: *Make sure students handle scissors carefully. Review the safety guidelines in Appendix A.* Encourage students to begin examining and analyzing packaging materials of various products. Advise them to think about the purpose of the packages and how they are discarded.

Writing in Science

Writing Mode Description

Scoring Rubric
4 Includes several senses and a variety of adjectives to describe the attributes of soil
3 Includes criteria, but adjectives are not as vivid
2 Includes only brief description
1 Includes only a list with no description

Section

2 Waste Disposal and Recycling

Objectives

After this lesson, students will be able to

E.4.2.1 Name three methods of solid waste disposal.

E.4.2.2 Identify ways people can help control the solid waste problem.

E.4.2.3 Explain how hazardous wastes can be safely disposed of.

Target Reading Skill

Asking Questions Explain that changing a head into a question helps students anticipate the ideas, facts, and events they are about to read.

Answers

Possible questions and answers include the following: **What is the problem with waste disposal?** *(Each disposal method has advantages and disadvantages.)* **What is recycling?** *(Reclaiming raw materials and reusing them to create new products.)* **How can people help control the solid waste problem?** *(Reduce, reuse, and recycle.)* **Why are some wastes hazardous?** *(Some are explosive, flammable, corrosive, or radioactive.)*

All in One Teaching Resources

• Transparency E34

Preteach

Build Background Knowledge L2

Getting Rid of Solid Waste

Ask: **What kinds of things does your family throw away?** *(Used paper, metal cans, glass jars, plastic milk jugs, and so on)* **How does your family get rid of its trash?** *(Trash may be collected in the students' community, or families may bring it to a "dump" themselves. Some families may recycle part of their trash.)*

Reading Preview

Key Concepts

• What are three methods of handling solid waste?

• What can people do to help control the solid waste problem?

• How can hazardous wastes be safely disposed of?

Key Terms

• municipal solid waste
• incineration • leachate
• sanitary landfill • recycling
• biodegradable • composting
• hazardous waste

Target Reading Skill

Asking Questions Before you read, preview the red headings. In a graphic organizer like the one below, ask a *why, what,* or *how* question for each heading. As you read, write the answers to your questions.

The Problem of Waste Disposal

Question	Answer
What is the problem with waste disposal?	Each disposal method has . . .

Lab zone Discover Activity

What's in the Trash?

Your teacher will give you a trash bag. The items in the bag represent the most common categories of household waste in the United States.

1. Before you open the bag, predict what the two most common categories are.

2. Put on some plastic gloves. Open the bag and sort the trash items into categories based on what they are made of.

3. Count the number of trash items in each category. Construct a bar graph showing the number of pieces of trash in each category.

Think It Over
Interpreting Data Based on your graph, what are the two most common types of household waste? Was your prediction correct?

How much trash does your family throw away in a year? If it's your job to take the trash out, you might say that it's a large amount. Now imagine that amount multiplied by every family in the United States! Consider these facts:

• Every hour, people throw away about 2.5 million plastic bottles.

• Every day, the average person produces about 2 kilograms of trash.

• Every year, people throw away 2.8 million metric tons of plastic bags and 230 million automobile tires.

You can see why some people call the United States a "throw-away society"! Disposable products can be cheap and convenient. But they have created a big problem—what to do with all the trash.

Lab zone Discover Activity

Skills Focus Interpreting data

Materials trash bag containing common household wastes, plastic gloves, graph paper, ruler. For each group of students, prepare a trash bag containing the following items: 4 paper items; 2 items of yard waste such as leaves; 1 piece of rubber, cloth, or wood waste; 1 soda can or other metal item; 1 glass jar or bottle;

1 plastic item; 1 food-waste item, such as an orange peel

Time 20 minutes

Tips Have students work on the floor so glass containers do not fall and break.

Expected Outcome Students will sort the items into the categories listed.

Think It Over Paper and yard waste

The Problem of Waste Disposal

In their daily activities, people generate many types of waste, including used paper, empty packages, and food scraps. The waste materials produced in homes, businesses, schools, and other places in a community are called **municipal solid waste.** Other sources of solid waste include construction debris and certain agricultural and industrial wastes. **Three methods of handling solid waste are burning, burying, and recycling. Each method has advantages and disadvantages.**

Incineration The burning of solid waste is called **incineration** (in sin ur AY shun). Incineration has some advantages. The burning facilities, or incinerators, do not take up much space. They do not pose a risk of polluting groundwater. The heat produced by burning solid waste can be used to generate electricity. These "waste-to-energy" plants supply electricity to many homes in the United States.

Unfortunately, incinerators do have drawbacks. Even the best incinerators release some pollution into the air. And although incinerators reduce the volume of waste by as much as 90 percent, some waste still remains. This waste needs to be disposed of somewhere. Finally, incinerators are expensive to build.

FIGURE 6
Waste Disposal
Billions of tons of municipal solid waste are created in the United States each year. More than one third of that waste is paper.
Reading Graphs *What percentage of solid waste does food waste represent?*

Landfill Wastes

- Paper and cardboard 38%
- Yard wastes 13%
- Food wastes 10%
- Plastics 9%
- Metals 8%
- Glass 6%
- Other wastes 16%

E ◆ 123

For: Landfill activity
Visit: PHSchool.com
Web Code: cep-5042

Students learn about the components of a well-designed sanitary landfill.

Go Online
active art

For: Sanitary Landfill activity
Visit: PHSchool.com
Web Code: cep-5042

Lab zone — Teacher **Demo**

Making a Model of a Landfill

Materials beaker, coffee filter, food coloring, jar, rubber band, soil, water

Time 10 minutes

Focus Review the meaning of *leachate.*

Teach Put a coffee filter over the mouth of a jar, letting it hang into the jar, and secure it in place with a rubber band. Fill the filter about halfway with soil. Put several drops of food coloring on the soil, and then pour water into the jar. After the water has collected in the jar, ask: **What do you see in the jar?** *(Colored water)* **Where did the color come from?** *(The food coloring)* **What does the food coloring represent in this landfill model?** *(Chemicals in the soil)*

Apply Ask: **In a real landfill, where do chemicals come from?** *(The wastes in the landfill)* **learning modality: visual**

Use Visuals: Figure 7 `L2`
Reducing Health and Safety Risks

Focus Remind students why sanitary landfills were developed.

Teach Ask different volunteers to read the captions aloud. Ask: **How is this landfill designed to reduce health risks?** *(Vent pipes release gases that might cause an explosion. Wells are monitored for wastes polluting groundwater. Leachate forms at the bottom rather than running off into surrounding water. Liners keep liquids from leaking into the soil.)*

Apply Remind students that even well-designed landfills do not prevent all leakage. Ask: **What can people do to further decrease the risk of pollution from landfills?** *(Reduce the amount of landfill waste that could be poisonuous, such as pesticides.)* **learning modality: visual**

Landfills Until fairly recently, people usually disposed of waste in open holes in the ground. But these open dumps were dangerous and unsightly. Rainwater falling on a dump dissolved chemicals from the wastes, forming a polluted liquid called **leachate.** Leachate could run off into streams and lakes, or trickle down into the groundwater below the dump.

In 1976, the government banned open dumps. Now much solid waste is buried in landfills that are constructed to hold the wastes more safely. A **sanitary landfill** holds municipal solid waste, construction debris, and some types of agricultural and industrial waste. Figure 7 shows the parts of a well-designed sanitary landfill. Once a landfill is full, it is covered with a clay cap to keep rainwater from entering the waste.

However, even well-designed landfills still pose a risk of polluting groundwater. And while capped landfills can be reused in certain ways, including as parks and sites for sports arenas, they cannot be used for housing or agriculture.

✓ **Reading Checkpoint** What are two possible uses of a capped sanitary landfill?

FIGURE 7
Sanitary Landfill
A well-designed sanitary landfill contains the waste and prevents it from polluting the surrounding land and water.

Leachate Treatment
The collected leachate is pumped into holding tanks and treated with chemicals. Any leftover solids are collected and hauled to a safe disposal site.

Gas Recovery
Bacteria break down wastes in a landfill, producing methane and carbon dioxide. These gases could cause an explosion. To avoid that, vent pipes collect and release the gases.

Solid Waste Layers
Compacting the waste keeps the landfill from settling. Each layer is covered with clean soil or plastic.

Monitoring Wells
Testing wells surround the landfill. The wells are monitored to detect any wastes polluting the groundwater.

Leachate Collection
Water moving through the landfill dissolves substances from the wastes, forming leachate at the bottom.

Liners
Layers of clay and plastic line the bottom and sides of the landfill. The liners keep liquids from leaking into the soil.

124 ◆ E

Recycling

The process of reclaiming raw materials and reusing them to create new products is called **recycling.** Recycling reduces the volume of solid waste by enabling people to use the materials in wastes again. While recycling uses some energy, it also saves the energy that would be needed to obtain and process raw materials.

As you know, matter in ecosystems is naturally recycled through the water cycle, carbon cycle, and other processes. Any material that can be broken down and recycled by bacteria and other decomposers is **biodegradable** (by oh dih GRAY duh bul). Unfortunately, many of the products people use today are not biodegradable. Plastic containers, metal cans, rubber tires, and glass jars are examples of products that do not naturally decompose. Instead, people have developed techniques to recycle the raw materials in these products.

A wide range of materials, including motor oil, tires, and batteries, can be recycled. Most recycling focuses on four major categories of products: metal, plastic, glass, and paper.

Metal In your classroom, you are surrounded by metal objects that can be recycled. Your desk, scissors, staples, and paper clips are probably made of steel. Another very common metal, aluminum, is used to make soda cans, house siding, window screens, and many other products.

Metals such as iron and aluminum can be recycled. Recycling metal saves money and causes less pollution than making new metal. With recycling, no ore needs to be mined, transported to factories, or processed. In addition, recycling metals helps conserve these nonrenewable resources.

Lab zone Skills **Activity**

Graphing

What happens to trash? Use the data in the table below to construct a circle graph of methods of municipal solid waste disposal in the United States. Give your circle graph a title. (For help making a circle graph, see the Skills Handbook.)

Method of Disposal	Percentage of Waste
Landfills	56%
Recycling	27%
Incineration	17%

Lab zone Skills **Activity**

Skills Focus Graphing

Materials protractor, drawing compass

Time 15 minutes

Tips Tell students to determine the size of each wedge of the circle graph by multiplying 360° by each percentage.

Expected Outcome *(Landfills = 202°, Recycling = 97°, Incineration = 61°; Possible title: Methods of Waste Disposal in the U. S.)*

Extend Have students make a second circle graph to show what would happen if 15% more of the total waste were recycled instead of being sent to landfills. *(Landfills = 148°, Recycling = 151°)* **learning modality: logical/mathematical**

Recycling

Teach Key Concepts L2

Metal, Plastic, Glass, and Paper Recycling

Focus Ask students to give examples of items that are recyclable.

Teach Ask: **What is an example of recycling in nature?** *(Matter is naturally recycled through the water cycle, carbon cycle, and other processes.)* Explain that biodegradable matter naturally decomposes. Ask: **What are some items that are not biodegradable or that degrade very slowly?** *(Plastic containers, metal cans, glass containers)* **What are the benefits of recycling aluminum cans and other metals?** *(It takes less energy to recycle the cans than to mine the raw materials and process the ore. It also saves money and causes less pollution.)* **What are plastic products that can be recycled?** *(Milk jugs, detergent containers, and soda bottles)* **Why can most paper products be recycled only a few times?** *(Each time paper is recycled to make pulp, the new paper is rougher, weaker, and darker.)*

Apply Ask: **Do you think recycling is worth the extra effort? Why?** *(Accept logical responses. Most students will say that recycling is worth the effort because it helps prevent the supply of certain materials from running out or that it helps prevent landfills from filling up.)* **learning modality: verbal**

Monitor Progress _____ L2

Oral Presentation Call on students at random to explain why metal, plastic, glass, and paper should be recycled instead of being discarded in landfills.

Answers
Figure 8 The supply might be used up.

✓ Reading Checkpoint Parks and sites for sports arenas

Integrating Technology

L1

Have small groups of students select a product labeled "biodegradable" to bury on the school grounds. Advise each group to select an item made of a different material. At the end of this chapter, have the groups dig up their items to see which materials began to decompose. Ask students to explain why some items may not appear to have begun decomposing. *(Possible answer: The materials in the item may take longer to break down.)* **CAUTION:** *Have students wear plastic gloves when handling trash and wash their hands afterward. Students who are allergic to molds should not participate.* **learning modality: kinesthetic**

Build Inquiry

L2

Calculating Trees to Make Newspaper

Materials calculator (optional), metric ruler, newspapers

Time 10 minutes

Focus Show students a stack of one week's issues of newspaper that you have collected. Ask them to estimate how many newspapers they think one tree can make.

Teach Explain that one tree 10.5 to 12 m tall produces a stack of newspapers 1.2 m high. Have a volunteer measure the height of the stack. Ask: **In how many weeks would I use up one tree by reading the newspaper?** *(120 cm ÷ height of stack)* **How many trees in a year?** *(52 ÷ weeks to use one tree)*

Apply Ask: **If every one of your families also read the newspaper every day, how many trees would we all use up in a year?** *(Above answer × [number of students] + yourself)* **learning modality: logical/ mathematical**

FIGURE 9
Plastic Recycling
Plastic bottles can be recycled and made into many products, including polyester fleece for jackets.

Try This Activity

It's in the Numbers

Plastic bottles and other plastic products usually have a number inside a triangle indicating the type of plastic they are made of. Plastics must be sorted by type before they can be recycled.

Sort the plastic products your teacher gives you into groups according to their recycling numbers.

Classifying Compare and contrast the pieces in each group with one another and with the pieces in other groups. Describe the characteristics of each group.

Plastic When oil is refined to make gasoline and other petroleum products, solid materials called resins are left over. Resins can be heated, stretched, and molded into plastic products. Common plastic products that can easily be recycled include milk jugs, detergent containers, and soda bottles. When these products are recycled, they take on very different forms: as fleece jackets, carpeting, park benches, shower stalls, floor tiles, trash cans, fiber filling for sleeping bags, or even dock pilings!

Glass Glass is made from sand, soda ash, and limestone mixed together and heated. Glass is one of the easiest products to recycle because glass pieces can be melted down over and over to make new glass containers. Recycled glass is also used to make fiberglass, bricks, tiles, and the reflective paints on road signs.

Recycling glass is less expensive than making glass from raw materials. Because the recycled pieces melt at a lower temperature than the raw materials, less energy is required. Recycling glass also reduces the environmental damage caused by mining for soda and limestone.

Paper It takes about 17 trees to make one metric ton of paper. Paper mills turn wood into a thick liquid called pulp. Pulp is spread out and dried to produce paper. Pulp can also be made from old newspapers and old used paper. The paper must be washed to remove the inks and dyes. Then the paper is mixed with more water and other chemicals to form pulp.

Most paper products can only be recycled a few times. Recycled paper is not as smooth or strong as paper made from wood pulp. Each time paper is recycled to make pulp, the new paper is rougher, weaker, and darker.

Reading Checkpoint What are three reasons to recycle glass?

Try This Activity

Skills Focus Classifying

Materials pieces of plastic products. Assemble a set of plastic pieces by selecting several examples from each of these recycling categories: 1 (polyethylene terphthalate) soft-drink bottles, 2 (high-density polyethylene) milk and water jugs, 3 (vinyl) shampoo bottles, 4 (low-density polyethylene) ketchup bottles, 5 (polypropylene) squeeze bottles,

6 (polystyrene) fast-food containers and coffee cups, 7 (all other resins and layered multi-materials). To reduce preparation time, assemble one set of plastic pieces and let students take turns sorting the pieces.

Time 10 minutes

Tips CAUTION: *Use only empty containers that have not held any hazardous materials. Rinse or wash out containers thoroughly.*

Expected Outcome The plastics can be sorted into at least four or five groups according to the plastics' color, clarity, and rigidity.

Extend Have students make a compare/ contrast table listing the types, descriptions, and uses of the different groups of plastics. **learning modality: logical/mathematical**

Is Recycling Worthwhile? Besides conserving resources, recycling also saves energy. For example, making aluminum products from recycled aluminum rather than from raw materials uses about 90 percent less energy overall. For certain materials, recycling is usually worthwhile.

But recycling is not a complete answer to the solid waste problem. For some cities, recycling is not cost-effective. Scientists have not found good ways to recycle some materials, such as plastic-coated paper and plastic foam. Some recycled products, such as low-quality recycled newspaper, have few uses. And all recycling processes require energy and create pollution. The value of recycling must be judged on a case-by-case basis.

What People Can Do

The good news is that there are ways individuals can help control the solid waste problem. **These are sometimes called the "three R's"—reduce, reuse, and recycle.** *Reduce* refers to creating less waste in the first place. For example, you can use a cloth shopping bag rather than a disposable paper or plastic bag. *Reuse* refers to finding another use for an object rather than discarding it. For example, you could refill plastic drink bottles with drinking water instead of buying new bottles of water.

As you have read, *recycle* refers to reclaiming raw materials to create new products. You can take the first step in the recycling process by recycling at home and by encouraging others to recycle. You can also make an effort to buy products made from recycled materials. This makes it more profitable for companies to use recycled materials in their products.

Another way to reduce the amount of solid waste your family produces is to start a compost pile. **Composting** is the process of helping biodegradable wastes to decompose naturally. The moist, dark conditions in a compost pile allow natural decomposers to break down waste more quickly. Compost piles can be used to recycle grass clippings, raked leaves, and some food wastes. Compost is an excellent natural fertilizer for plants.

FIGURE 10
Composting
Many kinds of food and yard waste can be composted.
Interpreting Photographs *How does composting help reduce household waste?*

E ◆ 127

Hazardous Wastes

Teach Key Concepts L2

Types of Hazardous Materials

Focus Tell students that hazardous wastes are sometimes not easy to identify.

Teach Have students look at each of the signs pictured in Figure 11 and read the captions. Discuss each type of waste and how it might be harmful. Ask: **What is a radioactive material?** *(A material that contains unstable atoms that give off radiation that can cause health problems)* **What is a flammable material?** *(A material that can catch fire easily)* **How do corrosive substances affect materials?** *(They eat through them.)* **What effect would a toxic substance have on the body?** *(It acts as a poison to harm the body.)* **How should hazardous wastes be disposed of?** *(In carefully designed landfills, by incineration, by being broken down by living organisms, or by storage in deep rock layers)*

Apply Have students brainstorm ways to reduce the use of hazardous materials. *(Possible answers: Use rechargeable batteries. Buy only nontoxic arts and crafts supplies.)* **learning modality: logical/mathematical**

Help Students Read

Active Comprehension Have students read the subheads under the main heading. Then ask: **What would you like to know about hazardous wastes?** *(Possible answers: What types of waste are considered hazardous? What are the effects of hazardous wastes?)* Write student questions on the board. After students finish reading pages 128–129, ask them to respond to each question.

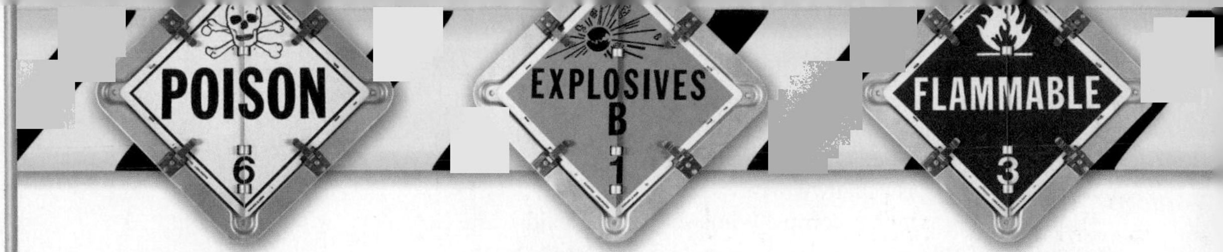

Category: Toxic
Example: Chlorine

Category: Explosive
Example: Nitroglycerin

Category: Flammable
Example: Kerosene

FIGURE 11
Hazardous Materials
Vehicles transporting dangerous materials must use signs like these to alert people of the potential dangers of their loads.

Hazardous Wastes

Many people picture hazardous wastes as bubbling chemicals or oozing slime. But any material that can be harmful to human health or the environment if it is not properly disposed of is a **hazardous waste.**

Types of Hazardous Wastes Hazardous wastes are classified into four main categories. Toxic, or poisonous, wastes, can damage the health of humans and other organisms. Explosive wastes either react very quickly when exposed to air or water, or explode when they are dropped. Flammable wastes catch fire easily. Corrosive wastes can dissolve many materials.

Other wastes that require special disposal are radioactive wastes. Radioactive wastes give off radiation that can cause cancer and other diseases. Some radioactive waste can remain dangerous for thousands of years.

Health Effects A person can be exposed to hazardous wastes by breathing, eating, drinking, or touching them. Even short-term exposure to hazardous wastes can cause health problems such as skin irritation or breathing difficulties. Long-term exposure can cause diseases, such as cancer, damage to body organs, or death.

Disposal Methods It is difficult to dispose of hazardous wastes safely. Hazardous wastes are most often disposed of in carefully designed landfills. The landfills are lined and covered with clay and plastic. These materials prevent chemicals from leaking into the soil and groundwater. **Hazardous wastes that are not disposed of in carefully designed landfills may be incinerated or broken down by living organisms. Liquid wastes may be stored in deep rock layers.**

Scientists are still searching for methods that will provide safe, permanent disposal of radioactive wastes. Some radioactive wastes are currently stored in vaults dug hundreds of meters underground or in concrete and steel containers above ground.

Category: Corrosive
Example: Hydrochloric acid

Category: Radioactive
Example: Uranium

Disposal Sites It is even a challenge to decide where to build hazardous waste disposal facilities. In general, people would prefer to have a single large facility located in an area where few people live. However, it may be safer, cheaper, and easier to transport wastes to small local facilities instead.

Reducing Hazardous Waste The best way to manage hazardous wastes is to produce less of them in the first place. Industries are eager to develop safe alternatives to harmful chemicals. At home, you can find substitutes for some hazardous household chemicals. For example, use citronella candles instead of insect spray to repel insects.

✓ **Reading Checkpoint** What is the best way to manage hazardous wastes?

Section 2 Assessment

◉ **Target Reading Skill** Asking Questions Use the answers to the questions you wrote about the headings to help you answer the questions below.

Reviewing Key Concepts

1. **a. Reviewing** Name three ways of dealing with solid waste.
   b. Comparing and Contrasting Describe one advantage and one disadvantage of each method.
   c. Developing Hypotheses Near a former open dump, there is a stream in which your older relatives used to fish. No one fishes there anymore, however, because there are no fish. What might have happened?
2. **a. Identifying** What is meant by the "three R's"?
   b. Problem Solving Give one example of how you could practice each of the "three R's."

3. **a. Listing** What are four ways to dispose of hazardous wastes safely?
   b. Comparing and Contrasting How do hazardous waste landfills differ from normal landfills?
   c. Making Judgments Do you think hazardous wastes should be treated and disposed of at one large central facility? Explain.

Lab zone **At-Home Activity**

Trash Weigh-In For one week, have your family collect its household trash in large bags. Do not include food waste. At the end of the week, hold a trash weigh-in. Multiply the total amount by 52 to show how much trash your family produces in a year. Can you come up with any ways to reduce your family trash load?

Chapter 4 E ◆ 129

Lab zone **Chapter Project**

Keep Students on Track Advise students to finish selecting a product package to redesign. Encourage them to brainstorm several ideas for improving the product, including materials to use, and write down all of their ideas. Pair students to help each other weigh the pros and cons of each idea.

Lab zone **At Home Activity**

Trash Weigh-In If students' families already recycle, tell students to weigh the materials being recycled separately from the other materials. Let students report their findings in class.

Answers

✓ **Reading Checkpoint** Produce less of them in the first place.

Assess

Reviewing Key Concepts

1. a. Burning, burying, recycling **b.** Possible answers: Incineration doesn't pollute groundwater but it can pollute air. Burying waste in a sanitary landfill can possibly pollute groundwater, but the land later can be used for parks and sports arenas. Recycling conserves nonrenewable resources, but for some cities, it is not cost-effective. **c.** The dump may have produced a leachate that polluted the stream, killing all the fish.
2. a. Reduce, reuse, recycle **b.** Possible answers: Use fewer paper towels to do a job; reuse plastic food containers to hold other household items; build a compost pile.
3. a. Disposing of them in carefully designed landfills, incinerating, breaking down by organisms, and storing in deep rock layers **b.** Hazardous waste landfills are designed with liners and covers of clay and plastic. **c.** Answers may vary. Possible answer: A central facility might dispose of hazardous waste more efficiently, but transporting hazardous waste to a central facility would be more costly, difficult, and potentially dangerous than using several, small, local facilities.

Reteach L1

Name common consumer items, and ask students to tell whether each can be reduced, reused, or recycled, or a combination.

Performance Assessment L2
Writing Have each student write a paragraph in favor of or against mandatory recycling in a community using facts from this section to support their point of view.

All in One Teaching Resources

- Section Summary: *Waste Disposal and Recycling*
- Review and Reinforce: *Waste Disposal and Recycling*
- Enrich: *Waste Disposal and Recycling*

Waste, Away!

Prepare for Inquiry

Key Concept
A sanitary landfill prevents groundwater pollution more effectively than a poorly designed landfill or an open dump does.

Skills Objectives
Students will be able to
- observe how well different models of landfills protect groundwater from leachate
- make models of a sanitary landfill, a poorly designed landfill, and an open dump

Prep Time 20 minutes
Class Time Day 1, 40 minutes; Day 2, 20 minutes

All in One **Teaching Resources**
- Lab Worksheet: *Waste, Away!*

Advance Planning
Cut the cheesecloth and plastic pieces large enough to overlap the top of the jar when they are suspended in it, as shown in the photo. Cut extra pieces in case some tear when students add pebbles to them. Check the plastic pieces to make sure there are no holes in them.

Alternative Materials
If supplies are limited, have one third of the groups construct System 1, one third construct System 2, and one third construct System 3.

Safety
Remind students to wear lab aprons and safety goggles and handle the glass jars carefully. Review the safety guidelines in Appendix A.

Waste, Away!

Problem
How do different kinds of landfills work?

Skills Focus
observing, making models

Materials
- measuring cup
- metric ruler
- soil
- small pebbles
- cheesecloth
- scissors
- plastic wrap
- water
- newspaper
- 5 rubber bands
- red food coloring
- tweezers
- heavy-duty plastic bag
- 12 small sponge cubes
- 3 transparent, wide-mouthed jars

Procedure
Read over the entire procedure to preview the three landfill systems you will model. Determine which parts of the models represent potential drinking water, rainfall, solid waste, leachate, and the landfill systems themselves. Write a prediction about the way each system will repond to the test you'll conduct in Part 2.

PART 1 Modeling Three Different Landfill Systems

1. Obtain three identical jars. Label them System 1, System 2, and System 3. Pour clean, clear water into each jar to a depth of 5 cm.

2. Add equal amounts of small pebbles to each jar. The pebbles should be just below the surface of the water.

3. For System 1, cover the pebble and water mixture with 2.5 cm of soil.

4. For System 2, hang a piece of cheesecloth in the jar about 5 cm above the waterline, as shown in the photograph. Hold the cheesecloth in place with a rubber band around the outside mouth of the jar. Gently pour a handful of small pebbles into the cheesecloth.

5. For System 3, suspend a plastic bag in the jar about 5 cm above the waterline. Hold the bag in place with a rubber band around the outside mouth of the jar. Gently pour a handful of small pebbles into the plastic bag.

6. Observe the water and pebbles at the bottom of each of the systems. Record your observations.

PART 2 Testing the Systems

7. Soak 12 identical sponge cubes in water tinted with red food coloring. Use tweezers to place four soaked sponge cubes onto the top surface in each jar.

8. Cover the sponge cubes in Systems 2 and 3 with a thin layer of soil. Leave the sponge cubes in System 1 uncovered.

9. Make a labeled drawing of each system. Explain what each part of each of the models represents.

10. Pour 150 mL of water over each system. Then cover each jar with plastic wrap, and hold the wrap in place with a rubber band. Let the systems stand overnight.

11. Observe each landfill system. Note especially any changes in the color or clarity of the "groundwater." Record your observations.

Guide Inquiry

Invitation
Hold up a transparent drinking glass of clean tap water, and then drop a few small pieces of household waste into it. Ask: **Would you want to drink this water? Why or why not?** (*No; chemicals and disease-causing organisms in the trash pollute the water.*)

Introduce the Procedure
Invite students to read the entire lab procedure. Answer any questions they have. Explain that the models will represent three different types of landfills, but at this point do not discuss which type each model represents.

Analyze and Conclude

1. **Observing** Which part of each model represents the leachate? How well did each landfill system protect the groundwater from the leachate?

2. **Making Models** Identify which of your three models represent each of these three common types of landfills: a well-designed, or sanitary, landfill; a landfill with a poor design; and an open dump. Compare the way the three systems work.

3. **Predicting** If a community's landfill were not located immediately above its groundwater source, do you think its water supply would be completely protected? Explain.

4. **Communicating** Write a paragraph describing which landfill system would be safest for the environment. Use your observations to support your answer.

Design an Experiment

Solid waste can be compacted (crushed into smaller pieces), and the liquid in it can be removed before it is placed in a landfill. Does preparing the waste in this way make it safer for the environment? Write a hypothesis, and then use the ideas and procedures from this lab to design an experiment that tests your hypothesis. Obtain your teacher's permission before trying your experiment.

Extend the Inquiry

Design an Experiment Compacting the waste takes less space and extends the life of the landfill, but does not remove harmful substances from the waste. It also keeps the wastes from settling inside the landfill. Removing liquid from the waste could reduce the amount of leachate produced. Students could model reduced-liquid waste by soaking the sponge cubes in food coloring, then squeezing the liquid out and allowing the cubes to dry thoroughly before placing them in the landfill models.

Troubleshooting the Experiment

- Circulate among groups as they build the models to make sure that the cheesecloth and plastic pieces are draped well down into the jars and are secured tightly with rubber bands.
- In Steps 4 and 5, caution students to add the pebbles gently so they do not tear the cheesecloth and plastic.
- When students draw the systems in Step 9, tell them to label the following elements: *groundwater* (water at bottom of jar), *soil*, *liner* (cheesecloth and plastic pieces), and *trash* (colored sponge cubes). Students could also label the pebbles *permeable layer*.

Expected Outcome

The groundwater in Systems 1 and 2 will turn red with "leachate"—food coloring from the sponge cubes. The water may also be cloudy with dissolved soil particles that have washed out of the landfills. The groundwater in System 3 will remain clear, with all of the leachate contained by the plastic liner.

Analyze and Conclude

1. The red-tinted water represented the leachate. Only System 3 protected the groundwater.

2. In System 1, an open dump, there is no barrier to separate waste from the soil and keep leachate from seeping into the groundwater. In System 2, a poorly designed landfill, the permeable liner contains the waste but allows leachate to seep into the groundwater. In System 3, a well-designed sanitary landfill, the plastic liner contains the leachate and keeps it from seeping into the groundwater.

3. Locating a landfill in an area that is not immediately above groundwater is safer. However, groundwater can still become contaminated if surface runoff from the landfill carries leachate to nearby rivers and streams or to permeable soil layers above groundwater supplies.

4. Paragraphs should include that a well-designed sanitary landfill (like System 3) is safest because it protects groundwater the best.

Section

3 Water Pollution and Solutions

Objectives

After this lesson, students will be able to

E.4.3.1 Explain why fresh water is a limited resource.

E.4.3.2 Identify the major sources of water pollution.

E.4.3.3 Describe how water pollution can be reduced.

Target Reading Skill

Previewing Visuals Explain that looking at the visuals before they read helps students activate prior knowledge and predict what they are about to read.

Answers

Possible questions and answers include the following: **What are some household causes of water pollution?** *(Water and human wastes that are washed down sinks, toilets, and showers)* **What is sediment?** *(Rock and sand that has been eroded by water)*

All in One Teaching Resources

• Transparency E36

Preteach

Build Background Knowledge   **L2**

Locating Earth's Water

Display a world map or globe, and ask: **How much of Earth's surface is covered by oceans?** *(Nearly 75%; accept all reasonable estimates.)* **Where else does some form of water exist?** *(In glaciers and polar ice, in freshwater lakes and rivers, in soil, deep underground in aquifers, and in the air as vapor)* Record students' responses on the board, but do not comment on any omissions at this time.

Reading Preview

Key Concepts

• Why is fresh water a limited resource?

• What are the major sources of water pollution?

• How can water pollution be reduced?

Key Terms

• groundwater • pollutant
• sewage • pesticide
• sediment

Target Reading Skill

Previewing Visuals Before you read, preview Figure 13. Then write two questions that you have about the diagram in a graphic organizer like the one below. As you read, answer your questions.

Water Pollution

Q.	What are some household causes of water pollution?
A.	
Q.	

Lab zone Discover **Activity**

How Does the Water Change?

1. Shine a flashlight through a clear plastic cup of water.
2. Add six drops of milk to the water and stir.
3. Shine the flashlight through the cup again. Note any differences.

Think It Over

Observing Where in the cup of water is the milk located? Could you easily separate the milk from the water?

Most of Earth's surface is covered by some form of water. Oceans cover nearly three fourths of Earth's surface. Around the poles are vast sheets of ice. From space you cannot even see many parts of Earth because they are hidden behind clouds of tiny water droplets. There seems to be so much water—it's hard to believe that it is a scarce resource in much of the world.

Water—A Limited Supply

How can water be scarce when there is so much of it on Earth's surface? **The reason is that most of the water on Earth—about 97 percent—is salt water. Salt water cannot be used for drinking or for watering crops.** In addition, about three quarters of the fresh water on Earth is in the form of ice. Finally, the supplies of liquid fresh water that do exist are not always close to where people live. For example, many cities in the southwestern United States draw their drinking water from rivers hundreds of kilometers away. And about half the people in the United States use groundwater for their drinking water. **Groundwater** is the water stored in soil and rock beneath Earth's surface.

Lab zone Discover **Activity**

Skills Focus Observing

Materials flashlight, clear plastic cup, water, plastic dropper, milk

Time 5 minutes

Tips In Step 3, encourage students to shine the light downward at the cup and from different angles.

Expected Outcome The mixture will appear cloudy; solid particles in the milk will reflect the light so the beam does not pass easily through the cup.

Think It Over The milk is scattered evenly throughout the water and cannot be easily separated from it. The milk's solid particles can be separated by evaporating the mixture.

Renewing the Supply Fortunately, Earth's supply of fresh water is renewable. As you recall from Chapter 2, water continually moves between the atmosphere and Earth's surface in the water cycle. Even though fresh water is a renewable resource, there is not always enough of it in a given place at a given time.

Water Shortages Water shortages occur when people use water in an area faster than the water cycle can replace it. This is more likely to happen during a drought, when less rain than normal falls in an area. During a drought, people have to limit their water use. If a drought is severe, crops may die from lack of water.

Many places in the world never receive enough rain to meet the water needs of their growing populations. These places must obtain water from distant sources or by other means. For example, the desert nation of Saudi Arabia obtains more than half of its fresh water by removing salt from ocean water.

 Reading Checkpoint What is groundwater?

Water Pollution

Since fresh water supplies are scarce, water pollution can be devastating. Substances that cause pollution are called **pollutants.** Some pollutants, such as iron and copper, make water unpleasant to drink or wash in. Other pollutants, such as mercury or benzene, can cause sickness or even death.

If you did the Discover activity, you saw that a few drops of milk quickly spread throughout a cup of water. You could not tell where the milk first entered the water. In the same way, pollutants can dissolve and move throughout a body of water. This is how pollution can affect areas far from its source.

Most water pollution is the result of human activities. **Wastes produced by households, agriculture, industry, mining, and other human activities can end up in water.**

FIGURE 12
Fresh Water
If you were to look out at the ocean, water would seem to be in plentiful supply. But only fresh water, not salt water, can be used for drinking and household tasks.

Land, Water, and Air Resources

Video Preview
▶ Video Field Trip
Video Assessment

E ◆ 133

E ● 133

Water—A Limited Supply

Teach Key Concepts [L2]
Earth's Limited Water

Focus Remind students that most of Earth's water is ocean.

Teach Ask: **Why is fresh water scarce?** *(Most water on Earth is salt water, much of the fresh is in the form of ice, and fresh water is not always located near where people live.)* **If water is renewable, why do water shortages occur?** *(The processes of the water cycle do not produce enough water in useable form to meet human needs. The problem is worsened when droughts occur.)*

Apply Have students find out where their local drinking water comes from. *(Most likely from a surface reservoir, well, or freshwater lake)* **learning modality: logical/mathematical**

Land, Water, and Air Resources

Show the Video Field Trip to let students observe beluga whales and help them understand how pollution affects these animals. Discussion question: **What are the probable sources of the insecticides being found in beluga whales?** *(Waste materials from factories; pesticides.)*

Independent Practice

All in One Teaching Resources

• Guided Reading and Study Worksheet: *Water Pollution and Solutions*

⊙ Student Edition on Audio CD

Monitor Progress _____ [L2]

Answers

✓ **Reading Checkpoint** Water stored in soil and rock beneath Earth's surface

Water Pollution

Teach Key Concepts L2
Sources of Water Pollution

Focus Review the effects of pollutants.

Teach Have different student volunteers read each caption in Figure 13. Explain that pesticides build up in the food chain because as organisms take in pollutants, they eliminate some pesticides but the remainder is stored in body tissue to be consumed by the next animal up the food chain. Ask: **What is a major pollutant from agriculture that affects the food chain?** (*Pesticides*) **What are sources of pollutants from industry and mining?** (*Chemicals, metal wastes, heat, oil, and gasoline*) **What is a natural source of pollutants?** (*Sediments*)

Apply Encourage students to share with the class any observations they have made of examples of water pollution in their community. **learning modality: visual**

 **Teaching Resources**

• Transparency E37

▶ Address Misconceptions L2
Pollution From Motor Oil Changes

Focus Students may think that spills from tankers cause most of the water pollution from oil.

Teach Tell students that more oil is dumped in water from households than from oil tankers. Over 2 million people who change their own motor oil pour more than 200 million gallons of oil per year down a drain or into the garbage. This amount is more than 50 times the amount of oil released by accidental tanker spills in 2000. The used oil from one oil change can pollute 1 million gallons of groundwater.

Apply Ask: **How should motor oil be safely disposed of?** (*It should be taken to a recycling center.*) **learning modality: logical/mathematical**

Go Online
PHSchool.com

For: More on cleaning up oil spills
Visit: PHSchool.com
Web Code: ced-5043

Students can review oil spills in an online interactivity.

 **Lab zone Try This Activity**

Is There Tea There?

In this activity, you will see how difficult it can be to remove pollutants from water.

1. Pour some cooled herbal tea into a clear plastic cup. Observe the color of the tea.
2. Place a paper filter in a funnel. Fill it half way with crushed charcoal. Put the funnel on top of another clear plastic cup.
3. Slowly pour the tea into the funnel so it collects in the plastic cup.
4. Observe the filtered liquid.

Observing How successful were you in removing the pollutant (tea) from the water?

Go Online
PHSchool.com

For: More on cleaning up oil spills
Visit: PHSchool.com
Web Code: ced-5043

Household Sewage The water and human wastes that are washed down sinks, toilets, and showers are called **sewage.** If sewage is not treated to kill disease-causing organisms, the organisms quickly multiply. People can become ill if they drink or swim in water containing these organisms.

Agricultural Wastes Animal wastes, fertilizers, and pesticides are also sources of pollution. Rain can wash animal wastes and fertilizers into ponds, where they cause algae to grow quickly. The algae soon cover the pond, blocking light from reaching plants in the pond and killing the plants.

Pesticides are chemicals that kill crop-destroying organisms. Because pesticides are usually spread over large, open areas, they can pollute bodies of water. Even low levels of chemicals in the water can build up to harmful concentrations as they move through the food chain.

Industry and Mining Wastes Some plants, mills, factories, and mines produce wastes that can pollute water. Chemicals and metal wastes can harm organisms that live in bodies of water. Animals that drink from polluted bodies of water or eat the organisms that live in them can also become ill.

Sediments Water that causes erosion picks up **sediments,** or particles of rock and sand. Sediments can cover up the food sources, nests, and eggs of organisms in bodies of water. Sediments also block sunlight, preventing algae and plants from growing. This affects organisms that rely on the algae and plants.

Heat A pollutant is usually thought of as an added material. But heat can also have a negative effect on a body of water. Some factories and power plants release water that has been used to cool machinery. This heated water can kill organisms living in the body of water into which it is released.

Oil and Gasoline One of the most dramatic forms of water pollution is an oil spill. You may have seen news reports showing beaches covered with sticky black oil, or volunteers cleaning oil from birds. It can take many years for an area to recover from an oil spill.

Another water pollution problem is caused by oil and gasoline that leak out of damaged underground storage tanks. The pollution can be carried far away from a leaking tank by groundwater.

 **Reading Checkpoint** Why is heat considered a water pollutant?

Lab zone Try This Activity

Skills Focus Observing

Materials cooled herbal tea, 2 clear plastic cups, paper filter, funnel, crushed charcoal

Time 10 minutes

Tips Use a tea that has a distinct color, and brew a strong solution.

Expected Outcome The filtered tea will be lighter in color than the unfiltered tea.

Extend Have students suggest an explanation for any changes they observe in the tea after pouring it through the funnel. (*The charcoal and filter will remove some but not all of the tea.*) **learning modality: visual**

FIGURE 13
Water Pollution
Most water pollution is caused by human activities.
Interpreting Diagrams *What are five specific sources of water pollution shown in the diagram?*

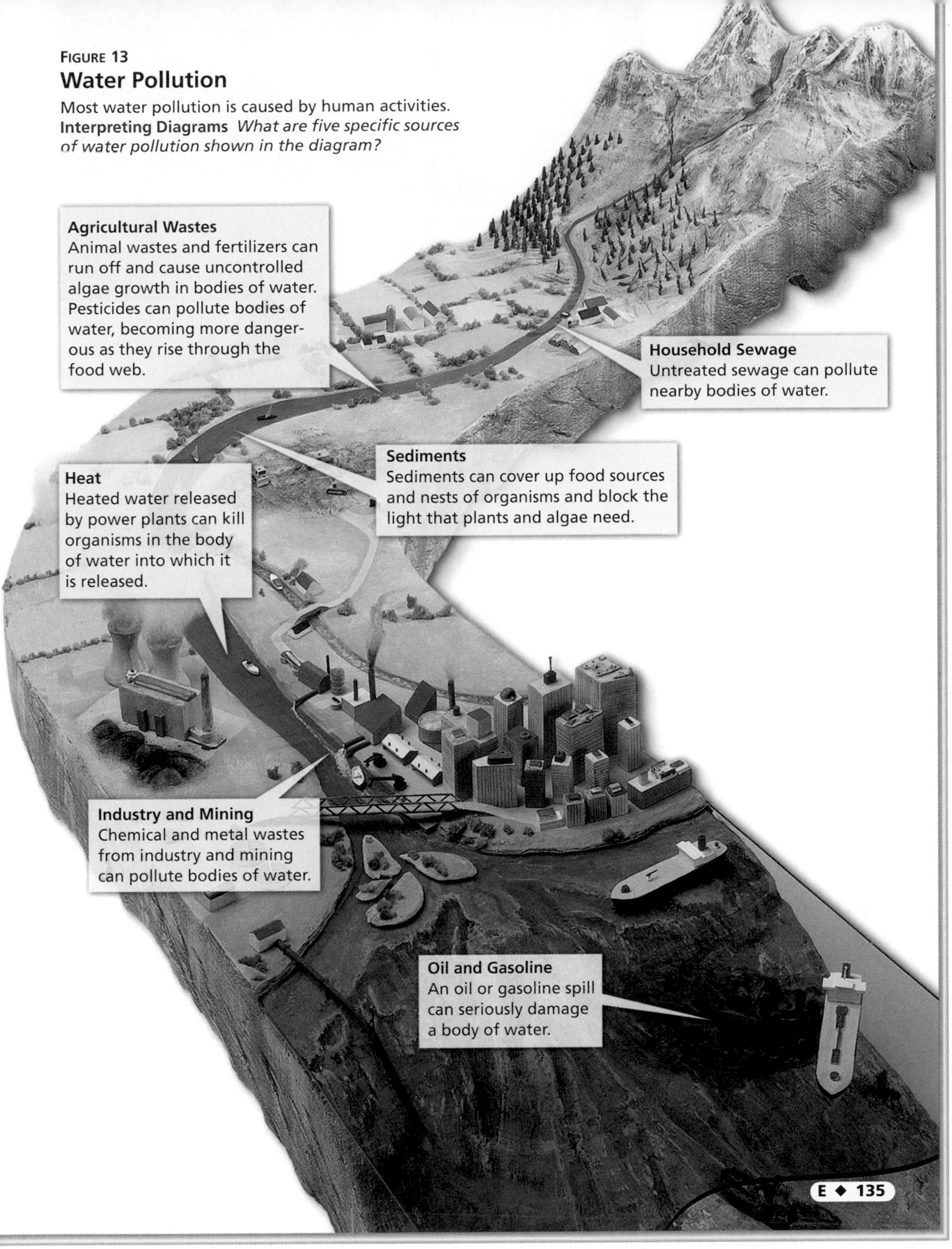

Agricultural Wastes
Animal wastes and fertilizers can run off and cause uncontrolled algae growth in bodies of water. Pesticides can pollute bodies of water, becoming more dangerous as they rise through the food web.

Household Sewage
Untreated sewage can pollute nearby bodies of water.

Sediments
Sediments can cover up food sources and nests of organisms and block the light that plants and algae need.

Heat
Heated water released by power plants can kill organisms in the body of water into which it is released.

Industry and Mining
Chemical and metal wastes from industry and mining can pollute bodies of water.

Oil and Gasoline
An oil or gasoline spill can seriously damage a body of water.

E ◆ 135

Cleaning Up Oil Spills

Materials small bowl, water, cooking oil, dropper, paper towels, graduated cylinder or cup calibrated in mL

Time 15 minutes

Focus Ask students how difficult they think it is to clean up an oil spill.

Teach Have students work in groups to fill a bowl halfway with water and then add 25 mL of cooking oil. Instruct them to wipe out the cylinder with a paper towel. Then have students try to remove the oil from the water with the dropper, placing the removed oil into the graduated cylinder. After students have worked for about 15 minutes, have them observe the liquid in the graduated cylinder and note that the water and oil have separated. Ask: **How much oil have you removed?** *(Students probably will have recovered very little oil.)* **Is oil still on the water in the bowl? How can you tell?** *(Students will most likely respond that the water surface still has an oily sheen or globules of oil.)*

Apply Tell students that many methods are used to clean up large oil spills, such as mechanically or chemically breaking up the oil into smaller amounts. **learning modality: kinesthetic**

Monitor Progress _____ L2

Oral Presentation Call on students at random to name sources of water pollution and their effects.

Answers
Figure 13 Any five of the following: animal wastes, fertilizers, pesticides, heated water, untreated sewage, sediments, chemical wastes, metal wastes, oil and gasoline spills

✓ **Reading Checkpoint** Heated water can kill organisms living in the body of water into which it is released.

E ● 135

Keeping Water Clean

Teach Key Concepts
Reducing Water Pollution

Focus Remind students that everyone is responsible for water quality.

Teach Ask: **How are disease-causing organisms kept out of drinking water?** (*Wastewater is treated to kill the organisms.*) **What can industries do to keep water clean?** (*Recycle or reduce their wastes, or produce less harmful waste*) **Why can't bacteria that break down oil take care of large oil spills?** (*There is too much oil for them to break down.*) **What can an individual do to help prevent water pollution?** (*Never pour hazardous chemicals down the drain*)

Apply Work with students to help them identify places (through the phone directory, the Internet, or state EPA office) where their families can drop off hazardous materials. The EPA can provide information about hazardous household materials that should not be disposed of down the drain or in the regular trash. **learning modality: verbal**

Help Students Read
Identifying Main Ideas Have students write a main idea sentence for each subheading under *Keeping Water Clean*. For example, for *Sewage Treatment*, a main idea sentence might be: A typical sewage treatment plant uses several steps to clean water before returning it to the environment.

FIGURE 14
Sewage Treatment
Riverbank State Park in New York City is a huge recreational complex built over a sewage treatment plant. **Problem Solving** *Why is this a good solution for a big city?*

Keeping Water Clean

By working together, government, industries, and individuals can improve water quality in the United States. Federal laws such as the Clean Water Act regulate the use of certain substances that can pollute water. State and local laws also regulate the use and cleanup of water pollutants.

The keys to keeping water clean are proper sewage treatment, the reduction of pollutants, and the effective cleanup of oil and gasoline spills. There are also some important ways that people can reduce water pollution at home.

Sewage Treatment Most communities treat wastewater before returning it to the environment. A typical treatment plant handles the waste in several steps. During primary treatment, the wastewater is filtered to remove solid materials. Then it is held in tanks where heavy particles settle out. During secondary treatment, bacteria in the system break down the wastes. Sometimes the water is then treated with chlorine to kill disease-causing organisms.

Some communities have come up with creative ways to deal with sewage treatment plants. In Figure 14, you can see Riverbank State Park in New York City. It is a park, marketplace, and sports facility built on top of a sewage treatment plant. The city now has a treatment plant and a park in half the usual space.

Reducing Pollutants Instead of releasing wastes into the environment, industries can recycle their wastes to recover useful materials. Once such programs are underway, companies often find they save money as well as reduce pollution. Other companies change their processes to produce less waste or less harmful waste. For example, some industries use natural fruit acids as cleaning agents rather than toxic solvents. Likewise, farmers are finding alternatives to toxic pesticides and fertilizers.

Lab zone Try This **Activity**

Getting Clean
In this activity you will see how Earth's fresh water is purified in the water cycle.

1. Pour 15 mL of water into a plastic cup.
2. Add a few drops of food coloring and half a teaspoon of sugar. Stir until the sugar is dissolved.
3. Put the cup in the sunlight in a place where it will not be disturbed.
4. Check on the cup twice a day until all the water has evaporated. Observe what remains in the cup.

Making Models What do the sugar and food coloring represent? What happens to the water in this activity?

Lab zone Try This **Activity**

Skills Focus Making models

Materials water, plastic cup, spoon, graduated cylinder, food coloring, sugar

Time 10 minutes, plus 5 minutes for follow-up observations on several days

Tips Supply room-temperature water, not hot water, as hot water will produce a super-saturated solution.

Expected Outcome Sugar crystals and a tint from the food coloring will remain in the cup. These materials represent dissolved substances that are left behind when water evaporates. The liquid water changes to water vapor.

Extend Let students repeat the activity, using other substances in the water, such as milk, salt, and baking soda. **learning modality: visual**

Cleaning Up Oil and Gasoline Spills Oil is a pollutant that nature can handle in small amounts. Bacteria that break down oil live in the ocean. When oil is present, the bacteria multiply quickly as they feed on it. As the oil disappears, the bacteria population dies down. But in the case of a large spill, bacteria cannot clean up the spill fast enough. It takes the hard work of many scientists and volunteers to minimize environmental damage from large spills.

Gasoline or oil that leaks from an underground tank is hard to clean up. If the pollution has not spread far, the soil around the tank can be removed. But pollution that reaches groundwater may be carried far away. Groundwater can be pumped to the surface, treated, and then returned underground. This, however, can take many years.

What You Can Do It is easy to prevent water pollution at home. Some common household water pollutants are paints and paint thinner, motor oil, and garden chemicals. You can avoid causing water pollution by never pouring these chemicals down the drain. Instead, save these materials for your community's next hazardous waste collection day.

FIGURE 15
Cleaning Up Oil Spills
After an oil spill, a volunteer gently cleans oil from the feathers of a gannet, a large seabird.

✓ **Reading Checkpoint** Why are leaks from underground oil tanks hard to clean up?

Section 3 Assessment

🎯 **Target Reading Skill** Previewing Visuals Refer to your questions and answers about Figure 13 to help you answer Question 2 below.

Reviewing Key Concepts

1. a. **Reviewing** If most of Earth is covered with water, why is fresh water a scarce resource?
   b. **Calculating** If only 3 percent of the water on Earth is fresh water, and 75 percent of that fresh water is frozen, what percent of the water on Earth is liquid fresh water?
   c. **Predicting** A classmate suggests that the solution to water shortages is to melt some icebergs and transport the water to areas that need water. What are two problems with this plan?

2. a. **Listing** Name four types of human activities that can be sources of water pollution.
   b. **Relating Cause and Effect** Explain how a farmer spraying fields with pesticides can pollute a river miles away.

3. a. **Identifying** What are three ways that water pollution can be reduced?
   b. **Sequencing** List in order the steps of wastewater treatment.
   c. **Making Judgments** What kinds of laws do you think would result in the greatest reduction in water pollution? Explain.

Writing in Science

Dialogue Suppose that a sewage treatment and recreation complex like the one in Figure 14 has been proposed for your town. Write a one-page dialogue in which you and another person from your town debate whether this is a good idea. (*Hint:* The speakers must hold opposing viewpoints.) Be sure to support all opinions with specific details.

Chapter 4 E ◆ 137

Lab zone Chapter **Project**

Keep Students on Track Advise students to finish the drawings of their models and attach a list of the materials they plan to use in their product. Meet with students individually to offer guidance if they are having difficulty designing their product.

Writing in Science

Writing Skill Persuasion

Scoring Rubric

4 Includes clear opinions from opposing viewpoints; support is clear and strong
3 Includes all criteria, but one or both arguments are not convincing
2 Includes little support for either side
1 Includes vague opinions and lacks support

Objectives

After this lesson, students will be able to

E.4.4.1 Identify the causes of smog and acid rain.

E.4.4.2 Describe the causes of indoor air pollution.

E.4.4.3 Explain the key to reducing air pollution.

Target Reading Skill

Relating Cause and Effect Explain that cause is the reason for what happens. The effect is what happens because of the cause. Relating cause and effect helps students relate the reason for what happens to what happens as a result.

Answers

Possible causes include the following: Factory and power plant emissions that produce nitrogen oxides and sulfur oxides when they burn coal and oil; gases emitted by automobiles and trucks; indoor air pollutants, such as toxic chemicals

All in One Teaching Resources

• Transparency E38

Preteach

Build Background Knowledge L2

Air Pollution Examples

Encourage students to describe specific examples of air pollution that they have seen in person or in pictures, such as smog hanging over a city, smoke coming from factory smokestacks, and grime or pollen settling on cars parked outdoors. Ask: **Which of these types of air pollution do you think we could control?** *(Accept all responses without comment at this time.)*

Section
4 Air Pollution and Solutions

Reading Preview

Key Concepts
• What are the causes of smog and acid rain?
• What are the causes of indoor air pollution?
• What is the key to reducing air pollution?

Key Terms
• emissions
• photochemical smog • ozone
• temperature inversion
• acid rain • radon

Target Reading Skill

Relating Cause and Effect As you read, identify three causes of air pollution. Write the information in a graphic organizer like the one below.

Causes

Factory and power plant emissions	→	**Effect**
	→	Air pollution
	→	

◄ Traffic jam

Lab zone **Discover Activity**

How Does the Scent Spread?

1. Choose a place to stand so that you and your classmates are evenly distributed around the room.
2. Your teacher will spray some perfume in one corner of the room.
3. Raise your hand when you first smell the perfume.

Think It Over
Inferring Describe the pattern you observed as people raised their hands. How do you think the scent traveled across the room?

You can't see, taste, or smell it, but you are surrounded by it. It's air, of course! But what is air? Air is a mixture of nitrogen, oxygen, carbon dioxide, water vapor, and other gases. Almost all living things depend on these gases to carry out their life processes. Recall from Chapter 2 that these gases cycle between the atmosphere and living things. These cycles guarantee that the air supply will not run out. But they don't guarantee that the air will be clean.

What causes air pollution? Perhaps you picture a smoke-stack belching thick, black smoke into the sky. Until the mid-1900s, in the United States, factories and power plants that burned coal produced most of the **emissions,** or pollutants that are released into the air. Today, there is a larger source of emissions: motor vehicles such as cars and trucks. There are some natural causes of air pollution, as well. For example, an erupting volcano sends an enormous load of pollutants into the atmosphere.

Lab zone **Discover Activity**

Skills Focus Inferring

Materials spray bottle with perfume

Time 5 minutes

Tips Make sure students are evenly spaced throughout the room so that the scent will reach different students at different times.

Expected Outcome Students closest to you will smell the perfume first, and those standing farthest away will smell it last.

Think It Over Students will see a "wave" of raised hands traveling from you to the farthest parts of the room. Students should infer that molecules of perfume traveled across the room in the air.

Smog

Have you ever heard a weather forecaster talk about a "smog alert"? A smog alert is a warning about a type of air pollution called photochemical smog. **Photochemical smog** is a thick, brownish haze formed when certain gases in the air react with sunlight. When the smog level is high, it settles as a haze over a city. Smog can cause eye and throat irritation and breathing problems. Exercising outdoors can make these problems worse.

Sources of Smog The major sources of smog are the gases emitted by automobiles and trucks. Burning gasoline in a car engine releases some gases into the air. These gases include hydrocarbons (compounds containing hydrogen and carbon) and nitrogen oxides. The gases react in the sunlight and produce a form of oxygen called **ozone**. Ozone, which is toxic, is the major chemical found in smog. Ozone can cause lung infections and damage the body's defenses against infection.

Temperature Inversion Normally, air close to the ground is heated by Earth's surface. As the air warms, it rises into the cooler air above it. Any pollutants in the air are carried higher into the atmosphere where they blow away from the place where they are produced.

Certain weather conditions cause a condition known as a temperature inversion. During a **temperature inversion,** a layer of warm air prevents the rising air from escaping. The polluted air is trapped and held close to Earth's surface. The smog becomes more concentrated and dangerous.

Reading Checkpoint What is the major chemical found in smog?

Go Online
PHSchool.com

For: More on air pollution
Visit: PHSchool.com
Web Code: ced-5044

FIGURE 16
Temperature Inversion
Normally, pollutants rise into the atmosphere and blow away. But during a temperature inversion, a layer of warm air traps pollutants close to the ground.
Interpreting Photographs *What is the brownish haze?*

Coolest Air

Warm Air

Cool Air

E ◆ 139

Smog

Teach Key Concepts L2
Causes of Smog

Focus Ask: **How would you describe smog?** *(Possible answer: A brown, hazy layer of gas in the air)*

Teach Ask: **What gases are the sources of smog?** *(Hydrocarbons and nitrogen oxides emitted by automobiles and trucks)* **How do these gases form smog?** *(They react with sunlight to form ozone.)* **What other factor must be present for smog to form?** *(Temperature inversion)* Point out that ozone is harmful when it is close to Earth's surface. Ozone in the upper atmosphere filters ultraviolet radiation.

Apply Ask: **Why are most smog alerts issued in summer?** *(The gases react with sunlight, which is more intense in summer.)*
learning modality: logical/mathematical

All in One Teaching Resources
• Transparency E39

Independent Practice

All in One Teaching Resources
• Guided Reading and Study Worksheet: *Air Pollution and Solutions*

Student Edition on Audio CD

Go Online
PHSchool.com

For: More on air pollution
Visit: PHSchool.com
Web Code: ced-5044

Students can review air pollution in an online interactivity.

Differentiated Instruction

English Learners/Beginning L1
Vocabulary: Word Analysis Explain that the word *smog* comes from parts of two other words put together. To clarify how the word *smog* was created, write *smoke + fog* on the board, and have students tell what each word means. Then erase *oke* and *f*, and write = *smog*. **learning modality: verbal**

English Learners/Intermediate L2
Vocabulary: Word Analysis Repeat the Beginning activity. Then ask students to look up the word *photochemical* and give the meaning of *photo (light)*. Show them a familiar item, a photograph, and point out that the connection between the word parts in *photograph* is the same as the connections in *photochemical*. **learning modality: verbal**

Monitor Progress L2

Skills Check Have students sequence how smog is formed.

Answers
Figure 16 Smog

Reading Checkpoint Ozone

Acid Rain

Teach Key Concepts $\boxed{\text{L2}}$

Causes and Effects of Acid Rain

Focus Remind students that an acid is a substance that has a pH lower than 7.0.

Teach Ask: **How is acid rain formed?** *(Nitrogen oxides and sulfur oxides react with water vapor to form nitric acid and sulfuric acid, which fall to Earth as precipitation.)* **How does acid rain affect living things?** *(It damages trees and other plants, and can kill fish and other aquatic organisms.)*

Apply Tell students that each whole pH value below 7 is ten times more acidic than the next higher value. Normal rain has a pH of 5.5. The most acidic rain in the U.S. has a pH of about 4.3. Ask: **How much more acidic is acid rain than normal rain?** *(About ten times)* **learning modality: logical/mathematical**

Observing Effects of Air Pollutants

Materials hand lens, foam cup, piece of nylon-stocking fabric, scissors, tape

Time 10–15 minutes for setup, plus follow-up observations

Focus Ask: **Do you think the air you are breathing today is clean?** *(Unless pollution is obvious, most will say yes.)*

Teach Have students examine the fabric with a hand lens. Ask them to pull and twist the fabric to test its strength and flexibility and to make notes about their observations. Then have each student cut out the bottom of the cup and tape a piece of stocking over the opening. Have students hang the cups outdoors where they will be exposed to air and rain. After a week, have students observe the fabric for strength, flexibility, and broken fibers or other signs of damage.

Apply Ask: **Do you agree with your original answer?** *(Most students will think that the air is polluted because of the negative effects on the nylon.)* Point out that air pollution can affect the nylon but sunlight also has a negative effect on it. **learning modality: visual**

FIGURE 17
Acid Rain
Acid rain can react with stone. **Inferring** *Why do these statues look like they are melting?*

Lab zone — Try This Activity

How Acid Is Your Rain?

In this activity you will test whether rain in your area is more or less acidic than lemon juice (citric acid).

1. Collect some rainwater in a clean plastic cup.
2. Indoors, dip a piece of pH paper into the cup. Compare the color of the paper to the chart on the package to find the pH. (The lower the pH of a substance, the more acidic it is.)
3. Pour a little lemon juice into a plastic cup. Repeat Step 2 with the lemon juice.

Measuring What is the pH of the rainwater? How does it compare to the pH of the lemon juice?

140 ◆ E

Acid Rain

Precipitation that is more acidic than normal because of air pollution is called **acid rain.** Acid rain can be in the form of snow, sleet, or fog as well as rain. **Acid rain is caused by the emissions from power plants and factories that burn coal and oil.** These fuels produce nitrogen oxides and sulfur oxides when they are burned. These gases react with water vapor in the air, forming nitric acid and sulfuric acid. The acids return to Earth's surface dissolved in precipitation.

As you can imagine, acid falling from the sky has some negative effects. When acid rain falls into a pond or lake, it changes the conditions there. Many fish, and particularly their eggs, cannot survive in more acidic water. When acid rain falls on plants, it can damage their leaves and stems. Acid rain that falls on the ground can also damage plants by affecting the nutrient levels in the soil. Whole forests have been destroyed by acid rain. Fortunately, some of the effects of acid rain are reversible. Badly damaged lakes have been restored by adding substances such as lime that neutralize the acid.

Acid rain doesn't just affect living things. The acid reacts with stone and metal in buildings and statues. Statues and stonework damaged by acid rain may look as if they are melting. Automobiles rust more quickly in areas with acid rain. These effects are not reversible.

Reading Checkpoint How can acid rain affect nonliving things?

Lab zone — Try This Activity

Skills Focus Measuring

Materials rainwater, 2 plastic cups, pH paper, pH chart, lemon juice

Time 10 minutes

Tips Collect rainwater ahead of time for this activity.

Expected Outcome Rainwater is normally slightly acidic (pH 5–6); a pH lower than 5 indicates acid rain. Lemon juice has a pH of 2.

Extend Have students measure the pH of tap water and compare it with their pH measurements of rainwater and lemon juice. **learning modality: logical/mathematical**

Indoor Air Pollution

You might think that you can avoid air pollution by staying inside. But in fact, the air inside buildings can be polluted, too. **Some substances that cause indoor air pollution, such as dust and pet hair, bother only those people who are allergic to them. Other indoor air pollutants, such as toxic chemicals, can affect anyone.** Glues and cleaning supplies may give off toxic fumes. And cigarette smoke, even from another person's cigarette, can damage the lungs and heart.

Carbon Monoxide One particularly dangerous indoor air pollutant is carbon monoxide. Carbon monoxide is a colorless, odorless gas that forms when wood, coal, oil, or gas are incompletely burned. When carbon monoxide builds up in an enclosed space such as an apartment or house, it can be deadly. Any home heated by wood, coal, oil, or gas should have a carbon monoxide detector.

Radon Another indoor air pollutant that is difficult to detect is radon. **Radon** is a colorless, odorless gas that is radioactive. It is formed naturally by certain types of rocks underground. Radon can enter homes through cracks in basement walls or floors. Research indicates that breathing radon gas over many years may cause lung cancer and other health problems. But the level of radon necessary to cause these effects is unknown. To be safe, some homeowners have installed ventilation systems to prevent radon from building up in their homes.

✓ Reading Checkpoint What is carbon monoxide?

FIGURE 18
Indoor Air Pollution
Air inside buildings can be polluted, too. *Observing How many sources of pollution can you spot in this room?*

Differentiated Instruction

Special Needs L1
Writing Captions Pair students with more able students. Distribute photocopies of Figure 18. Suggest that students write a caption for each source of indoor pollution shown. Then have students add other sources of air pollution to the drawing (indoors or from outdoors) and write captions for those. **learning modality: visual**

Less Proficient Readers L1
Analyzing Word Parts Write *carbon dioxide* and *carbon monoxide* on the board, and ask students to identify the difference between the words. Explain that *di* means "two," and *mono* means "one." Carbon dioxide has two atoms of oxygen, and carbon monoxide has one atom. Draw a diagram of each molecule. **learning modality: visual**

Indoor Air Pollution

Teach Key Concepts L2
Sources of Indoor Air Pollution

Focus Remind students that many different sources can pollute indoor air.

Teach Ask: **What are some sources of indoor air pollution?** *(Dust, pet hair, glues, and cleaning supplies)* **Why are carbon monoxide and radon difficult to detect?** *(They are colorless and odorless.)*

Apply Have students contact the local health department or environmental agency to find out if radon is found in your area. **learning modality: logical/mathematical**

Identifying Indoor Pollutants

Materials containers of products that give off toxic fumes

Time 10 minutes

Focus Review the names of products that can cause indoor air pollution.

Teach Tell students that many product labels have information about safe handling and use. Display the products, and have volunteers read aloud the cautionary statements on the labels. **CAUTION:** *Instruct students not to open any container.*

Apply Ask: **How can these products be used safely?** *(Usually outside or in well-ventilated areas)* **learning modality: verbal**

Monitor Progress L2

Oral Presentation Call on students to name one source of air pollution.

Answers
Figure 17 Acid rain has reacted with the statues, eating away some of the stone.
Figure 18 Cigarette smoke, cat and dog dander, glue, nail polish, paint, cleansers

✓ Reading Checkpoint Acid rain reacts with stone and metal in buildings and statues and damages them.

✓ Reading Checkpoint A colorless, odorless gas that forms when wood, coal, oil, or gas is incompletely burned

Reducing Air Pollution

Teach Key Concepts   L2
Controlling Emissions

Focus Review with students the various sources of air pollution.

Teach Tell students that the amount of emissions that can be released into the air by automobiles and factories is regulated by law. Ask: **How are emissions controlled in cars and trucks?** *(By pollution-control devices such as catalytic converters)* Have students study Figure 19. Ask a volunteer to describe how gas is cleaned in this smokestack scrubber.

Apply Ask: **How can individuals help reduce emissions?** *(Use less energy by reducing use of electricity and gas)* **learning modality: visual**

Integrating Health   L2

Ask students to hypothesize why some respiratory problems, such as asthma, bronchitis, and emphysema, are caused or worsened by breathing polluted air. *(Possible answer: Pollutants damage the lungs.)* Provide brochures or Internet printouts from reliable sources, such as the American Lung Association and the U.S. Environmental Protection Agency. Encourage students to make posters that include a labeled diagram of the respiratory system and a brief description of how the system is affected. **learning modality: visual**

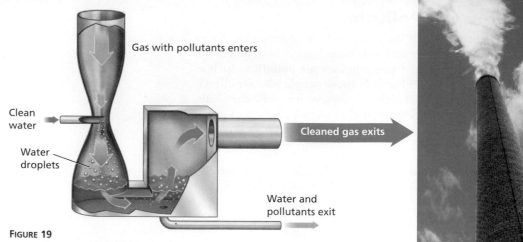

Gas with pollutants enters

Clean water

Water droplets

Cleaned gas exits

Water and pollutants exit

FIGURE 19
Controlling Factory Emissions
A smokestack scrubber removes pollutants such as sulfur dioxide from emissions. The dirty gas passes through a tube containing water droplets. Pollutants dissolve in the water, leaving clean gas to flow out of the chamber. The dirty water still must be properly disposed of. **Inferring** *Why aren't scrubbers a perfect solution to the emissions problem?*

Reducing Air Pollution

The key to reducing air pollution is to control emissions. In the United States, laws such as the Clean Air Act regulate the amount of certain pollutants that can be released into the air. These laws also encourage the development of new technology that reduces air pollution. But reducing emissions requires not only new technology but also the efforts of people like you.

Controlling Emissions From Factories At one time, industries dealt with emissions by building tall smokestacks. The stacks released wastes high in the air, where they could blow away. But the pollutants still ended up somewhere. Now factories place devices in the stacks to treat emissions. The device in Figure 19, called a scrubber, removes pollutants from emissions using a stream of water droplets. Pollutants dissolve in the water and fall into a container. The use of scrubbers explains why "smoke" from factories is white—it's not smoke, it's steam.

Controlling Emissions From Vehicles Cars and trucks now contain pollution-control devices. For example, a catalytic converter is a device that reduces emissions of carbon monoxide, hydrocarbons, and nitrogen oxides. This device causes the gases to react, forming less-harmful carbon dioxide and water.

Laws can ensure that people use pollution-control devices. For example, in many states, cars must pass emissions tests. The state of California's strict emissions-testing laws have helped reduce the smog problem in Los Angeles in recent years.

What You Can Do You may not think there is much you can do to reduce air pollution. But in fact, some small changes in people's behavior can make a big difference.

You can help reduce air pollution by reducing certain types of energy use. Much air pollution is a result of burning fuels to provide electricity and transportation. Using less energy conserves fuel resources and also reduces emissions. When you take public transportation, carpool, walk, or ride a bicycle, there is one fewer car on the road. This means there are fewer emissions that contribute to air pollution.

✓ **Reading Checkpoint** What are two things you can do to help reduce air pollution?

FIGURE 20
Reducing Air Pollution
Commuting to school or work by bicycle is one way to reduce the emissions that cause air pollution.

Section 4 Assessment

🎯 **Target Reading Skill** Relating Cause and Effect Refer to your graphic organizer about air pollution to help you answer Question 1 below.

Reviewing Key Concepts

1. **a. Reviewing** What causes smog? What causes acid rain?
   b. Comparing and Contrasting How are the causes of smog and acid rain similar? How are they different?
2. **a. Listing** Give four examples of indoor air pollutants.
   b. Classifying Which of the indoor air pollutants you listed bother only those people who are allergic to them? Which can affect anyone?
   c. Predicting New homes today are better insulated and more airtight than older homes. How might this affect indoor air pollution problems?
3. **a. Identifying** What is the one key to the reduction of air pollution?

   b. Applying Concepts Use an example to explain how new technology can help reduce emissions.
   c. Inferring One bus produces more emissions than one car. Yet increasing the number of people who travel by bus results in fewer emissions overall. Explain.

Lab zone At-Home **Activity**

It's in the Air What solid particles are in your air? With a family member, set up two particle collectors. Smear petroleum jelly on the inside of two clean, empty glass jars. Place one inside your home and the other outside. Make sure both jars are in locations where they will not be disturbed. Predict what you will find if you leave the jars in place for a few days. Compare the solid particles in each jar. How similar are they? Can you identify any of the particles?

Chapter 4 E ◆ 143

Lab zone Chapter **Project**

Keep Students on Track Advise students to complete their project models and begin testing them. Remind students that they must show how the product is protected, using fewer materials in the packaging. Encourage students to change their models at this time if necessary.

Lab zone At Home **Activity**

It's in the Air Suggest that students place the inside jar in a busy room, such as the kitchen or living room, and the outside jar in their yard or close to a driveway or street. Depending on the time of year, students may observe pollen grains as well as dust, pet hair, soot, and the like.

E ● 143

How Does the Garden Grow?

Prepare for Inquiry

Key Concept
Pollutants in water reduce seed germination and injure growing plants.

Skills Objectives
Students will be able to
- control the correct variables
- interpret data on seed germination and plant growth
- design an experiment to test the effect of a possible pollutant on the growth of radish seeds

Prep Time 30 minutes

Class Time Day 1, 30 minutes; Days 2–6, 5 minutes each

All in One Teaching Resources
- Lab Worksheet: *How Does the Garden Grow?*

Advance Planning
Let tap water stand uncovered for 24–48 hours to allow chlorine to dissipate. Prepare each polluted solution by mixing 5 mL of the pollutant with 100 mL of water. (For acid, use vinegar; for oil, use vegetable oil.)

Safety
Stress to students the importance of washing their hands well with soap after handling the seeds and soil. Review the safety guidelines in Appendix A.

How Does the Garden Grow?

Problem
How do pollutants affect seed growth?

Skills Focus
controlling variables, interpreting data, designing experiments

Suggested Materials
- 2 plastic petri dishes with lids
- wax pencil
- potting soil
- acid solution
- 20 radish seeds
- oil solution
- detergent solution
- salt solution
- day-old tap water
- masking tape
- 10-mL graduated cylinder
- metric ruler

Procedure

PART 1 Observing the Effects of a Known Pollutant

1. Read all the steps of the lab. Write a hypothesis about how an acid solution might affect the growth of radish seeds. Then copy the data table into your notebook.

2. Write your initials on the lids of the petri dishes. Then write "Control" on one lid. Label the other lid "Acid Solution."

3. Fill each dish with potting soil. Do not pack down the soil.

4. Pour 10 mL of water into the control dish. Pour 10 mL of the acid solution into the pollutant dish. Lightly scatter ten seeds on the soil surface in each dish.

5. Cover each dish with the correct lid. Tape the lids firmly in place. Store the dishes where they will receive light and will not be moved. Wash your hands with soap.

6. Once a day for the next five days, observe the seeds (do not open the lids). Record your observations in the data table. Use a metric ruler to measure the length of any roots or shoots that develop. If you do not observe any change, record that observation.

PART 2 Observing the Effects of a Possible Pollutant

7. Using the procedures you followed in Part 1, design an experiment that tests the effect of a possible pollutant on the growth of radish seeds. (*Hint:* You may use one of the remaining solutions listed under Suggested Materials.) Be sure to write a hypothesis and control all necessary variables.

8. Submit your experimental plan to your teacher for review. After making any necessary changes, create a data table in which to record your observations. Then carry out your experiment.

Data Table				
Date	Number of Seeds That Germinated		Condition of Seedlings	
	Control	Pollutant (Acid Solution)	Control	Pollutant (Acid Solution)

Guide Inquiry

Invitation
Ask: **Why is it important to know how pollutants affect seed growth?** (*Accept all reasonable answers, such as how to use this information to reduce pollution or clean it up.*)

Then have students brainstorm a list of reasons for having healthy plant growth in ecosystems, gardens, and farms based on what they already know about biogeochemical cycles, worldwide human hunger, and pollution.

Analyze and Conclude

1. **Observing** In Part 1, how many seeds germinated each day in the control dish? In the pollutant dish? What was the total number of seeds that germinated in each dish?

2. **Controlling Variables** In Part 1, how did the preparation of the two petri dishes differ? How was this difference important to the investigation?

3. **Interpreting Data** In Part 1, did the seedlings grown under the two conditions differ? If so, how?

4. **Drawing Conclusions** In Part 1, did your results support your hypothesis? Explain.

5. **Designing Experiments** What was the manipulated variable in Part 2? What was the responding variable?

6. **Inferring** In Part 2, did the solution you chose act as a pollutant? Explain.

7. **Communicating** Write a paragraph explaining what the effect would be if the pollutant you investigated in Part 2 reached a vegetable garden or farm.

More to Explore

Do you think the pollutant you studied in Part 1 has the same effect on all types of plants? Explain your reasoning. How might you test your hypothesis?

Extend the Inquiry

More to Explore Students' plans should involve controlling all variables except the types of plants.

Troubleshooting the Experiment
- Advise students to make sure the hypothesis is a testable statement.
- Monitor students' choices of places to put the two dishes.

Expected Outcome
All or most seeds in the control dish should germinate within two or three days, and grow well. Some or all seeds in the pollutant dish will fail to germinate, and any sprouts will not grow well.

Analyze and Conclude

1. Answers will vary. Pollutants usually reduce the number of seeds that germinate.

2. Water was added to one dish while acid was added to the other. It showed that the cause of any differences in the growth of seeds was due to this one variable.

3. Yes; seedlings in the acid dish did not grow as well as those in the control dish.

4. Answers will depend on hypotheses.

5. Answers will depend on the solution chosen to test. The detergent, oil, or salt preparations will act as a pollutant and inhibit germination and/or growth.

6. Yes; the solution would not normally be found in healthy soil and the solution damaged the seeds, which is how pollutants would affect seeds.

7. Paragraphs may include that fewer seeds would germinate, and the seedlings that did sprout would not grow into healthy plants.

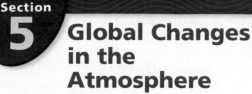

Global Changes in the Atmosphere

Objectives

After this lesson, students will be able to

E.4.5.1 Describe how human activities have damaged the ozone layer.

E.4.5.2 Identify ways that human activities might be linked to global climate changes.

Target Reading Skill

Outlining Explain that using an outline format helps students organize information by main topic, subtopic, and details.

Answers

Outlines should have Roman numerals followed by major headings and capital letters followed by minor headings.

Global Changes in the Atmosphere
  I. The thinning of the ozone layer
     A. The source of ozone
     B. The ozone hole
     C. What's being done
  II. Global climate change
     A. The greenhouse effect
     B. Global warming
     C. Possible consequences
     D. The difficulty of predicting climate change

All in One Teaching Resources

• Transparency E40

Preteach

Build Background Knowledge   **L1**

Beneficial Ozone

Invite volunteers to tell the class about how they got a sunburn. Ask: **What in sunlight causes a sunburn?** *(Accept all reasonable responses without comment at this time.)* Tell them that without ozone high in the atmosphere, we would not be able to go outside. They will learn why in this section.

Global Changes in the Atmosphere

Reading Preview

Key Concepts

• How have human activities damaged the ozone layer?

• How might human activities be linked to global climate changes?

Key Terms

• ozone layer
• chlorofluorocarbon
• greenhouse effect
• global warming

Target Reading Skill

Outlining As you read, make an outline about global atmospheric changes that you can use for review. Use the red headings for the main ideas and the blue headings for the supporting ideas.

Global Changes in the Atmosphere
I. The thinning of the ozone layer
A. The source of ozone
B.
C.
II. Global climate change
A.
B.
C.
D.

Lab zone · Discover Activity

What Happens to the Beads?

1. Your teacher will give you beads that change color under certain conditions, along with two pipe cleaners and a small piece of T-shirt material.
2. Thread half of the beads on one pipe cleaner, twisting the ends together.
3. Repeat Step 2 with the remaining beads. Cover the beads on this pipe cleaner with the T-shirt fabric.
4. Take both sets of beads outdoors. After two minutes, go inside. Then remove the fabric covering. Immediately observe the two sets of beads and compare their colors.

Think It Over

Developing Hypotheses Was there any difference in color between the two sets of beads? Form a hypothesis to explain your observations.

It's the first day of vacation, and it's a perfect day for the beach. It's hot, and there's not a cloud in the sky. You've found the perfect spot to read your new book. But as you begin to read, the heat and the sound of the ocean start to make you sleepy. The next thing you know, you're waking up with your head in your book! You've been asleep for two hours! And the redness on your arms reminds you that you forgot to apply sunscreen. Ouch!

Beach ▶ supplies

Lab zone · Discover Activity

Skills Focus Developing hypotheses

Materials ultraviolet-light-sensitive beads, pipe cleaners, pieces of T-shirt fabric

Time 20 minutes

Tips When students return to the classroom, ask them to make observations quickly. The beads lose color when they are no longer exposed to ultraviolet light.

Expected Outcome Beads covered by fabric will not change color. Beads exposed to direct sunlight (even strong light on an overcast day) will change to various colors of the visible spectrum; they will vary in intensity according to the intensity of the ultraviolet light exposure.

Think it Over Yes; sunlight causes the beads to change color.

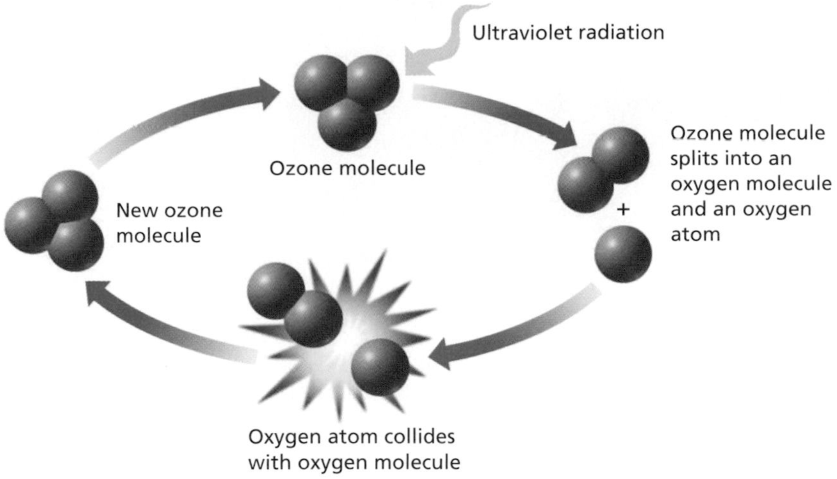

Ultraviolet radiation

Ozone molecule

New ozone molecule

+

Ozone molecule splits into an oxygen molecule and an oxygen atom

Oxygen atom collides with oxygen molecule

FIGURE 21
Ozone Cycle
When ultraviolet radiation from the sun strikes an ozone molecule, the ozone molecule splits into an oxygen molecule and a free oxygen atom.
Interpreting Diagrams *What happens when the free oxygen atom collides with an oxygen molecule?*

The Thinning of the Ozone Layer

If you have ever had a sunburn, you have experienced the painful effects of the sun's ultraviolet radiation. But did you know that such burns would be even worse without the protection of the ozone layer? The **ozone layer** is a layer of the upper atmosphere about 30 kilometers above Earth's surface. Actually, the concentration of ozone in this layer is very low—only a few parts per million. Yet even the small amount of ozone in the ozone layer protects people from the effects of too much ultraviolet radiation. These effects include sunburn, eye diseases, and skin cancer.

Since you read earlier that ozone is a pollutant, the fact that ozone can be helpful may sound confusing. The difference between ozone as a pollutant and ozone as a helpful gas is its location. Ozone close to Earth's surface in the form of smog is harmful. Higher in the atmosphere, where people cannot breathe it, ozone protects us.

The Source of Ozone Ozone is constantly being made and destroyed. When sunlight strikes an ozone molecule, the energy of the ultraviolet radiation is partly absorbed. This energy causes the ozone molecule to break apart into an oxygen molecule and an oxygen atom, as shown in Figure 21. The oxygen atom soon collides with another oxygen molecule. They react to form a new ozone molecule. Each time this cycle occurs, some ultraviolet energy is absorbed. That energy does not reach Earth's surface.

Math Skills

Calculating a Concentration

Levels of pollutants are often written as concentrations. A concentration is a ratio that compares the amount of one substance to the amount of another substance. For example, suppose that the concentration of ozone in part of the atmosphere is 3 parts per million. This means that there are 3 molecules of ozone in 1,000,000 molecules of air. This ratio can also be written in three other ways:

3 : 1,000,000

3 to 1,000,000

$$\frac{3}{1,000,000}$$

Practice Problems Express each of these concentrations in three different ways.

1. 7 parts per hundred
2. 25 parts per billion

The Thinning of the Ozone Layer

Teach Key Concepts [L2]

The Ozone Layer

Focus Remind students that ozone is a form of oxygen that is produced when gases react in sunlight. It is toxic and helps to form smog on Earth's surface.

Teach Ask: **How can ozone be both harmful and beneficial?** (*It is harmful when it is close to Earth's surface where people can breathe it. It is helpful when it is higher in the atmosphere and helps to absorb ultraviolet light.*) Ask: **How does ozone protect us from ultraviolet radiation?** (*It absorbs ultraviolet radiation so that it does not reach Earth's surface.*) **What has damaged the ozone layer?** (*The use of CFCs*) **How is this damage being corrected?** (*Many countries have banned the use of CFCs.*)

Apply Tell students that the dramatic ozone "hole" exists only over Antarctica, but currently, the ozone layer over the United States is depleted by about 6 percent.
learning modality: verbal

All in One Teaching Resources
• Transparency E41

Independent Practice

All in One Teaching Resources
• Guided Reading and Study Worksheet: *Global Changes in the Atmosphere*

⊙ **Student Edition on Audio CD**

Differentiated Instruction

Gifted and Talented [L3]
Researching Ozone Depletion Potential Have students research the Ozone Depletion Potential, (ODP), a number that refers to the amount of ozone depletion caused by a substance. Tell them to plan and present an oral report that includes how the number is determined (*it is compared to the impact of a similar mass of CFC-11*) and a list of common products and their ODPs.

Monitor Progress [L2]

Writing Have each student write a paragraph to explain how ozone protects organisms on Earth. Students can save their work in their portfolios.

Answers
Figure 21 It forms a new ozone molecule.

Math Skills Ratio and proportion

Focus Tell students that small concentrations, such as three parts per million, are difficult to visualize.

Teach Give each student a sheet of graph paper ruled in tenths of an inch, and have them calculate the total number of small squares in an 8-by-10-inch block on the sheet. *(8,000)* Tell students to shade in any four squares on the sheet. Ask: **What is the concentration of black squares?** *(4 parts per 8,000)* Have volunteers write on the board the four ways to express this ratio. *(4 parts per 8,000; 4:8,000; 4 to 8,000; and 4/8,000)*

Answers
1. 7:100, 7 to 100, 7/100
2. 25:1,000,000,000; 25 to 1,000,000,000, and 25/1,000,000,000

Lab zone Build Inquiry L2

Modeling the Effects of CFCs on Ozone

Focus Review the ozone cycle shown in Figure 21.

Teach Explain that when sunlight hits a CFC molecule, it releases a chlorine atom. This atom hits an ozone molecule and interrupts the normal cycle. Chlorine breaks up the ozone molecule, and it becomes regular oxygen—it never re-forms into ozone. Challenge pairs of students to create a model to demonstrate the ozone cycle and its interruption by CFCs, and then present their models to the class.

Apply Ask: **Why is more oxygen not helpful in blocking ultraviolet radiation?** *(Because the oxygen molecule is not the right size and shape to absorb the sun's harmful rays)* Tell students that one chlorine atom can break apart 100,000 ozone molecules.
learning modality: kinesthetic

FIGURE 22
Ozone Hole
The ozone hole was first detected over Antarctica in the 1970s. The hole has grown steadily since then, though it varies a bit from year to year. In each of the globes at the right, the blue area indicates the extent of the ozone hole in the spring of that year.
Observing *How would you describe the change in the ozone hole from 1979 to 2000?*

◀ **1979**
Scientists detect a hole in the ozone layer over Antarctica. (The bluish area represents the extent of the ozone hole.)

The Ozone Hole In the late 1970s, scientists observed that the ozone layer over Antarctica was growing thinner each spring. The amount of ozone in the ozone layer was decreasing, causing an area of severe ozone depletion, or an ozone hole. In Figure 22, you can see how the size of the ozone hole has changed since 1979. What was to blame for the ozone hole?

Scientists determined that the major cause of the ozone hole is a group of gases called CFCs, which were used in many household products. CFCs, or **chlorofluorocarbons,** are human-made gases that contain chlorine and fluorine. CFCs had been used in refrigerators, air conditioners, fire extinguishers, aerosol spray cans, and other products. High in the atmosphere, CFCs react with ozone molecules. The CFCs block the natural cycle in which ozone molecules absorb ultraviolet radiation. As a result, more ultraviolet light reaches Earth's surface.

What's Being Done In the late 1970s, the United States and many other countries banned the use of CFCs in aerosol spray cans. Then in 1990, many nations signed an agreement to ban the use of almost all CFCs by 2000. Some uses of CFCs are still allowed, for example, in lung medications. But compared to the 1970s, few CFCs now enter the atmosphere. Unfortunately, CFC molecules are very stable and remain in the atmosphere for a long time. But scientists predict that if the ban is maintained, the ozone layer will gradually recover.

When scientists discovered that CFCs were harming the atmosphere, they immediately began to search for substitutes. Refrigerators and air conditioners were redesigned to use less harmful substances. Most spray cans were either replaced by pump sprays or redesigned to use other gases. Researchers developed new ways to make products such as plastic foam without using CFCs. As a result of this research and invention, far fewer CFCs now enter the atmosphere.

✓ Reading Checkpoint What do scientists predict will happen if the ban on CFCs is maintained?

148 ◆ E

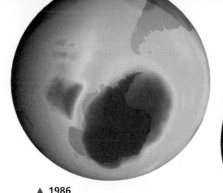

▲ 1986
The ozone hole has grown to
cover much of Antarctica.

1993 ▲
The ozone hole covers
nearly all of Antarctica.

2000 ▶
The ozone hole covers
Antarctica and extends north
over the tip of South America.

Math ▸ Analyzing Data

Chlorine Levels

The line graph shows a scientist's predictions
of how the ban on CFCs might affect
chlorine levels in the atmosphere. The red
line shows the levels of chlorine without the
ban on CFCs. The blue line shows the levels
with the ban on CFCs.

1. **Reading Graphs** What variable is plotted
   on the horizontal axis? What variable is
   plotted on the vertical axis?

2. **Interpreting Data** Which graphed line
   shows rising levels of chlorine? What
   trend does the other line show?

3. **Inferring** Why do the two lines start at the
   same point?

4. **Drawing Conclusions** How does the
   relationship between the two lines change as
   time goes on?

Chlorine Levels in the Atmosphere, 1985–2005

Without
CFC ban

With
CFC ban

Chlorine Level
(parts per billion)

Year

Math ▸ Analyzing Data

Math Skill Making and interpreting graphs

Focus Ask a volunteer to identify the type of
graph shown. *(Line graph)*

Teach Explain that line graphs are used to
show how something has changed over time.
Ask: **Why was a line graph used to represent
this data?** *(To show how chlorine levels in the
atmosphere have changed over time)* Tell
students that line graphs can also be used to
compare data. Ask: **What data does this
graph compare?** *(Chlorine levels with the ban
and without the ban)*

Answers
1. Year; chlorine level
2. The red line; the blue line shows gradually
diminishing chlorine levels.
3. The ban did not exist in 1985, so
predictions of the levels without the ban
could not be made before then.
4. The difference in chlorine levels becomes
greater over time.

Monitor Progress _____ L2

Writing Have students write a brief
paragraph explaining how CFCs harm the
atmosphere.

Answers
Figure 22 It is getting larger.

✓ **Reading
Checkpoint** Scientists predict that the
ozone hole will slowly
recover.

Global Climate Change

Teach Key Concepts L2
Greenhouse Effect And Global Warming

Focus Remind students that when sunlight hits objects on Earth, its light energy is transformed into thermal energy.

Teach Point out that although light energy can travel through Earth's atmosphere, some thermal energy is blocked by gases in the air, producing the greenhouse effect. Ask: **Is the greenhouse effect harmful?** (*No; without the greenhouse effect the Earth would not be warm enough to support life.*) **How is the greenhouse effect related to global warming?** (*Rising levels of carbon dioxide may intensify the greenhouse effect and cause temperatures on Earth to rise.*) **Do scientists know for certain that burning coal and oil is causing global warming?** (*No; natural factors also can effect climate change.*)

Apply Ask students to hypothesize how rising sea levels and warmer temperatures might affect where people live. (*Possible answer: People would have to move inland and farther from the equator.*) **learning modality: logical/mathematical**

All in One **Teaching Resources**
• Transparency E42

Go Online
SciLINKS NSTA

For: Links on changes in climate
Visit: www.SciLinks.org
Web Code: scn-0545

Download a worksheet that will guide students' review of Internet resources on changes in climate.

Go Online
SciLINKS NSTA

For: Links on changes in climate
Visit: www. SciLinks.org
Web Code: scn-0545

FIGURE 23
Greenhouse Effect
When energy in the form of sunlight strikes Earth's surface, it changes to heat. Certain gases in the atmosphere trap some of the heat, preventing it from escaping back into space. This trapping of heat is known as the greenhouse effect. *Applying Concepts What gases in the atmosphere trap heat near Earth's surface?*

Global Climate Change

Some changes to the atmosphere could affect the climate of the whole planet. To understand why, you need to know more about the atmosphere.

The Greenhouse Effect Think about the sun shining through a window on a cool day. The window lets light enter the room. The light strikes objects in the room and is converted to heat. The closed windows then trap the warm air inside, and the room becomes warmer.

In the atmosphere, water vapor, carbon dioxide, and certain other gases act like windows. These gases allow sunlight to reach Earth's surface, but they prevent some of the heat from escaping back into space. The trapping of heat near Earth's surface is called the **greenhouse effect.** Without the greenhouse effect, Earth would be much colder—about 33 degrees colder, on average.

Global Warming Since the 1800s, coal and oil have been the main sources of energy in many parts of the world. As you have read, burning these substances produces carbon dioxide. As a result, the amount of carbon dioxide in the atmosphere has increased from 280 parts per million to 350 parts per million. This amount is increasing more quickly every year.

Human activities that increase carbon dioxide levels may be intensifying the greenhouse effect. One theory, called **global warming,** predicts that the increase in carbon dioxide levels will cause the average temperature to continue to rise. Scientists have estimated that in this century, the average global temperature could rise by as much as 3.5 Celsius degrees.

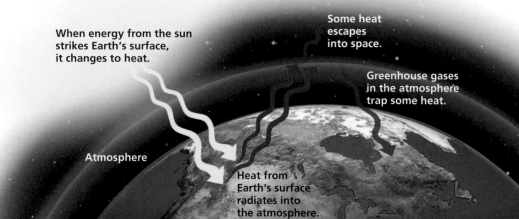

When energy from the sun strikes Earth's surface, it changes to heat.

Some heat escapes into space.

Greenhouse gases in the atmosphere trap some heat.

Atmosphere

Heat from Earth's surface radiates into the atmosphere.

Differentiated Instruction

English Learners/Beginning L1
Vocabulary: Link to Visual Explain the greenhouse effect by using Figure 23. Explain that the yellow arrows represent light energy from the sun, and the red arrows represent thermal energy. Point to the captions and read them aloud. Then have students tell in their own words what is happening in the picture. **learning modality: visual**

English Learners/Intermediate L2
Vocabulary: Link to Visual Repeat the procedure for Beginning students, but have students write their own captions for the picture. **learning modality: visual**

Possible Consequences Although the predicted increase in temperature may not sound like a big change, it could have a huge impact. Parts of the Antarctic ice cap would melt, raising the level of the oceans and causing increased flooding. The temperature change would affect climate patterns all over the world. This change would, in turn, affect where crops could be grown. There might also be more hurricanes and other severe storms.

The Difficulty of Predicting Climate Change It is difficult to predict how Earth's climate will be affected by changes in the atmosphere. The systems that determine climate are very complex. For example, Earth's oceans, forests, clouds, and volcanoes all affect carbon dioxide levels in the atmosphere. It is difficult to know what impact each of these factors might have on climate change.

Scientists have studied climate systems for less than a century, a very short time to understand processes that can take thousands of years. Most scientists base their global climate predictions on computer models. But only time will tell if these predictions have been accurate.

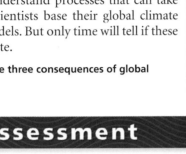

FIGURE 24
Computer Climate Model
Computer models are important tools for scientists trying to predict climate change. The model shown uses ocean temperatures near North and South America. The lightest colors indicate the warmest temperatures. The darkest colors indicate the coolest temperatures.

✓ **Reading Checkpoint** What might be three consequences of global warming?

Section 5 Assessment

🎯 **Target Reading Skill** Outlining Use the information in your outline about global atmospheric changes to help you answer the questions below.

Reviewing Key Concepts

1. a. Reviewing How have human activities affected the ozone layer?
   b. Relating Cause and Effect What part of the ozone cycle do CFCs interrupt? What effect does this have?
   c. Predicting Exposure to ultraviolet radiation can cause skin cancer. How would you expect the thinning of the ozone layer to affect skin cancer rates? Explain.
2. a. Identifying What human activities have led to increased levels of carbon dioxide in the atmosphere?
   b. Explaining Explain how increased carbon dioxide levels could be linked to global climate changes.
   c. Problem Solving What are some steps people could take to reduce the amount of carbon dioxide that enters the atmosphere?

Math Practice

3. Calculating a Concentration Draw a picture to show what is meant by each of the following concentrations. Then express each concentration in three different ways.
a. 4 parts per 10
b. 19 parts per 100
c. 7 to 10
d. 27 : 100

Chapter 4 E ◆ 151

Study Guide

interactive Textbook

- Complete student edition
- Section and chapter self-assessments
- Assessment reports for teachers

Help Students Read

Developing Vocabulary

Word Forms Ask students to use a dictionary to write definitions in their own words of the terms *depletion* and *inversion*. Then have students explain how these definitions relate to the terms *nutrient depletion* and *temperature inversion*.

Words in Context Select Key Terms from the chapter. Have students write a sentence for each term that places the term in a correct context. Provide them with one example before they begin: **litter: The very top layer of fertile soil is litter, made of dead leaves and grass.**

Connecting Concepts

Concept Maps Help students develop one way to show how the information in this chapter is related. Earth's land, water, and air resources must be protected from pollution and conserved through recycling, proper disposal and cleanup, and reducing pollutants. Have students brainstorm to identify the key concepts, key terms, details, and examples. Then tell them to write each item on a sticky note and attach it at random to chart paper or to the board.

Tell students that this concept map will be organized in hierarchical order, and have them begin at the top with key concepts. Ask students these questions to guide them in categorizing the information on the stickies: **What are ways to conserve land and manage solid waste? What causes pollution of land, air, and water resources? How can air and water pollution be reduced?**

Prompt students by using connecting words or phrases such as "includes" and "can be prevented by" to indicate the basis for the organization of the map. The phrases should form a sentence between or among a set of concepts.

Chapter 4 **Study Guide**

1 Conserving Land and Soil

Key Concepts

- Three uses that change the land are agriculture, mining, and development.
- Fertile soil is made up of several layers, including litter, topsoil, and subsoil.
- Poor soil management can result in three problems: erosion, nutrient depletion, and desertification. Fortunately, damaged soil can sometimes be restored.

Key Terms

development	nutrient depletion
litter	fertilizer
topsoil	desertification
subsoil	drought
bedrock	land reclamation
erosion	

2 Waste Disposal and Recycling

Key Concepts

- Three methods of handling solid waste are burning, burying, and recycling. Each method has advantages and disadvantages.
- One way to help solve the solid waste problem is to practice the "three R's"—reduce, reuse, and recycle.
- Hazardous wastes that are not disposed of in carefully designed landfills may be incinerated or broken down by living organisms. Liquid wastes may be stored in deep rock layers.

Key Terms

municipal solid waste
incineration
leachate
sanitary landfill
recycling
biodegradable
composting
hazardous waste

3 Water Pollution and Solutions

Key Concepts

- Fresh water is scarce because about 97 percent of the water on Earth is salt water.
- Wastes produced by households, agriculture, industry, and mining can end up in water.
- Keeping water clean requires proper sewage treatment, the reduction of pollutants, and the effective cleanup of oil and gasoline spills.

Key Terms

groundwater	pesticide
pollutant	sediment
sewage	

4 Air Pollution and Solutions

Key Concepts

- The major sources of smog are emissions from vehicles. Acid rain is caused by the emissions from power plants and factories that burn coal and oil.
- Some indoor air pollutants only affect people who are sensitive to them. Other indoor air pollutants can affect anyone.
- The key to reducing air pollution is to control emissions.

Key Terms

emissions	temperature inversion
photochemical smog	acid rain
ozone	radon

5 Global Changes in the Atmosphere

Key Concepts

- The major cause of the ozone hole is a group of gases called CFCs, or chlorofluorocarbons.
- Human activities that increase carbon dioxide levels may add to the greenhouse effect.

Key Terms

ozone layer	greenhouse effect
chlorofluorocarbon	global warming

152 ◆ E

Answer

Accept all logical presentations by students.

All in One Teaching Resources

- Key Terms Review: *Land, Water, and Air Resources*

Review and Assessment

Go Online
PHSchool.com
For: Self-Assessment
Visit: PHSchool.com
Web Code: cea-5040

Organizing Information

Concept Mapping Copy the concept map about air pollution onto a separate sheet of paper. Then complete it and add a title. (For more on Concept Mapping, see the Skills Handbook.)

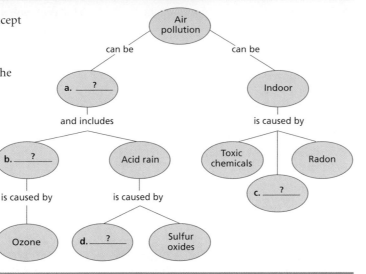

Reviewing Key Terms

Choose the letter of the best answer.

1. The advance of desert-like conditions into areas that previously were fertile is called
   a. desertification.
   b. crop rotation.
   c. nutrient depletion.
   d. land reclamation.

2. Which of the following is a biodegradable waste?
   a. a glass jar   b. a metal can
   c. an apple core   d. a plastic bag

3. The water and waste materials washed down toilets and sinks are called
   a. pesticides.
   b. sewage.
   c. industrial chemicals.
   d. fertilizers.

4. A device that removes pollutants from emissions is a
   a. scrubber.
   b. catalytic converter.
   c. filter.
   d. CFC substitute.

5. Which gas is thought to be one of the causes of global warming?
   a. radon
   b. ozone
   c. carbon dioxide
   d. carbon monoxide

Writing in Science

Research Report Suppose that you are an ecologist studying animals that live in a body of water near a big city. Write a report explaining how human activities might affect the body of water and the animals that rely on it.

Discovery CHANNEL SCHOOL

Land, Water, and Air Resources
Video Preview
Video Field Trip
▶ Video Assessment

Chapter 4 E ◆ 153

Go Online
PHSchool.com
For: Self-Assessment
Visit: PHSchool.com
Web Code: cea-5040

Students can take an online practice test that is automatically scored.

All in One Teaching Resources
- Transparency E40: Concept Map
- Chapter Test
- Performance Assessment Teacher Notes
- Performance Assessment Student Worksheet
- Performance Assessment Scoring Rubric

ExamView® Computer Test Bank CD-ROM

Review and Assessment

Organizing Information
a. outdoor
b. smog
c. any one: carbon monoxide, cigarette smoke, pet hair, dust
d. sulfuric acid or sulfur dioxide
   Possible title: Causes of Air Pollution

Reviewing Key Terms
1. a   **2.** c   **3.** b   **4.** a   **5.** c

Writing in Science

Writing Skill Research

Scoring Rubric
4 Includes a detailed description of human activities that can cause pollution, the types of pollution caused by each activity, and the effect on animals that rely on the body of water
3 Includes all criteria, but details are not as elaborate
2 Includes few examples or only brief descriptions
1 Includes inaccurate descriptions

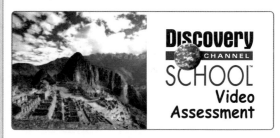

Discovery CHANNEL SCHOOL Video Assessment

Land, Water, and Air Resources

Show the Video Assessment to review chapter content and as a prompt for the writing assignment. Discussion questions: **How does the toxic pollution of water affect the wildlife that lives downstream?** *(Wildlife that eat organisms that swim downstream from areas of polluted water take in pollutants from the food they eat.)* **What are two effects of toxins in the beluga whale population?** *(Toxins can cause cancerous tumors, infertility, and severe health problems in offspring.)*

Checking Concepts

6. Possible answers can include any two of the following: Leaving fields fallow, leaving crop wastes in the fields, and rotating crops.

7. A drought is a period when less rain than normal falls on an area.

8. Possible answers can include one of the following: Institute curbside recycling with trash pickup; place recycling bins in public places.

9. The substance might have leached out of the soil and seeped into groundwater, thus contaminating the water supply.

10. Bacteria that live in the ocean feed on the oil and break it down.

11. Coal and oil produce nitrogen oxides and sulfur oxides when they are burned. These gases react with water vapor in the air to form nitric acid and sulfuric acid. The acids return to Earth's surface dissolved in precipitation.

12. Water vapor and carbon dioxide act like windows, allowing sunlight to reach Earth's surface but preventing the heat from escaping back into space.

Thinking Critically

13. The topsoil and subsoil could be replaced in their original order. Then the area could be replanted.

14. Radioactive waste remains dangerous for thousands of years. Burning the waste might pollute the air, and burying it could pollute the groundwater or add radioactive substances to the food chain.

15. The levels of photochemical smog would be worse in cities because the major sources of photochemical smog are the gases emitted by motor vehicles, which are more concentrated in cities.

16. The gray haze is smog. It is confined to the cool layer because a temperature inversion prevents the polluted air from rising.

Checking Concepts

6. Describe two techniques for preventing nutrient depletion.

7. What is a drought?

8. What is one way that communities can encourage residents to produce less solid waste?

9. Explain how a person might be exposed to a hazardous substance that was buried underground many years ago.

10. How can a small oil spill in the ocean be naturally cleaned up?

11. How does acid rain form?

12. What role do water vapor and carbon dioxide play in the greenhouse effect?

Thinking Critically

13. Problem Solving In strip mining, a layer of soil is removed to expose a resource, such as coal, underneath. What methods could be used to restore this damaged land?

14. Applying Concepts Why is it unsafe to bury or incinerate radioactive waste?

15. Making Generalizations Would you expect the levels of photochemical smog to be worse in cities or in rural areas? Explain.

16. Interpreting Diagrams What is represented by the gray haze in the diagram? Why is it confined to the cool layer?

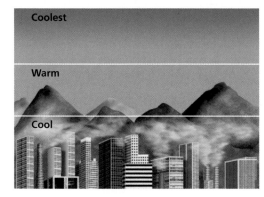

Coolest

Warm

Cool

Math Practice

17. Calculating a Concentration The concentration of iron in one water sample is 500 parts per million. The iron concentration in a second sample is 300 parts per million. Which sample has the higher iron concentration? Explain.

Applying Skills

Use the graph showing carbon dioxide levels to answer Questions 18–20.

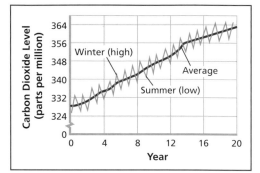

18. Interpreting Data What was the average level of carbon dioxide in the atmosphere at the beginning of the study? What was the average level of carbon dioxide in Year 20 of the study?

19. Calculating How much did the average level of carbon dioxide increase during the study?

20. Developing Hypotheses In each year of the study, the winter level of carbon dioxide was higher than the summer level. Suggest an explanation for this.

Lab zone Chapter **Project**

Performance Assessment Share your project with your classmates. Explain the difference between your package and the original package, including the amount and type of materials. Then demonstrate how your package protects the product at least as well as the original package.

Lab zone Chapter **Project**

Project Wrap-Up Give students the opportunity to explain their design goals and criteria. Criteria should focus on the ease and convenience of disposal, and how the materials reduce harm to the environment. Ask students to describe any challenges they faced and how they resolved them.

Reflect and Record Ask students to write a short evaluation of their product. What part of their package do they think is better than the original package? Does their design have applications to other types of products?

Standardized Test Prep

Choose the letter of the best answer.

1. The diagram shows the different layers of soil. In which soil layer would you expect to find many species of organisms as well as rock fragments, nutrients, and decaying matter?

   A Layer W
   B Layer X
   C Layer Y
   D Layer Z

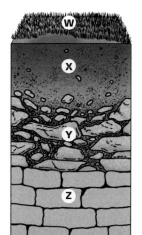

2. Farmer Brown plants corn in all of his fields every year. What is the MOST likely result of his farming methods?

   F soil erosion
   G nutrient depletion
   H desertification
   J land reclamation

3. How can sediments affect the water supply?

   A They can block sunlight, preventing algae and plants from growing.
   B They can cause the growth of bacteria, which use up oxygen in the water.
   C They can cause algae to grow, preventing light from reaching other organisms in the water.
   D They can change the temperature of the water, causing fish and other organisms to die.

4. Suppose you were to perform an experiment measuring the soil erosion resulting from different amounts of rain. What would the manipulated variable in this experiment be?

   F time   **G** depth of soil
   H amount of rain   **J** type of soil

5. The Environmental Protection Agency (EPA) monitors air quality around the country. According to the EPA, exposure to levels of sulfur dioxide in the air greater than 14 parts per million is harmful to public health and the environment. In which of the following ways could you also write this concentration of sulfur dioxide?

   A $\frac{14}{10,000,000}$

   B 14 to 1,000,000.
   C 14 : 1,100,000.
   D $\frac{140}{100,000}$

Constructed Response

6. Human activities are the most common causes of water pollution. List three types of human activities. Then explain how each type of activity can pollute water.

Math Practice

17. Sample 1 has the higher iron concentration because the denominator is the same; 500 is more than 300.

Applying Skills

18. The average level was about 328 ppm at the beginning of the study and about 363 ppm in Year 20.

19. The average level increased by 35 ppm.

20. Possible answers include the following: In the summer, more plants are growing and removing carbon dioxide from the air. Also, more heating fuels are burned in the winter, so carbon dioxide emissions increase.

Standardized Test Prep

1. B   **2.** G   **3.** A   **4.** H   **5.** B
6. Possible answers include the following: Farming—fertilizers and pesticides can be washed by rain into waterways and are a source of pollution; industry—some factories and power plants release water that has been used to cool machinery, which can kill organisms living in waterways; use of fossil fuels—oil spills on the oceans take many years to recover from the pollution of sticky black oil, and gasoline can leak from underground tanks into groundwater.

Chapter at a Glance

PRENTICE HALL
Teacher**EXPRESS**™
Plan • Teach • Assess

 Chapter Project *Energy Audit*

Technology	**Local Standards**

All in One Teaching Resources

- Chapter Project Teacher Notes, pp. 304–305
- Chapter Project Student Overview, pp. 306–307
- Chapter Project Student Worksheets, pp. 308–309
- Chapter Project Scoring Rubric, p. 310

Discovery CHANNEL SCHOOL™
Video Preview

Section 1

Fossil Fuels

1–2 periods
1/2–1 block

E.5.1.1 Explain how fuels provide energy.

E.5.1.2 Name the three major fossil fuels.

E.5.1.3 Explain why fossil fuels are considered nonrenewable resources.

Go Online
SciLINKS™ NSTA

Section 2

Renewable Sources of Energy

2–3 periods
1–1 1/2 blocks

E.5.2.1 Explain the forms of energy provided by the sun.

E.5.2.2 Identify and describe various renewable sources of energy.

Go Online
SciLINKS™ NSTA

Discovery CHANNEL SCHOOL™
Video Field Trip

Section 3

Nuclear Energy

1–2 periods
1/2–1 block

E.5.3.1 Describe what happens during a nuclear fission reaction.

E.5.3.2 Explain how a nuclear power plant produces electricity.

E.5.3.3 Describe what takes place in a nuclear fusion reaction.

Go Online
active art

Section 4

Energy Conservation

1–2 periods
1/2–1 block

E.5.4.1 Name ways to ensure that there will be enough energy for the future.

E.5.4.2 Identify ways individuals can conserve energy.

Go Online
PHSchool.com

Review and Assessment		**Test Preparation**

All in One Teaching Resources

- Key Terms Review, p. 346
- Transparency E57
- Performance Assessment Teacher Notes, p. 355
- Performance Assessment Scoring Rubric, p. 356
- Performance Assessment Student Worksheet, p. 357
- Chapter Test, pp. 358–361

Go Online
PHSchool.com

Discovery CHANNEL SCHOOL™
Video Assessment

Test Preparation Blackline Masters

Lab zone Chapter Activities Planner

For more activities

LAB ZONE Easy Planner CD-ROM

Student Edition	Inquiry	Time	Materials	Skills	Resources
Chapter Project	Open-Ended	Ongoing (2–3 weeks)	**All in One** Teaching Resources See p. 304	Observing, creating data tables, interpreting data, drawing conclusions, communicating	**Lab zone Easy Planner** **All in One** Teaching Resources Support pp. 304–310
Section 1					
Discover Activity, p. 158	Guided	10 minutes	Lignite coal, hand lens	Observing	**Lab zone Easy Planner**
Skills Activity, p. 160	Guided	15 minutes	Drawing compass, protractor, calculator (optional)	Graphing	**Lab zone Easy Planner**
Section 2					
Discover Activity, p. 165	Directed	Prep: 10 minutes Class: 5 minutes	500 mL water, 2 sealable clear plastic bags, 2 thermometers	Developing hypotheses	**Lab zone Easy Planner**
Try This Activity, p. 168	Guided	20 minutes	Pinwheels; sticks or pencils, spools, string or monofilament, paper squares, coins, or bottle caps, tape, fans	Making models	**Lab zone Easy Planner**
Technology Lab, pp. 172–173	Open-Ended	Prep: 20 minutes Class: 40 minutes	Scissors, frozen vegetables, 3 sheets of aluminum foil, 3 sheets of oaktag paper, wooden or plastic stirrers, glue, 3 thermometers, tape, clock or watch; optional materials as selected	Designing a solution, evaluating the design	**Lab zone Easy Planner** **Lab Activity Video** **All in One** Teaching Resources Technology Lab: *Design and Build a Solar Cooker*, p. 327
Section 3					
Discover Activity, p. 174	Directed	10 minutes	15 dominoes	Inferring	**Lab zone Easy Planner**
Skills Activity, p. 175	Guided	5 minutes	Calculator (optional)	Calculating	**Lab zone Easy Planner**
Section 4					
Discover Activity, p. 179	Directed	20 minutes	light bulbs in packages (60-watt incandescent and 15-watt compact fluorescent), lamp, thermometer, clock or watch	Inferring	**Lab zone Easy Planner**
Consumer Lab, p. 183	Guided	Prep: 20 minutes Class: 40 minutes	Watch or clock, beakers, ice water, hot water, thermometers or temperature probes, containers and lids made of paper, glass, plastic, plastic foam, and metal	Measuring, controlling variables	**Lab zone Easy Planner** **Lab Activity Video** **All in One** Teaching Resources Consumer Lab: *Keeping Comfortable*, pp. 343–345

Section 1 Fossil Fuels

1–2 periods, 1/2–1 block

Objectives

E.5.1.1 Explain how fuels provide energy.
E.5.1.2 Name the three major fossil fuels.
E.5.1.3 Explain why fossil fuels are considered nonrenewable resources.

Local Standards

Key Terms

• fuel • energy transformation • combustion • fossil fuel • hydrocarbon
• petroleum • refinery • petrochemical

Preteach

Build Background Knowledge

Prompt students to define the term *energy*.

Lab zone Discover Activity *What's in a Piece of Coal?*

Targeted Print and Technology Resources

Reading Strategy : Building Vocabulary

Presentation-Pro CD-ROM

Instruct

Energy Transformation and Fuels Discuss the processes fuels go through to provide energy and describe how energy changes from one form to another.

What Are Fossil Fuels? Help students identify and learn properties of the three major fossil fuels.

Fuel Supply and Demand Hold a class discussion on why fossil fuels are considered nonrenewable and consider problems caused by their depletion.

Targeted Print and Technology Resources

All in One Teaching Resources
L2 Guided Reading, pp. 313–316
L2 Transparencies, E45, E46, E47

www.SciLinks.org Web Code: scn-0551

Student Edition on Audio CD

Transparencies E45, E46, E47

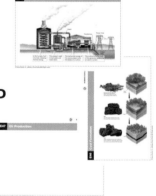

Assess

Section Assessment Questions

Have students use their sentences that include Key Terms to help answer the questions.

Reteach

Allow students to debate the advantages and disadvantages of the three major fossil fuels.

Targeted Print and Technology Resources

All in One Teaching Resources
• Section Summary, p. 312
L1 Review and Reinforce, p. 317
L3 Enrich, p. 318

Section 2 Renewable Sources of Energy

🕐 *2–3 periods, 1–1 1/2 blocks*

ABILITY LEVELS KEY
L1 Basic to Average
L2 For All Students
L3 Average to Advanced

Objectives

E.5.2.1 Explain the forms of energy provided by the sun.

E.5.2.2 Identify and describe various renewable sources of energy.

Key Terms

• solar energy • hydroelectric power • biomass fuel • gasohol
• geothermal energy

Local Standards

Preteach

Build Background Knowledge

Direct students to name and discuss other forms of energy that they know of besides oil, gas, and coal.

Lab zone **Discover Activity** *Can You Capture Solar Energy?*

Targeted Print and Technology Resources

All in One Teaching Resources

L2 Reading Strategy Transparency E48: Previewing Visuals

⊙ **Presentation-Pro CD-ROM**

Transparency E48

Instruct

Harnessing the Sun's Energy Discuss how the sun provides energy and use section figures to describe ways to collect this energy.

Hydroelectric Power Explain how the water cycle plays a role in how electricity is produced by flowing water.

Capturing the Wind Help students evaluate the advantages and disadvantages of wind-generated electricity.

Biomass Fuels List with students the types of biomass fuels and discuss their use.

Tapping Earth's Energy Use an illustration of a geothermal power plant to discuss the use and characteristics of geothermal energy.

The Promise of Hydrogen Power Help students consider the likelihood that hydrogen power will become a major energy source in the future.

Lab zone **Technology Lab** *Design and Build a Solar Cooker*

Targeted Print and Technology Resources

All in One Teaching Resources

L2 Guided Reading, pp. 321–324
L2 Transparencies, E49, E50
L2 Technology Lab: *Design and Build a Solar Cooker*, p.327

📼 **Lab Activity Video/DVD**
www.SciLinks.org Web Code: scn-0552

⊙ **Student Edition on Audio CD**

Transparency E49, E50

Assess

Section Assessment Questions

🔖 Have students use their completed Previewing Visuals graphic organizers to answer the questions.

Reteach

Challenge students to weigh the benefits and limitations of each renewable energy source.

Targeted Print and Technology Resources

All in One Teaching Resources

• Section Summary, p. 320
L1 Review and Reinforce, p. 325
L3 Enrich, p. 326

Section 3 **Nuclear Energy**

🕐 *1–2 periods, 1/2–1 block*

Objectives

E.5.3.1 Describe what happens during a nuclear fission reaction.

E.5.3.2 Explain how a nuclear power plant produces electricity.

E.5.3.3 Describe what takes place in a nuclear fusion reaction.

Key Terms

• nucleus • nuclear fission • reactor vessel • fuel rod • control rod • meltdown
• nuclear fusion

Local Standards

Preteach

Build Background Knowledge

Allow student volunteers to sketch diagrams of what they think an atom looks like, then have the class discuss the drawings and suggest changes.

Lab zone **Discover Activity** *Why Do They Fall?*

Targeted Print and Technology Resources

All in One **Teaching Resources**
L2 Reading Strategy Transparency E51: Comparing and Contrasting

💿 **Presentation-Pro CD-ROM**

Transparency E51

Instruct

Nuclear Fission Use section illustrations to help students explore how nuclear fission produces energy that can be harnessed to produce electricity.

Nuclear Power Plants Display a figure that prompts student discussion of the major parts of a nuclear power plant, the stages of fission-generated electricity, and the risks associated with nuclear power.

The Quest to Control Fusion Refer to a diagram illustrating fusion to describe a nuclear fusion reaction and explore the current limits on our ability to use this source of energy.

Targeted Print and Technology Resources

All in One **Teaching Resources**
L2 Guided Reading, pp. 331–333
L2 Transparencies, E52, E53, E54

www.PHschool.com Web Code: cep-5053

💿 **Student Edition on Audio CD**

Transparencies E52, E53, E54

Assess

Section Assessment Questions

Have students use their Venn diagrams comparing fission and fusion to answer the questions.

Reteach

Have students compare and contrast fission and fusion, and voice their opinions on these energy sources.

Targeted Print and Technology Resources

All in One **Teaching Resources**
• Section Summary, p. 330
L1 Review and Reinforce, p. 334
L3 Enrich, p. 335

Section 4 Energy Conservation

1–2 periods, 1/2–1 block

ABILITY LEVELS KEY
L1 Basic to Average
L2 For All Students
L3 Average to Advanced

Objectives

E.5.4.1 Name ways to ensure that there will be enough energy for the future.

E.5.4.2 Identify ways individuals can conserve energy.

Key Terms

• efficiency • insulation • energy conservation

Local Standards

Preteach

Build Background Knowledge

Encourage students to share what they already know about energy efficiency and energy conservation.

Discover Activity *Which Bulb Is More Efficient?*

Targeted Print and Technology Resources

All in One Teaching Resources

L2 Reading Strategy Transparency E55: Using Prior Knowledge

⊙ **Presentation-Pro CD-ROM**

Transparency E55

Instruct

Energy Efficiency Direct students to explore what determines energy efficiency and learn how it can affect the amount of energy used in heating and cooling, lighting, and transportation.

Energy Conservation Instruct students to list ways of reducing individual energy use, then to log their energy conservation efforts.

Consumer Lab *Keeping Comfortable*

Targeted Print and Technology Resources

All in One Teaching Resources

L2 Guided Reading, pp. 338–340

L2 Consumer Lab: *Keeping Comfortable,* pp. 343–345

Lab Activity Video/DVD Consumer Lab: *Keeping Comfortable*

www.PhSchool.com Web Code: cep-5042

⊙ **Student Edition on Audio CD**

Assess

Section Assessment Questions

Have students use their Using Prior Knowledge graphic organizers to answer the questions.

Reteach

With students, identify ways to improve energy efficiency and promote energy conservation.

Targeted Print and Technology Resources

All in One Teaching Resources

• Section Summary, p. 337

L1 Review and Reinforce, p. 341

L3 Enrich, p. 342

Chapter 5 Content Refresher

Go Online
NSTA-PD LINKS

For: Professional development support
Visit: www.SciLinks.org/PDLinks
Web Code: scf-0550

Professional Development

Section 1 Fossil Fuels

Fuel Supplies Fossils fuels take hundreds of millions of years to form, thus making their supplies limited. They form from the decomposing remains of plants and animals. Over time, the remains become buried under hundreds, even thousands, of feet of mud, rock, sand, and sometimes water.

The type of fuel that forms—oil, coal, natural gas—is determined by the combination of the plant and animal matter that is present, how long the material is buried, and the temperature and pressure that exists while the remains decompose.

As you can see in the graph below, the United States depends heavily on fossil fuels, with 86 percent of the nation's energy provided by coal, oil, and natural gas. Geologists, analysts, and economists predict that even with improvements in exploration technology, oil production could peak anytime between 2050 and 2100, and natural gas production could peak about 10 years after oil begins to decline. Advanced mining technology might allow access to coal deposits that are currently too expensive to recover. According to the U.S. Department of Energy, based on known domestic supplies, fossil fuels are expected to last no more than another ten generations.

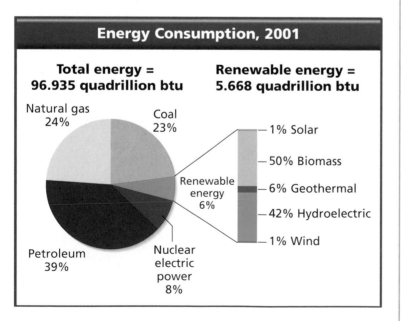

Energy Consumption, 2001

Total energy = 96.935 quadrillion btu

Renewable energy = 5.668 quadrillion btu

Natural gas 24%
Coal 23%
Renewable energy 6%
Petroleum 39%
Nuclear electric power 8%

1% Solar
50% Biomass
6% Geothermal
42% Hydroelectric
1% Wind

Section 2 Renewable Sources of Energy

Use of Renewable Energy Sources Renewable sources of energy exist in an inexhaustible or replaceable supply. They are generally considered less polluting than fossil fuels. Even the burning of biomass fuels, which produces carbon dioxide, a greenhouse gas, is considered less environmentally damaging than burning fossil fuels because harvested biomass is often replaced by new biomass crops that consume carbon dioxide.

In spite of these advantages, renewable energy sources are not widely used in the United States. As the graph indicates, only 6 percent of the total U.S. energy consumed in 2001 was produced through renewable energy. In fact, U.S. consumption of renewable energy actually declined by more than 12 percent in 2001. Fossil fuel prices are so low that consumers have no incentive to pursue alternative energy sources. Also, the performance of renewable energy sources can be erratic, affected by weather, water levels (for hydropower), wind, and land availability.

Address Misconceptions

Renewable energy sources were developed only recently as an alternative to fossil fuels. If true, this would ignore centuries of human history. For more on this misconception, see **Address Misconceptions** on page 169.

Biomass Feuls Besides reducing our dependence on fossil fuels, using biomass fuels helps reduce our waste-disposal problems. At the Mesquite Lake Resource Recovery Project in California, an electric power plant burns cow manure to produce enough electricity for thousands of homes. The manure would otherwise pose a disposal problem because of its high salt content and the presence of seeds that make it undesirable for use as a fertilizer.

Some problems are associated with the use of biomass materials. Growing biomass crops takes up land that could be used for growing food crops. Removing the stalks, leaves, and roots from biomass crops means crop wastes will not decay and enrich the soil. Unprotected soil is also more susceptible to erosion.

Section 3 Nuclear Energy

Storage of Radioactive Wastes Nuclear power production docs not produce greenhouse gas emissions, but it creates its own environmental problems. Radioactive wastes are a byproduct of nuclear power generation and include the spent fuel, as well as protective clothing, trash, or tools that have been contaminated by radioactive dust or particles. The safe disposal and isolation of these wastes are regulated.

One environmental issue is the storage of the highly radioactive spent fuel. Currently, it is stored at the nuclear plant where it was used. You can see these locations on the map. But many people are concerned about the potential for environmental contamination. The U.S. Department of Energy is carrying out a long-range plan for all of the nation's spent fuel to be stored deep underground at a geologic storage site at Yucca Mountain, Nevada. This option will reduce the potential for accidents at local storage sites. However, there is the potential for environmental contamination during transport of the spent fuel to Nevada.

U.S. Nuclear Power Plants

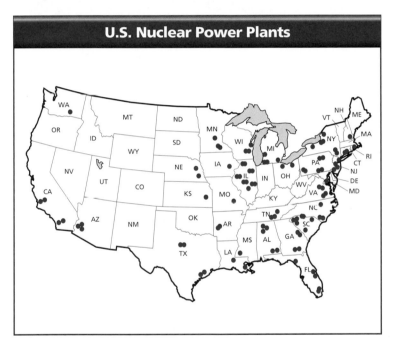

Chernobyl Investigation of the Chernobyl accident revealed two basic causes. First, the reactor was not housed in a containment building and therefore was unstable at low power. This type of reactor is not used commercially in North America or Western Europe because nuclear engineers consider it unsafe. Second, many of the plant's operators lacked scientific or technical expertise and made major errors when dealing with the initial problems.

The long-term health effects of the Chernobyl disaster are still being studied. Increases in birth defects and thyroid cancer in children have been documented. Other cancers are not expected to increase until 20 or more years after the accident.

Section 4 Energy Conservation

Making Informed Decisions Preserving energy resources for the future can certainly begin at home by promoting energy efficiency and energy conservation. But citizens don't have to "go it alone" in their energy conservation efforts, as the federal government offers resources and programs on these issues. A portion of the U.S. Department of Energy's web site (www.energysmartschools.gov) provides a quiz, especially designed for young people, which allows individuals to assess the energy efficiency of their homes.

The federal government also offers consumers a chance to make informed decisions when purchasing household appliances or homes. Appliances or homes earn the distinction of an "Energy Star" label when they meet energy efficiency standards established jointly by the Department of Energy and the U.S. Environmental Protection Agency (www.energystar.gov). The Energy Star program estimates that a family can reduce its energy consumption by one third by choosing designated energy-efficient appliances. More impressively, energy savings from the Energy Star program in 2002 were equivalent to the energy needed to power 15 million homes and reduce the emission of greenhouse gases by 14 million cars.

Help Students Read

Identifying Main Idea
Paragraph and Subheading Organization

Strategy Help students become aware of text organization and help them identify key information. By identifying the main idea and supporting details under each subheading, student will be able to distinguish important and unimportant information. Before you begin, assign students two paragraphs, each with a subhead, within the chapter to read.

Example
1. Main idea of a Paragraph Review with students the fact that most paragraphs have a topic sentence expressing the paragraph's main idea, while the other sentences provide supporting details.
2. Main Idea of a Subheading Guide students to make the connection that just as a paragraph has a main idea, the text under each subheading has a main idea carried within the paragraphs.
3. Inferring or Synthesizing a Main Idea State that it may be necessary to infer an unstated main idea by combining information carried in several paragraphs.
4. Practice Have students read through a section, noting each of the subheads as they read.

Energy Resources

- Complete student edition
- Video and audio
- Simulations and activities
- Section and chapter activities

 Chapter **Project**

Objectives

This project will give students an opportunity to examine energy use in various areas of their school and to suggest ways to reduce the school's energy consumption. After this Chapter Project, students will be able to

- create a data table for recording the types and amounts of energy used in the selected areas
- make observations and record data
- interpret data and draw conclusions as the basis for recommending ways to reduce energy use
- communicate findings and recommendations in a written report

Skills Focus

Observing, creating data tables, interpreting data, drawing conclusions, communicating

Project Time Line 2–3 weeks

All in One Teaching Resources

- Chapter Project Teacher Notes
- Chapter Project Worksheet 1
- Chapter Project Worksheet 2
- Chapter Project Worksheet 3
- Chapter Project Scoring Rubric

Well-maintained power lines ensure that electricity flows to homes and businesses. ▶

Developing a Plan

Each group should collect and evaluate numerical data, including the school's utility bills and readings of electric meters and fuel gauges. For purposes of comparison, making observations of the same area on different days and at different times of day should help students detect average and unusual uses.

Possible Materials

- No special materials are required, but students might benefit from a mock-up of a data collection table that provides some cues for sources of energy information.
- Students will find it helpful to use calculators and to have computer access to prepare group reports and a class proposal to the school administration.

Energy Resources

Show the Video Preview to introduce the Chapter Project and overview the chapter content. Discussion question: **What are some of the devices that Louie has converted to run on French fry oil?** (*Several cars, a boat engine, and a lawn mower*)

Lab zone Chapter **Project**

Energy Audit

How much energy does it take to keep your school running? In this chapter's project, you will work in a group to study energy use in your school.

Your Goal To report on one type of energy use in your school and make suggestions for saving energy

To complete this project, you must

- survey the types and amount of energy used in one area of your school
- identify ways to conserve energy in that area
- prepare a written report summarizing your observations and proposing your suggestions
- follow the safety guidelines in Appendix A

Plan It! Select an area of the school to study, such as a classroom, the cafeteria, or the school grounds. You could also consider the school's heating or cooling system or transportation to and from school. Then decide what type of data you will collect. When you begin your study, look for ways to reduce energy use.

Chapter 5 E ◆ 157

the project responsibilities among themselves as they see fit, *every* group member should take part in identifying the types and amounts of energy use in that group's area, recording and analyzing data, developing the written report, and suggesting energy conservation measures for their area of the school.

Performance Assessment

The Chapter Project Scoring Rubric will help you evaluate how well students complete the Chapter Project. You may want to share the scoring rubric with your students so they are clear about what will be expected of them. Students will be assessed on

- their ability to identify and evaluate all the types of energy used in the area studied
- their ability to make recommendations for reducing those energy uses and to communicate their findings and recommendations to others
- their participation in their group

Portfolio

Launching the Project

Discuss with your school principal what students will be doing in this project, and obtain approval for them to enter areas that are usually off-limits to them. If necessary, arrange for an adult to accompany students to these areas. Obtain copies of the school's utility and fuel bills for students' use in determining the amount of energy used.

Invite students to read the Chapter Project description. Lead students in brainstorming a list of areas in the school that they could

study. Take the class on a tour of the school building and grounds. Encourage students to keep track of the different energy uses they observe—electricity for lighting, fuel oil or natural gas for heating, electricity or natural gas for cooking, gasoline for the school buses, and so on.

Divide the class into groups of three or four, and let the groups meet briefly to choose areas to study. Monitor the groups' choices to avoid duplication. Emphasize that although each group's members may divide

Objectives
After completing the lesson, students will be able to

E.5.1.1 Explain how fuels provide energy.

E.5.1.2 Name the three major fossil fuels.

E.5.1.3 Explain why fossil fuels are considered nonrenewable resources.

Target Reading Skill

Building Vocabulary Explain that knowing the definitions of key-concept words helps students understand what they read.

Answers
Example sentences include:

- An example of **energy transformation** is **combustion,** when a **fuel** is burned and chemical energy is released.
- Oil, also called **petroleum,** is one of the **fossil fuels,** which are all made up of energy-rich **hydrocarbons.**
- Many products that come from oil are produced in a **refinery,** where oil is heated and separated.
- **Petrochemicals,** which are also made oil, are used to make medicines, from plastics, paints, and cosmetics.

Preteach

Build Background Knowledge `L2`

Defining Energy

Have students share how they got to school today. Point out that getting to school required energy. Then ask: **What is energy?** *(Answers will vary depending on students' prior science learning. Responses may include strength, power, or something that makes something happen.)* If necessary, point out that the scientific definition of *energy* is "the capacity to do work."

Reading Preview

Key Concepts
- How do fuels provide energy?
- What are the three major fossil fuels?
- Why are fossil fuels considered nonrenewable resources?

Key Terms
- fuel • energy transformation
- combustion • fossil fuel
- hydrocarbon • petroleum
- refinery • petrochemical

Target Reading Skill

Building Vocabulary Using a word in a sentence helps you think about how best to explain the word. After you read the section, reread the paragraphs that contain definitions of Key Terms. Use all the information you have learned to write a meaningful sentence using each Key Term.

Lab zone Discover **Activity**

What's in a Piece of Coal?
1. Observe a chunk of coal. Record your observations in as much detail as possible, including its color, texture, and shape.
2. Now use a hand lens to observe the coal more closely.
3. Examine your coal for fossils—imprints of plant or animal remains.

Think It Over
Observing What did you notice when you used the hand lens compared to your first observations? What do you think coal is made of?

How did you travel to school today? Whether you traveled in a car or a bus, walked, or rode your bike, you used some form of energy. The source of that energy was a fuel. A **fuel** is a substance that provides energy—such as heat, light, motion, or electricity—as the result of a chemical change.

Energy Transformation and Fuels

Rub your hands together quickly for several seconds. Did they become warmer? When you moved your hands, they had mechanical energy, the energy of motion. The friction of your hands rubbing together converted the mechanical energy to thermal energy, which you felt as heat. A change from one form of energy to another is called an **energy transformation,** or an energy conversion.

A fuel ▶

Lab zone Discover **Activity**

Skills Focus Observing

Materials lignite coal, hand lens

Time 10 minutes

Tips Lignite—the second stage of coal formation after peat—is the only form of coal that may contain recognizable plant remains.

Expected Outcome Students may or may not find fossils of plant remains in the coal samples. If fossils are present, they will be more noticeable with a hand lens.

Think It Over The lignite's texture, layering, and fossils (if present) can be seen more clearly with a hand lens. If fossils are visible, students should be able to infer that coal is made of plant remains.

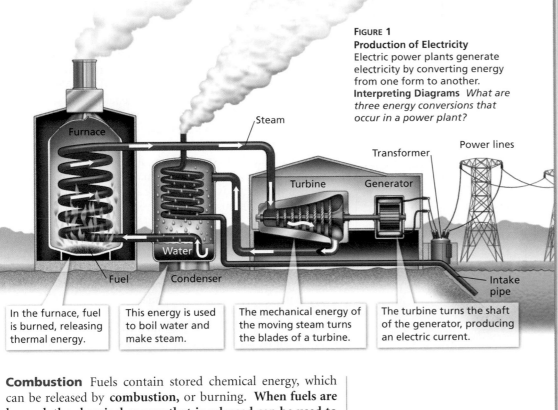

FIGURE 1
Production of Electricity
Electric power plants generate electricity by converting energy from one form to another.
Interpreting Diagrams *What are three energy conversions that occur in a power plant?*

Steam

Transformer

Power lines

Furnace

Turbine

Generator

Fuel

Water

Condenser

Intake pipe

| In the furnace, fuel is burned, releasing thermal energy. | This energy is used to boil water and make steam. | The mechanical energy of the moving steam turns the blades of a turbine. | The turbine turns the shaft of the generator, producing an electric current. |

Combustion Fuels contain stored chemical energy, which can be released by **combustion,** or burning. **When fuels are burned, the chemical energy that is released can be used to generate another form of energy, such as heat, light, motion, or electricity.** For example, when the gasoline in a car's engine is burned, it undergoes a chemical change. Some of the chemical energy stored in the gasoline is converted into thermal energy. This thermal energy is then converted to mechanical energy that moves the car.

Production of Electricity The chemical energy stored in fuels can be used to generate electricity. In an electric power plant, the thermal energy produced by burning fuel is used to boil water, making steam, as shown in Figure 1. The mechanical energy of the steam then turns a turbine. The turbine is connected to a generator, which consists of powerful magnets surrounded by coils of copper wire. As the magnets turn inside the wire coil, an electric current is produced. This current flows through power lines to homes and industries.

 Reading Checkpoint What energy transformations occur in a car's engine?

Go Online
SciLINKS NSTA
For: Links on fossil fuels
Visit: www.SciLinks.org
Web Code: scn-0551

Chapter 5 E ◆ 159

Differentiated Instruction

English Learners/Beginning L1
Vocabulary: Science Glossary
Pronounce and define aloud vocabulary words for students, such as *hydrocarbon, petroleum,* and *petrochemical.* Suggest that students start a glossary of vocabulary terms, with each term and its definition in English on one side of an index card and in the student's primary language on the other side. **learning modality: verbal**

English Learners/Intermediate L2
Vocabulary: Science Glossary Students can expand on the science glossary activity described in Beginning by adding other vocabulary words in this section: *combustion, fossil fuel, refinery.* Students can write a sentence that uses each of these words. Then, to give students an opportunity to practice pronunciation, call on individuals to read their sentences aloud.

Energy Transformation and Fuels

Teach Key Concepts L2
Changing Energy

Focus Remind students that rubbing hands together transforms mechanical energy into thermal energy.

Teach Ask: **What are other examples of energy conversions?** Some Examples include using a toaster (*Electrical energy changed to heat energy*), and burning a candle (*Chemical energy changed to light and heat energy*).

Apply Invite students who are interested in auto mechanics to explain how an internal combustion engine works. Ask: **What devices besides automobiles contain an internal combustion engine?** (*Gasoline-powered lawnmowers, snowblowers, chainsaws, portable generators, and the like*) **learning modality: verbal**

All in One Teaching Resources
• Transparency E45

Independent Practice L2

All in One Teaching Resources
• Guided Reading and Study Worksheet: *Fossil Fuels*

O Student Edition on Audio CD

Go Online
SciLINKS NSTA
For: Links on fossil fuels
Visit: www.SciLinks.org
Web Code: scn-0551

Download a worksheet that will guide students' review of Internet resources on fossil fuels.

Monitor Progress L2

Answers
Figure 1 When fuel is burned, chemical energy is converted to thermal energy (heat), some of which is converted to the mechanical energy of moving steam that turns turbines, converting mechanical energy into electrical energy.

 **Reading Checkpoint** Ignition (electrical energy) triggers an explosion of fuel (chemical energy) to create heat (thermal energy), which drives pistons that turn the crankshaft (mechanical energy).

What Are Fossil Fuels?

Teach Key Concepts　L2

High-Energy Fuels

Focus Review with students that all fossil fuels have similar energy-rich compositions and that all were formed over hundreds of millions of years.

Teach Emphasize that the high energy of fossil fuels arises from the hydrocarbons that compose them. Ask: **Why does the combustion of fossil fuels provide more energy per kilogram than the combustion of other fuels?** (*Hydrocarbons that make up fossil fuels contain compounds that are more energy-rich than other fuels.*)

Apply Challenge students to create a model showing how fossil fuels form over time. Provide materials: clay, soil, sand, pebbles, leaves, colored paper, and books or heavy weights. (*Models might include trapping materials such as leaves or colored paper between layers of soft material such as clay or soil, and then compressing these materials under heavy weights.*) Ask: **What happens to buried materials to turn them into fossil fuels?** (*Over time, heat and pressure change the materials into hydrocarbons.*) **learning modality: kinesthetic**

All in One　Teaching Resources

• Transparencies E46, E47

Help Students Read

Identifying Main Idea Refer to the Content Refresher, which provides guidelines for Identifying Main Ideas. Have students read the last sentence of the first paragraph, which is the main topic sentence. Ask: **Given this topic sentence, what are the main ideas that you should look for in this selection?** (*A description of each type of fossil fuel, how it is used, and the advantages and disadvantages of using each*) After reading What Are Fossil Fuels? have students work in pairs to create index cards with a summary of the information about each fossil fuel.

Lab zone　Skills Activity

Graphing

Use the data in the table below to make a circle graph showing the uses of energy in the United States. (To review circle graphs, see the Skills Handbook.)

End Use of Energy	Percent of Total Energy
Transportation	26.5
Industry	38.1
Homes and businesses	35.4

What Are Fossil Fuels?

Most of the energy used today comes from organisms that lived hundreds of millions of years ago. As these plants, animals, and other organisms died, their remains piled up. Layers of sand, rock, and mud buried the dead organisms. Over time, heat and the pressure of sediments changed the material into other substances. **Fossil fuels** are the energy-rich substances formed from the remains of organisms. **The three major fossil fuels are coal, oil, and natural gas.**

Fossil fuels are made of hydrocarbons. **Hydrocarbons** are energy-rich chemical compounds that contain carbon and hydrogen atoms. During combustion, the carbon and hydrogen atoms combine with oxygen from the air to form carbon dioxide and water. The combustion process releases energy in the forms of heat and light.

The combustion of fossil fuels provides more energy per kilogram than does the combustion of other fuels. One kilogram of coal, for example, can provide twice as much energy as one kilogram of wood. Oil and natural gas can provide three times as much energy as an equal mass of wood.

Coal Coal is a solid fossil fuel formed from plant remains. Figure 2 shows the process by which coal forms. People have burned coal to produce heat for thousands of years. Until the Industrial Revolution of the 1800s, however, wood was more convenient and cheaper than coal for most people. The huge energy needs of growing industries made it worthwhile to find, mine, and transport coal. Today, coal accounts for approximately 23 percent of the energy used in the United States. Most of that coal fuels electric power plants.

Before coal can be used to produce energy, it has to be mined, or removed from the ground. Miners use machines to chop the coal into chunks and lift it to the surface. Coal mining can be a dangerous job. Thousands of miners have been killed or injured in accidents in the mines. Many more suffer from lung diseases. Fortunately, modern safety procedures and better equipment have made coal mining safer.

Coal is the most plentiful fossil fuel in the United States. It is fairly easy to transport and provides a lot of energy when burned. But coal also has some disadvantages. Coal mining can increase erosion. Runoff from mines can cause water pollution. Also, burning most types of coal results in more air pollution than other fossil fuels. And, as mentioned above, coal mining can be dangerous.

Lab zone　Skills Activity

Skills Focus Graphing

Materials drawing compass, protractor, calculator (optional)

Time 15 minutes

Tips To determine the number of degrees for each use, students should first divide each percentage by 100. Then, they should multiply each of those numbers by 360° and round off so the three sections total 360°.

Expected Outcome Transportation 96°; Industry 137°; Homes and businesses 127°.

Extend Let students brainstorm specific types of energy uses included in each "end use" category—for example, oil for heating, electricity for refrigeration and lighting, gasoline for automobiles, and so on. **learning modality: logical/mathematical**

FIGURE 2
Coal Formation

Coal is formed from the remains of trees and other plants that grew in swamps hundreds of millions of years ago. **Relating Diagrams and Photos** *What are two ways that peat and coal differ?*

Decomposing Plant Matter
When swamp plants die, their decomposing remains build up.

Peat
Over time, plant remains pile up and form peat. Peat can be burned as fuel.

Coal
Under increasing pressure from sediments, peat is compacted. Eventually, peat becomes coal. Coal is a more efficient fuel than peat.

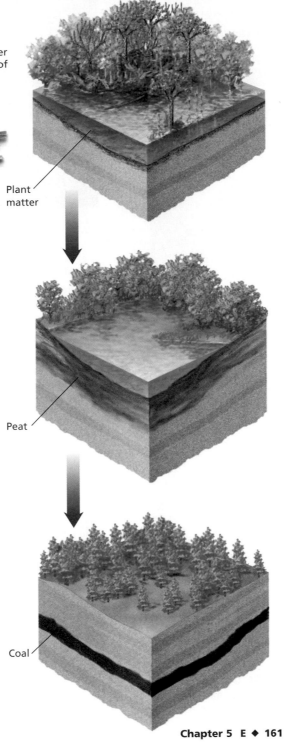

Plant matter

Peat

Coal

Chapter 5 E ◆ 161

Lab zone · Build Inquiry

L2

Classifying Peat and Coal

Materials samples of peat moss, lignite, bituminous coal, and anthracite; 2 small plastic bags; hand lenses

Time 10 minutes

Focus Explain to students that peat is the decayed remains of plants—the early stage of coal formation.

Teach Give each group hand lenses, a plastic bag containing a sample of peat moss, and a second bag containing the three types of coal. **CAUTION:** *Rinse the coal thoroughly to remove any dust. Make sure students wash their hands after handling the samples.* Let students examine the samples, noting similarities and differences between them. Then list the following names and characteristics on the board, and challenge students to identify each coal sample:

- *Lignite:* dark brown; layered; may contain recognizable fragments of plant remains
- *Bituminous coal:* denser than lignite; black; may have bands
- *Anthracite:* hardest type of coal; black; shiny

Apply Ask: **Why are the coal samples darker and harder than the peat?** *(Coal has been buried longer than peat and therefore subjected to much greater pressure.)* **learning modality: kinesthetic**

Monitor Progress _____ L2

Skills Check Have each student create a flowchart showing how fossil fuels are formed. Students can save their flowcharts in their portfolios.

Portfolio

Answer

Figure 2 Possible answers: Peat has a looser texture, is lighter in color, and is more mixed in composition. Coal has been buried deeper and therefore longer than peat. Coal is a more efficient fuel than peat.

E ● 161

Observing Oil's Consistency

Materials 2 small paper cups, 30 mL dark molasses, paper towel, aluminum pan

Time 10 minutes

Focus Explain to students that molasses is very similar to crude oil in consistency.

Teach CAUTION: *If you are concerned about spills, have a few volunteers perform this activity as a demonstration for the other students.* Give each student or group a paper towel, a small paper cup containing about 30 mL of dark molasses, and an empty cup. Invite students to pour the molasses from one cup to the other over the pan, try to pick some up with the paper towel, and touch some between the thumb and index finger. Students will find that the molasses is too thick to pour readily, is not absorbed by the towel, and is sticky.

Apply Ask: **How easy do you think it would be to clean up crude oil that spilled on a beach?** *(Extremely difficult)* Explain that techniques such as bioremediation must be used if cleanup is to be successful. Bioremediation involves using biological agents, such as bacteria, to digest the oil. **learning modality: kinesthetic**

Use Visuals: Figure 3

Refining Crude Oil

Focus Using the figure, review the basic processes involved in refining oil.

Teach Call on students to name several products made by refining crude oil. Ask: **Which products are separated out at the lowest temperatures?** *(Gasoline, other gases, jet fuel)* **Which are separated out at the highest temperatures?** *(Diesel fuel, grease and wax, asphalt)*

Apply Ask: **What must be done to all crude oil before any products can be obtained from it at a refinery?** *(It must be heated.)* **learning modality: visual**

FIGURE 3
Oil Production
Crude oil is first pumped out of the ground and then refined. In the refining process, crude oil is heated and separated to make different products.

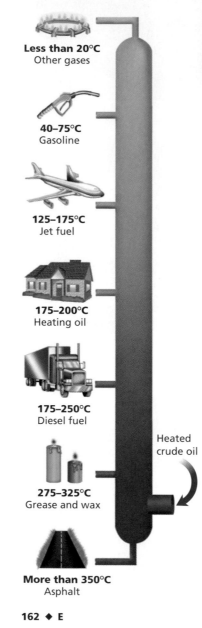

Less than 20°C
Other gases

40–75°C
Gasoline

125–175°C
Jet fuel

175–200°C
Heating oil

175–250°C
Diesel fuel

275–325°C
Grease and wax

Heated crude oil

More than 350°C
Asphalt

Oil Oil is a thick, black, liquid fossil fuel. It formed from the remains of small animals, algae, and other organisms that lived in oceans and shallow inland seas hundreds of millions of years ago. **Petroleum** is another name for oil, from the Latin words *petra* (rock) and *oleum* (oil). Petroleum accounts for more than one third of the energy produced in the world. Fuel for most cars, airplanes, trains, and ships comes from petroleum. In addition, many homes are heated by oil.

Most oil deposits are located underground in tiny holes in sandstone or limestone. The oil fills the holes somewhat like the way water fills the holes of a sponge. Because oil deposits are usually located deep below the surface, finding oil is difficult. Scientists can use sound waves to test an area for oil. Even using this technique, however, only about one out of every six wells drilled produces a usable amount of oil.

When oil is first pumped out of the ground, it is called crude oil. To be made into useful products, crude oil must undergo a process called refining. A factory in which crude oil is heated and separated into fuels and other products is called a **refinery**. In Figure 3, you can see some of the products made by refining crude oil. Many other products you use every day are also made from crude oil. **Petrochemicals** are compounds that are made from oil. Petrochemicals are used to make plastics, paints, medicines, and cosmetics.

Reading Checkpoint What is a refinery?

Natural Gas Natural gas is a mixture of methane and other gases. Natural gas forms from some of the same organisms as oil. Because it is less dense than oil, natural gas often rises above an oil deposit, forming a pocket of gas in the rock.

Pipelines transport natural gas from its source to the places where it is used. If all the gas pipelines in the United States were connected, they would reach to the moon and back—twice! Natural gas can also be compressed into a liquid and stored in tanks as fuel for trucks and buses.

Natural gas has several advantages. It produces large amounts of energy but lower levels of many air pollutants than coal or oil. It is also easy to transport once the network of pipelines is built. One disadvantage of natural gas is that it is highly flammable. A gas leak can cause a violent explosion and fire.

Gas companies help to prevent dangerous explosions from leaks. If you use natural gas in your home, you probably are familiar with the "gas" smell that alerts you whenever there is unburned gas in the air. You may be surprised to learn that natural gas actually has no odor at all. What causes the strong smell? Gas companies add a chemical with a distinct smell to the gas before it is piped to homes and businesses so that people can detect a gas leak.

FIGURE 4
Natural Gas
More than 700,000 kilometers of natural gas pipelines run underground in the United States. Here, a technician prepares a new section of pipe.

Math Analyzing Data

Fuels and Electricity
The circle graph shows which energy sources are used to produce electricity in the United States.

1. **Reading Graphs** What does each wedge of the circle represent?

2. **Interpreting Data** Which energy source is used to generate most of the electricity in the United States?

3. **Drawing Conclusions** What percentage of the electricity production in the United States relies on fossil fuels?

4. **Predicting** How might the circle graph differ 50 years from now? Give reasons to support your prediction.

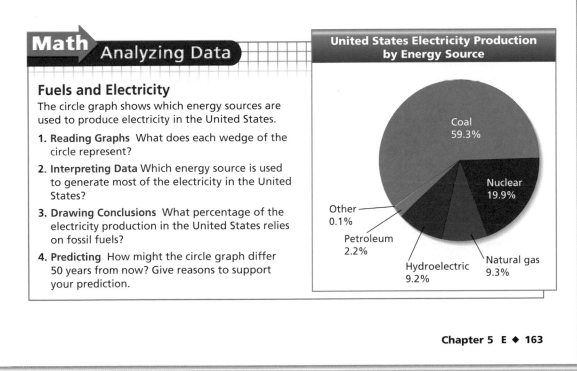

United States Electricity Production by Energy Source

- Coal 59.3%
- Nuclear 19.9%
- Natural gas 9.3%
- Hydroelectric 9.2%
- Petroleum 2.2%
- Other 0.1%

Lab zone  **Build Inquiry** L1

Calculating Lengths of Gas Pipeline

Materials calculator

Time 5 minutes

Focus Point out the text statement "If all the gas pipelines in the United States were connected, they would reach to the moon and back—twice!"

Teach Have students use the moon's average distance from Earth *(384,392 km)* to calculate the total length of U.S. gas pipelines *(384,392 km × 4 = 1,537,568 km).*

Apply Ask: **How does this distance compare to the width of your state?** *(Have that value ready.)* **learning modality: logical/mathematical**

Math Analyzing Data

Math Skill Making and interpreting graphs

Focus Point out that a circle graph can be used to show portions of a whole.

Teach Ask: **If the entire circle represents 100 percent, what does one fourth of the circle represent?** *(Twenty-five percent.)* **Why do you think a circle graph was chosen for this exercise?** *(Answers should explain that the graph emphasizes the differences between the proportions of the various energy sources.)*

Answers
1. The percentage of total U.S. electricity that is produced using the labeled energy source
2. Coal
3. 70.8% (59.3% coal, 9.3% natural gas, 2.2% petroleum)
4. Answers might include: Coal, petroleum, and natural gas might decrease because they are in limited supply; nuclear and hydroelectric energy sources might increase to replace fossil fuels.

Differentiated Instruction

Gifted and Talented L1
Researching Pipelines Challenge students to use reference books or online sources to find out where most natural gas pipelines are located in the United States. Have them learn how much natural gas moves through U.S. pipelines each day. **learning modality: logical/mathematical**

Special Needs L3
Observing States of Matter Have students compare samples that represent the states of matter most commonly associated with the three fossil fuels: solid—chunk of coal; liquid—molasses to represent oil; gas—closed, empty jar to represent natural gas. **learning modality: logical/mathematical**

Monitor Progress L2

Skills Check Have each student create a simple, three-column table listing the advantages and disadvantages of each type of fossil fuel. Students can save their tables in their portfolios.

Portfolio

Answer

✓ **Reading Checkpoint** A factory in which crude oil is heated and separated into fuels and other products.

Fuel Supply and Demand

Teach Key Concepts L2
Nonrenewable Resources

Focus Explain that fossil fuels are nonrenewable and unevenly distributed.

Teach Ask: **What evidence do we have that our demand for fossil fuels might use up our supply?** *(Oil reserves took 500 million years to form. New reserves can't form quickly enough to replace those used up.)*

Apply Ask: **How does uneven distribution contribute to global problems?** *(Answers should focus on fuel-rich and fuel-dependent nations.)* **learning modality: logical/ mathematical**

Monitor Progress L2
Answer

Reading Checkpoint They consume more energy resources than they produce.

Assess

Reviewing Key Concepts

1. a. a substance that provides energy as the result of a chemical change **b.** Stored chemical energy is converted into other forms of energy. **c.** Thermal energy from burning fuel is used to boil water, producing steam. Mechanical energy of the steam turns a turbine connected to a generator, and the generator produces electrical energy.
2. a. coal, oil, and natural gas **b.** Possible answer: Coal is easy to transport, but it pollutes air. Oil provides large amounts of energy but is hard to recover. Natural gas produces fewer air pollutants but is highly flammable. **c.** Answers will be based on the advantages and disadvantages identified in question 2b.
3. a. They take hundreds of millions of years to form. **b.** Sample answers: take public transportation, turn off lights not in use, drive fuel-efficient car.

Reteach L1
Have students debate the advantages and disadvantages of fossil fuels.

All in One Teaching Resources
• Section Summary: *Fossil Fuels*
• Review and Reinforcement: *Fossil Fuels*
• Enrich: *Fossil Fuels*

FIGURE 5
Supply and Demand
In the 1970s, a group of oil-exporting nations reduced their oil exports to the United States. Gasoline shortages resulted.

Fuel Supply and Demand

The many advantages of using fossil fuels as an energy source have made them essential to modern life. **But since fossil fuels take hundreds of millions of years to form, they are considered nonrenewable resources.** For example, Earth's known oil reserves took 500 million years to form. One fourth of this oil has already been used. If fossil fuels continue to be used more rapidly than they are formed, the reserves will eventually be used up.

Many nations that consume large amounts of fossil fuels have very small reserves. They have to buy oil, natural gas, and coal from nations with large supplies. The United States, for example, uses about one third of all the oil produced in the world. But only 3 percent of the world's oil supply is located in this country. The difference must be purchased from countries with large oil supplies. The uneven distribution of fossil fuel reserves has often been a cause of political problems in the world.

Reading Checkpoint Why are some nations dependent on others for fossil fuels?

Section 1 Assessment

Target Reading Skill Building Vocabulary Use your sentences to help you answer the questions below.

Reviewing Key Concepts
1. **a. Defining** What is a fuel?
   b. Explaining How do fuels provide energy?
   c. Sequencing Describe in order the energy transformations that occur in the production of electricity at a power plant.
2. **a. Listing** What are the three main fossil fuels?
   b. Comparing and Contrasting List an advantage and a disadvantage of each fossil fuel discussed in this section.
   c. Making Judgments Suppose you were designing a new power plant that would burn fossil fuel to generate electricity. Which fossil fuel would you recommend? Give two reasons for your answer.
3. **a. Reviewing** Why are fossil fuels considered nonrenewable resources?
   b. Problem Solving List three things you can do to reduce your dependence on fossil fuels.

Lab zone At-Home Activity

Heating Fuel Pros and Cons Talk to an adult family member to find out what type of fuel heats or cools your home. Then, with the family member, list some advantages and disadvantages of that type of fuel. Share what you learned with your classmates. What fuel source is used by the majority of students in your class?

Lab zone Chapter Project

Keep Students on Track Students should observe their areas at different times of day to determine which types of energy use take place. Explain that the school's meters and gauges show the amount of fuel used for the entire building. To estimate energy used in one area, students can divide the total amount of fuel used by the number of rooms in the school.

Lab zone At Home Activity

Heating Fuel Pros and Cons
Before students present the activity at home, ask volunteers to name advantages and disadvantages of the three fossil fuels. After students report the types of fuel that are used at home, create a class graph of the data.

Renewable Sources of Energy

Reading Preview

Key Concepts
- What forms of energy does the sun provide?
- What are some renewable sources of energy?

Key Terms
- solar energy
- hydroelectric power
- biomass fuel
- gasohol
- geothermal energy

⊙ Target Reading Skill
Previewing Visuals Before you read, preview Figure 7. Then write two questions that you have about the diagram in a graphic organizer like the one below. As you read, answer your questions.

Solar House

Q.	How does the house capture solar energy?
A.	
Q.	

Lab zone **Discover Activity**

Can You Capture Solar Energy?

1. Pour 250 milliliters of water into each of two resealable, clear plastic bags.
2. Record the water temperature in each bag. Seal the bags.
3. Put one bag in a dark or shady place. Put the other bag in a place where it will receive direct sunlight.
4. Predict what the temperature of the water in each bag will be after 30 minutes.
5. Record the temperatures after 30 minutes.

Think It Over
Developing Hypotheses How did the water temperature in each bag change? What could account for these results?

You've just arrived at the campsite for your family vacation. The sun streaming through the trees warms your face. A breeze stirs, carrying with it the smell of a campfire. Maybe you'll start your day with a dip in the warm water of a nearby hot spring.

You might be surprised to learn that even in these woods, you are surrounded by energy resources. The sun warms the air, the wind blows, and heat from inside Earth warms the waters of the spring. These sources of energy are all renewable—they are constantly being supplied. Scientists are trying to find ways to put these renewable energy resources to work to meet people's energy needs.

◄ Campers surrounded by renewable resources

E ◆ 165

Lab zone **Discover Activity**

Skills Focus Developing hypotheses
Materials 500 mL water, 2 sealable clear plastic bags, 2 thermometers
Time 10 minutes for setup; 5 minutes for follow-up
Tips Provide room-temperature water for Step 1. If your classroom does not have a sunny window, place bags in another location where there is direct sunlight.

Expected Outcome Specific temperatures will vary.

Think It Over The water temperature stayed the same in the dark/shaded bag, while the water temperature increased in the bag placed in sunlight. The water in that bag absorbed energy from the sun.

Objectives
After completing the lesson, students will be able to
E.5.2.1 Explain the forms of energy provided by the sun.
E.5.2.2 Identify and describe various renewable sources of energy.

Target Reading Skill ⊙

Previewing Visuals Explain that looking at the visuals before they read helps students activate prior knowledge and predict what they are about to read.

Answers
Possible questions and answers include: **How does the house capture solar energy?** (*Active solar collectors on the roof, large windows on south and west sides that act as passive solar collectors*) **What does the equipment that is on the roof and in the basement do?** (*Active solar cells on the roof generate electricity that can be stored in a battery in the basement. Water heated in an active solar collector on the roof is stored in a tank in the basement and used to heat the house.*) **What is the difference between active and passive solar heating systems?** (*Both convert sunlight into thermal energy, but only active systems use pumps and fans to distribute heat.*

All in One Teaching Resources
- Transparency E48

Preteach

Build Background Knowledge   L2

Identifying Alternate Energy Sources
Ask students: **What other sources of energy can you name besides coal, oil, and natural gas?** (*Answers will vary depending on students' prior learning but will likely include renewable sources covered in this section and nuclear energy covered in the next section.*)

Harnessing the Sun's Energy

Teach Key Concepts   L2
Solar Technologies

Focus Tell students that various technologies are associated with capturing solar energy.

Teach Ask: **Which approach to capturing solar energy involves the least complicated technology?** *(Passive solar heating)*

Extend Show students several examples of solar cells and small solar-powered motors, available from home-electronics stores. Ask: **What energy conversions are taking place?** *(Solar energy to electrical energy to mechanical energy)* **learning modality: kinesthetic**

All in One Teaching Resources

• Transparency E49

Independent Practice   L2

All in One Teaching Resources

• Guided Reading and Study Worksheet: *Renewable Sources of Energy*

🔘 **Student Edition on Audio CD**

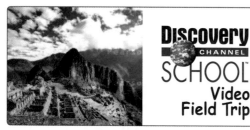

Energy Resources

Show the Video Field Trip to let students experience the excitement of a race with cars powered by solar energy and understand the energy transformation in these cars. Discussion questions: **What are the advantages of using solar energy as an energy source?** *(It does not pollute, is inexpensive, and can be stored for later use.)*

FIGURE 6
Solar Power Plant
This mirror collects energy from the sun and powers an electric plant in New South Wales, Australia. **Inferring** *Why is the Australian desert a practical location for a solar power plant?*

Energy Resources
Video Preview
▶ Video Field Trip
Video Assessment

Harnessing the Sun's Energy

The warmth you feel on a sunny day is **solar energy,** or energy from the sun. **The sun constantly gives off energy in the forms of light and heat.** Solar energy is the source, directly or indirectly, of most other renewable energy resources. In one day, Earth receives enough solar energy to meet the energy needs of the entire world for 40 years. Solar energy does not cause pollution, and it will not run out for billions of years.

So why hasn't solar energy replaced energy from fossil fuels? One reason is that solar energy is only available when the sun is shining. Another problem is that the energy Earth receives from the sun is very spread out. To obtain a useful amount of power, it is necessary to collect solar energy from a large area.

Solar Power Plants One way to capture the sun's energy involves using giant mirrors. In a solar power plant, rows of mirrors focus the sun's rays to heat a tank of water. The water boils, creating steam, which can then be used to generate electricity.

Solar Cells Solar energy can be converted directly into electricity in a solar cell. A solar cell has a negative and a positive terminal, like a battery. When light hits the cell, an electric current is produced. Solar cells power some calculators, lights, and other small devices. However, it would take more than 5,000 solar cells the size of your palm to produce enough electricity for a typical American home.

Passive Solar Heating Solar energy can be used to heat buildings with passive solar systems. A passive solar system converts sunlight into thermal energy, which is then distributed without using pumps or fans. Passive solar heating is what occurs in a parked car on a sunny day. Solar energy passes through the car's windows and heats the seats and other car parts. These parts transfer heat to the air, and the inside of the car warms. The same principle can be used to heat a home.

Active Solar Heating An active solar system captures the sun's energy, and then uses pumps and fans to distribute the heat. First, light strikes the dark metal surface of a solar collector. There, it is converted to thermal energy. Water is pumped through pipes in the solar collector to absorb the thermal energy. The heated water then flows to a storage tank. Finally, pumps and fans distribute the heat throughout the building.

✓ **Reading Checkpoint** How do solar cells work?

FIGURE 7
Solar House

A solar house uses passive and active heating systems to convert solar energy into heat and electricity.

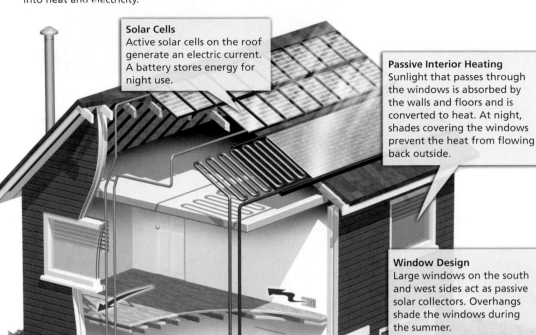

Solar Cells
Active solar cells on the roof generate an electric current. A battery stores energy for night use.

Passive Interior Heating
Sunlight that passes through the windows is absorbed by the walls and floors and is converted to heat. At night, shades covering the windows prevent the heat from flowing back outside.

Window Design
Large windows on the south and west sides act as passive solar collectors. Overhangs shade the windows during the summer.

Solar Water Heater
Water is pumped from a storage tank to an active solar collector on the roof. Sunlight heats the water, which is then returned to the tank. The water then heats pipes that heat the air throughout the house.

Backup Heat Source
The house has a wood stove to provide backup heat on cloudy days.

Chapter 5 E ◆ 167

Differentiated Instruction

Less Proficient Readers　**L1**
Previewing Visuals Have students study Figure 7 and record at least three questions about the information in the illustration. Then have students listen to this section, Harnessing the Sun's Energy, on the *Student Edition on Audio CD*. As students listen, have them write the answers to the questions they prepared. **learning modality: verbal**

Use Visuals: Figure 7　　L1
Exploring a Solar House

Focus Review the passive and active solar heating systems illustrated in Figure 7.

Teach Call on students to describe the various features labeled in the solar house. Ask: **Which of these solar systems do you have in your own home?** (*Most students will probably identify passive interior heating and window design.*) If any students say that their homes are equipped with active solar systems, invite those students to describe the devices and their operation to the class.

Apply Remind students that office buildings and institutions might use solar systems. Ask: **Where else in the community do you see examples of passive or active solar systems?** (*Allow a day or two for students to report examples.*) **learning modality: visual**

All in One Teaching Resources
• Transparency E49

Lab zone　Build Inquiry
　　　　　　　　　　　　　　　　L1

Observing Passive Solar Heating

Materials 2 thermometers, large glass jar
Time 10 minutes

Focus Tell students that they can measure the difference in temperature inside and outside a passive solar object.

Teach Take students outdoors on a sunny day away from the pavement to a spot that receives direct sunlight. Have students note the temperatures of the two thermometers. Put one thermometer in a glass jar turned upside down on the ground and leave the other thermometer in open air. Have students compare the temperatures after several minutes. Ask: **Why is the temperature higher inside the glass jar?** (*The glass allows light to pass into the jar but traps heat inside the jar.*) **learning modality: logical/mathematical**

Monitor Progress　　　　L2

Oral Presentation Call on students to describe an example of technology that captures solar energy for human use.

Answers
Figure 6 The Australian desert receives intense, consistent sunlight over a large area.

✓ **Reading Checkpoint** By converting solar energy into electrical energy

E ● 167

Hydroelectric Power

Teach Key Concepts L2
Power From Water

Focus Tell students that the water cycle plays a role in generating electricity from flowing water.

Teach Tell students that hydroelectric power depends on the controlled flow of water through tunnels (spillways or gates) in dams. Ask: **What energy conversion is taking place as flowing water turns turbines connected to a generator?** *(Mechanical energy is converted to electrical energy.)*

Apply Ask: **What are some negative effects that dams might have on the environment?** *(Possible answer: Dams can change ecosystems when they are built.)* **learning modality: logical/mathematical**

Capturing the Wind

Teach Key Concepts L2
Wind Energy

Focus Remind students that solar energy produces convection currents that produce wind for wind energy. It also provides energy for the water cycle, which is essential to hydroelectric power.

Teach Tell students that similar to the way flowing water produces electricity in a hydroelectric dam, wind generates power by moving turbines that are connected to generators. Ask: **What weather conditions are disruptive to harnessing wind energy?** *(Winds irregular; no winds; winds too strong; weather stagnant—no winds generated)* **Name two reasons why wind farms are best placed in remote locations.** *(Possible answers: Wind farms are noisy; they require a lot of space; other fuels may be difficult to transport to remote sites.)*

Apply Divide the class into two groups; assign one group water power and the other wind power. Ask: **What are the advantages of this source of electricity, and why should our community adopt it?** *(Students should consider climate and geographic restrictions, cost, potential environmental damage, and so on.)* Have each group give a brief presentation on its position. **learning modality: verbal**

FIGURE 8
Water and Wind Power
Both this dam in Arizona and this wind farm in California use renewable sources of energy to generate power.

Lab zone Try This **Activity**

Blowing in the Wind
You can make a model that shows how wind can do the work necessary to produce energy. Using a pinwheel and other materials, construct a device that lifts a small object when the wind blows. Then use a fan to test your device.

Making Models What parts of a wind power plant do the fan and pinwheel represent?

168 ◆ E

Hydroelectric Power

The sun is one source of renewable energy. **Other renewable sources of energy include water, the wind, biomass fuels, geothermal energy, and hydrogen.**

Solar energy is the indirect source of water power. Recall that in the water cycle, energy from the sun heats water on Earth's surface, forming water vapor. The water vapor condenses and falls back to Earth as rain and snow. As the water flows over the land, it provides another source of energy.

Hydroelectric power is electricity produced by flowing water. A dam across a river blocks the flow of water, creating a body of water called a reservoir. When a dam's floodgates are opened, water flows through tunnels at the bottom of the dam. As the water moves through the tunnels, it turns turbines, which are connected to a generator.

Today, hydroelectric power is the most widely used source of renewable energy. Unlike solar energy, flowing water provides a steady supply of energy. Once a dam and power plant are built, producing electricity is inexpensive and does not create air pollution. But hydroelectric power has limitations. In the United States, most suitable rivers have already been dammed. And dams can have negative effects on the environment.

Reading Checkpoint What is hydroelectric power?

Capturing the Wind

Like water power, wind energy is also an indirect form of solar energy. The sun heats Earth's surface unevenly. As a result of this uneven heating, different areas of the atmosphere have different temperatures and air pressures. The differences in pressure cause winds as air moves from one area to another.

Wind can be used to turn a turbine and generate electricity. Wind farms consist of many windmills. Together, the windmills generate large amounts of power.

Lab zone Try This **Activity**

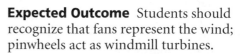

Skills Focus Making models

Materials pinwheels; sticks or pencils; spools; string or monofilament; paper squares, coins, or bottle caps; tape; fans

Time 20 minutes

Tips Tell students to use simple designs.

Expected Outcome Students should recognize that fans represent the wind; pinwheels act as windmill turbines.

Extend Compare models to actual windmills. **learning modality: kinesthetic**

Wind is the fastest-growing energy source in the world. Wind energy does not cause pollution. In places where fuels are difficult to transport, wind energy is the major source of power.

But wind energy has drawbacks. Few places have winds that blow steadily enough to provide much energy. Wind energy generators are noisy and can be destroyed by very strong winds. Still, as fossil fuels become more scarce, wind energy will become more important.

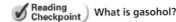 **Reading Checkpoint** How can wind be used to generate electricity?

Biomass Fuels

Wood was probably the first fuel ever used for heat and light. Wood belongs to a group of fuels called **biomass fuels,** which are made from living things. Other biomass fuels include leaves, food wastes, and even manure. As fossil fuel supplies shrink, people are taking a closer look at biomass fuels. For example, when oil prices rose in the early 1970s, Hawaiian sugar cane farmers began burning sugar cane wastes to generate electricity. At one point, these wastes provided almost one fourth of the electricity used on the island of Kauai.

Aside from being burned as fuel, biomass materials can also be converted into other fuels. For example, corn, sugar cane, and other crops can be used to make alcohol. Adding the alcohol to gasoline forms a mixture called **gasohol.** Gasohol can be used as fuel for cars. Bacteria can produce methane gas when they decompose biomass materials in landfills. That methane can be used to heat buildings. And some crops, such as soybeans, can produce oil that can be used as fuel, which is called biodiesel fuel.

Biomass fuels are renewable resources. But it takes time for new trees to replace those that have been cut down. And producing alcohol and methane in large quantities is expensive. As a result, biomass fuels are not widely used today in the United States. But as fossil fuels become scarcer, biomass fuels may play a larger role in meeting energy needs.

Reading Checkpoint What is gasohol?

FIGURE 9
Biomass Fuels
Biomass fuels are fuels that are made from living things.
Comparing and Contrasting *How are biomass fuels similar to energy sources such as wind and water? How are they different?*

▲ A woman uses a wood-fired oven in Nepal.

▲ This car runs on vegetable oil.

Biomass Fuels

Teach Key Concepts　L2
Fuels From Living Things

Focus Review the definition of *biomass fuels.*

Teach Explain that biomass can be burned as fuel and converted into other fuels. Ask: **Name five biomass products that can be burned as fuel.** (*Examples include: trees/wood, corn, sugar cane, landfill wastes, leaves, manure, food wastes.*)

Apply Ask: **Why do you think biomass fuels are commonly used in less developed nations?** (*They are easy to obtain and do not require special technology.*) **learning modality: verbal**

🚩 Address Misconceptions
New Renewables?

Focus Suggest to students that renewable energy has been around for a long time.

Teach Many people believe that renewable energy sources were developed only recently as environment-friendly alternatives to fossil fuels, but this is not the case. Ask: **What types of energy were used before people could generate electricity?** (*Burning wood, peat, other biomass fuels; wind, water*)

Apply Ask: **Why did renewable sources become less popular?** (*Energy from fossil fuels is easier to obtain, more convenient.*) **learning modality: verbal**

Monitor Progress ＿＿＿＿　L2

Answers
Figure 9 All derive their energy from the sun and are renewable, but biomass fuels are replenished slowly.

✔ Reading Checkpoint Hydroelectric power is electricity produced by flowing water.

✔ Reading Checkpoint Wind turns turbines connected to generators.

✔ Reading Checkpoint Gasohol is car fuel that is a mixture of gasoline and an alcohol made using biomass products.

Tapping Earth's Energy

Teach Key Concepts
Power From Geothermal Energy

Focus Remind students that geothermal energy is the intense heat from Earth's interior.

Teach Direct students' attention to Figure 10. Ask: **How is electricity generated in a geothermal power plant?** *(Cold water piped underground is heated by magma and turns into steam, which is used to generate electricity.)*

Apply Ask: **Why isn't geothermal energy more commonly used?** *(Magma comes close to the surface only in a few areas; deep wells required in other places would be expensive.)*
learning modality: visual

All in One Teaching Resources
• Transparency E50

The Promise of Hydrogen Power

Teach Key Concepts
Energy for the Future

Focus Tell students that scientists want to develop hydrogen power because of its potential to provide huge amounts of energy.

Teach Ask: **What are the advantages and disadvantages associated with hydrogen power?** *(Advantages: abundant, burns cleanly, doesn't pollute air; disadvantages: expensive to produce, almost all hydrogen is combined with oxygen in water.)*

Apply Ask: **What examples do we have of hydrogen power being supplied by fuel cells?** *(Experimental cars, space shuttle)* **learning modality: logical/mathematical**

Tapping Earth's Energy

Below Earth's surface are pockets of very hot liquid rock called magma. In some places, magma is very close to the surface. The intense heat from Earth's interior that warms the magma is called **geothermal energy.**

In certain regions, such as Iceland and New Zealand, magma heats underground water to the boiling point. In these places, the hot water and steam can be valuable sources of energy. For example, in Reykjavík, Iceland, 90 percent of homes are heated by water warmed underground in this way. Geothermal energy can also be used to generate electricity, as shown in Figure 10.

Geothermal energy is an unlimited source of cheap energy. But it does have disadvantages. There are only a few places where magma comes close to Earth's surface. Elsewhere, very deep wells would be needed to tap this energy. Drilling deep wells is very expensive. Even so, geothermal energy is likely to play a part in meeting energy needs in the future.

Reading Checkpoint How can geothermal energy be used to generate electricity?

FIGURE 10
Geothermal Energy
A geothermal power plant uses heat from Earth's interior as an energy source. Cold water is piped deep into the ground, where it is heated by magma. The resulting steam can be used for heat or to generate electricity.
Making Generalizations *What is one advantage and one disadvantage of geothermal energy?*

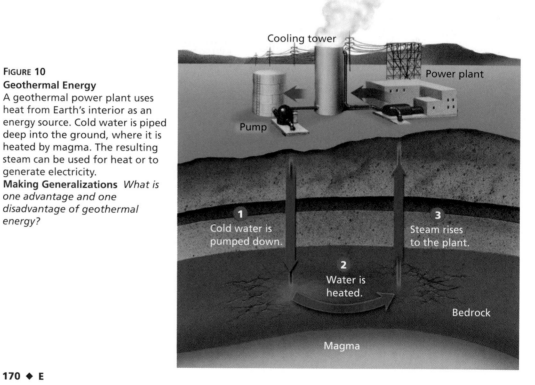

Cooling tower
Power plant
Pump
1 Cold water is pumped down.
3 Steam rises to the plant.
2 Water is heated.
Bedrock
Magma

Differentiated Instruction

Less Proficient Readers **L1**
Describing Geothermal energy Have students summarize in their own words the process for generating electricity with geothermal energy. Let students share their summaries with the class in a follow-up discussion. Guide students to agree on a "best sentence" for each step in the process.
learning modality: verbal

Gifted and Talented **L3**
Hydrogen Power Plants Hydrogen is the simplest of the elements and the most plentiful gas in the universe. Have students research the use of hydrogen to power electrical plants. Have them prepare diagrams to report their findings. **learning modality: logical/mathematical**

The Promise of Hydrogen Power

Now that you have read about so many energy sources, consider a fuel with this description: It burns cleanly. It creates no smog or acid rain. It exists on Earth in large supply.

This ideal-sounding fuel is real—it's hydrogen. Unfortunately, almost all the hydrogen on Earth is combined with oxygen in water. Pure hydrogen can be obtained by passing an electric current through water. But it takes more energy to obtain the hydrogen than is produced by burning it.

Still, scientists find hydrogen power promising. At present, hydroelectric plants decrease their activity when the demand for electricity is low. Instead, they could run at full capacity all the time, using the excess electricity to produce hydrogen. Similarly, solar power plants often generate more electricity than is needed during the day. This extra electricity could be used to produce hydrogen. Scientists are also searching for other ways to produce hydrogen cheaply from water.

Car manufacturers are now developing cars that run on hydrogen fuel cells. These would produce water as emissions. That water might then be used again as fuel. You can see that if scientists can find a way to produce hydrogen cheaply, it could someday be an important source of energy.

Reading Checkpoint In what common substance is most hydrogen on Earth found?

FIGURE 11
Hydrogen Power
The object fascinating these astronauts is a bubble of water—the harmless byproduct of the hydrogen fuel cells used on the space shuttle.

Section 2 Assessment

Target Reading Skill Previewing Visuals Compare your questions and answers about Figure 7 with those of a partner.

Reviewing Key Concepts

1. **a. Identifying** What two forms of energy does the sun supply?
   b. Explaining What are two reasons that solar energy has not replaced energy from fossil fuels?
   c. Applying Concepts A friend of yours argues that shopping malls should use solar energy to conserve fossil fuels. How would you respond?

2. **a. Listing** List five renewable energy sources other than solar energy.
   b. Classifying Which of the renewable energy sources that you listed are actually indirect forms of solar energy? Explain.
   c. Predicting Which source of renewable energy do you think most likely to be used in your community in 50 years? Give reasons to support your answer.

Writing in Science

Advertisement Write an advertisement for one of the renewable energy sources discussed in this section. Be sure to mention how its advantages make it superior to the other energy sources. Also mention how scientists might be able to overcome its disadvantages.

Chapter 5 E ◆ 171

Figure 10 Geothermal energy is an unlimited source, but it comes to Earth's surface only at a few places.

Reading Checkpoint Geothermal energy heats water, creating steam that can turn a turbine.

Reading Checkpoint Most hydrogen on Earth is found in water.

Assess

Reviewing Key Concepts

1. **a.** heat and light **b.** only available when the sun is shining; must be collected from a very large area **c.** Students might suggest that solar energy might be used to supplement the use of fossil fuels, but should not be the only source of energy because on cloudy days not enough solar energy could be captured to provide the mall's needs.
2. **a.** wind, water, biomass, geothermal, hydrogen **b.** wind and water energy because water power depends on the water cycle, which is driven by the sun, and wind energy depends on the uneven heating of the Earth by the sun; biomass because the sun is needed for photosynthesis **c.** Answers will reflect students' understanding of local climate, geography, and resources.

Reteach L1

As a class, weigh the benefits and limitations of each renewable energy source.

Performance Assessment L2

Have each student create a compare/contrast table that includes at least three of the renewable energy sources discussed in this section and identifies one advantage and one disadvantage of each source. Students can save their tables in their portfolios.

All in One Teaching Resources

- Section Summary: *Renewable Sources of Energy*
- Review and Reinforcement: *Renewable Sources of Energy*
- Enrich: *Renewable Sources of Energy*

Lab zone Chapter Project

Keep Students on Track Provide copies of the school's fuel and utility bills so students can determine the amount and actual cost of each type of energy used. If a group is studying energy used for transportation, encourage them to survey other students about transportation to school. They also may need to contact your school district's central office or the private company that owns and operates the school buses.

Writing in Science

Writing Mode Persuasion
Scoring Rubric
4 Includes several examples; tone creative, convincing
3 Includes all criteria; tone moderately convincing
2 Includes sufficient coverage; unconvincing
1 Includes incomplete or inaccurate descriptions of both topics

Design and Build a Solar Cooker

Prepare for Inquiry

Key Concept
A solar cooker that focuses the sun's rays in its center works best.

Skills Objectives
After this lab, students will be able to
- design an experiment to test how the shape of a solar cooker affects how it functions
- evaluate the effectiveness of various solar cooker designs

🕐 **Prep Time** 20 minutes
Class Time 40 minutes

Advance Planning
Identify a sunny area for the solar cookers.

Safety
Students should wear safety goggles and use caution in handling scissors and glass thermometers. Review the safety guidelines in Appendix A.

All in One Teaching Resources
- Lab Worksheet: *Design and Build a Solar Cooker*

Guide Inquiry

Invitation
Ask: **In what kind of places or under what conditions do you think people might cook with solar energy?** (*Accept all answers as part of the discussion; answers might include: places where the climate is hot, sunny, and dry, such as the desert; areas where electricity is not available, perhaps where people cannot afford it; places where people, such as scientists or explorers, are working under field conditions.*) **Why might the shape of a solar cooker affect how well it works?** (*The shape should influence how sunlight enters or is distributed throughout the cooker.*)

Design and Build a Solar Cooker

Problem
What is the best shape for a solar cooker?

Skills Focus
designing a solution, evaluating the design

Materials
- scissors
- frozen vegetables
- 3 sheets of aluminum foil
- 3 sheets of oaktag paper
- wooden or plastic stirrers
- glue
- 3 thermometers
- tape
- clock or watch
- optional materials provided by your teacher

Procedure

PART 1 Research and Investigate

1. Glue a sheet of aluminum foil, shiny side up, to each sheet of oaktag paper. Before the glue dries, gently smooth out any wrinkles in the foil.

2. Bend one sheet into a U shape. Leave another sheet flat. Bend another sheet into a shape of your own choosing.

3. Predict which shape will produce the largest temperature increase when placed in the sun. Write down your prediction and explain your reasons.

4. Place the aluminum sheets in direct sunlight. Use wood blocks or books to hold the sheets in position, if necessary.

5. Record the starting temperature on each thermometer.

6. Place the thermometer bulbs in the center of the aluminum shapes. After 15 minutes, record the final temperature on each thermometer.

PART 2 Design and Build

7. Using what you learned in Part 1, design a solar cooker that can cook frozen vegetables. Your solar cooker should
   - be no larger than 50 cm on any side
   - cook the vegetables in less than 10 minutes
   - be made of materials approved by your teacher

8. Prepare a written description of your plan that includes a sketch of your cooker. Include a list of materials and an operational definition of a "well-cooked" vegetable. Obtain your teacher's approval for your design. Then build your solar cooker.

Introducing the Procedure
Have students work in groups of three. Discuss sharing and rotating duties. If needed, review the meaning of *operational definition*.

Troubleshooting the Experiment
- In Step 2, make sure students have the foil on the inside of the U or inside their chosen shape.
- In Step 6, make sure students hold the thermometers with their bulbs at the same distance from the foil.

PART 3 Evaluate and Redesign

9. Test your solar cooker by spearing some frozen vegetables on the stirrers. Time how long it takes to cook the vegetables. Make note of any problems with your solar cooker design.

10. Based on your test, decide how you could improve the design of your cooker. Then make any desired changes to your cooker and test how the improved cooker functions.

Analyze and Conclude

1. **Identifying a Need** In what situations might it be important to have an efficient cooker that does not use fuel?

2. **Designing a Solution** How did you incorporate what you learned in Part 1 into your design in Part 2? For example, which shape did you use in your cooker design?

3. **Evaluating the Design** When you tested your solar cooker, what problems did you encounter?

4. **Redesigning** In what ways did you change your design for your second test? How did the redesign improve the performance of your cooker?

5. **Working With Design Constraints** Why might it be important for solar cookers to use inexpensive, readily available materials?

6. **Evaluating the Impact on Society** How can solar-powered devices help meet the world's future energy needs? What limitation do solar-powered devices have?

Communicate

Design an advertisement for your solar cooker that will appear in a camping magazine. Make sure your ad describes the benefits of solar cookers in general, and of your design in particular.

Objectives

After completing the lesson, students will be able to

E.5.3.1 Describe what happens during a nuclear fission reaction.

E.5.3.2 Explain how a nuclear power plant produces electricity.

E.5.3.3 Describe what takes place in a nuclear fusion reaction.

Target Reading Skill

Comparing and Contrasting Explain that comparing and contrasting information shows how ideas, facts, and events are similar and different. The results of the comparison can have importance.

Answers

Possible answers: Similarities—both types of reactions release large amounts of energy and involve small losses of mass; differences—fission uses uranium and splits nuclei, fusion uses hydrogen and combines nuclei.

All in One Teaching Resources
• Transparency E51

Preteach

Build Background Knowledge   L2

Picturing an Atom

Ask several students to come to the board, draw what they think an atom looks like, and label its parts. Encourage the rest of the class to discuss the drawings and suggest corrections or additions. You can return to the diagrams later in the lesson.

Reading Preview

Key Concepts
• What happens during a nuclear fission reaction?
• How does a nuclear power plant produce electricity?
• How does a nuclear fusion reaction occur?

Key Terms
• nucleus • nuclear fission
• reactor vessel • fuel rod
• control rod • meltdown
• nuclear fusion

Target Reading Skill

Comparing and Contrasting
As you read, compare fission and fusion reactions in a Venn diagram like the one below. Write the similarities in the space where the circles overlap and the differences on the left and right sides.

Nuclear Fission   Nuclear Fusion

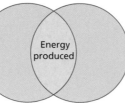

Energy produced

Lab zone Discover Activity

Why Do They Fall?

1. Line up 15 dominoes to form a triangle.
2. Knock over the first domino so that it falls against the second row of dominoes. Observe the results.
3. Set up the dominoes again, but then remove the dominoes in the third row from the lineup.
4. Knock over the first domino again. Observe what happens.

Think It Over

Inferring Suppose each domino produced a large amount of energy when it fell over. Why might it be helpful to remove the dominoes as you did in Step 3?

Wouldn't it be great if people could use the same method as the sun to produce energy? In a way, they can! The kind of reactions that power the sun involve the central cores of atoms. The central core of an atom that contains the protons and neutrons is called the **nucleus** (plural *nuclei*). Reactions that involve nuclei, called nuclear reactions, result in tremendous amounts of energy. Two types of nuclear reactions are fission and fusion.

Nuclear Fission

Nuclear reactions convert matter into energy. In 1905, Albert Einstein developed a formula that described the relationship between energy and matter. You have probably seen this famous equation: $E = mc^2$. In the equation, the E represents energy and the m represents mass. The c, which represents the speed of light, is a very large number. This equation states that when matter is changed into energy, an enormous amount of energy is released.

◀ Albert Einstein

Lab zone Discover Activity

Skills Focus Inferring

Materials 15 dominoes

Time 10 minutes

Tips Make sure students place the dominoes with less than a domino-length space between rows.

Expected Outcome In Step 2, all 15 dominoes will topple as those in one row fall back against those in the next row. With the third row removed in Step 4, the last two rows will remain standing.

Think It Over Removing the third row would stop the production of energy after a certain point.

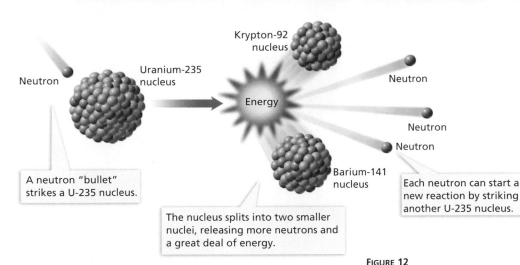

Neutron

Uranium-235 nucleus

Krypton-92 nucleus

Energy

Neutron

Neutron

Neutron

Neutron

Barium-141 nucleus

A neutron "bullet" strikes a U-235 nucleus.

The nucleus splits into two smaller nuclei, releasing more neutrons and a great deal of energy.

Each neutron can start a new reaction by striking another U-235 nucleus.

FIGURE 12
Nuclear Fission
A great deal of energy is released in a nuclear fission reaction.
Interpreting Diagrams *How does a nuclear fission reaction begin?*

Fission Reactions Nuclear fission is the splitting of an atom's nucleus into two smaller nuclei. The fuel for the reaction is a large atom that has an unstable nucleus, such as uranium-235 (U-235). A neutron is shot at the U-235 atom at high speed. **When the neutron hits the U-235 nucleus, the nucleus splits apart into two smaller nuclei and two or more neutrons.** The total mass of all these particles is a bit less than the mass of the original nucleus. The small amount of mass that makes up the difference has been converted into energy—a lot of energy, as described by Einstein's equation.

Meanwhile, the fission reaction has produced three more neutrons. If any of these neutrons strikes another nucleus, the fission reaction is repeated. More neutrons and more energy are released. If there are enough nuclei nearby, the process repeats in a chain reaction, just like a row of dominoes falling. In a nuclear chain reaction, the amount of energy released increases rapidly with each step in the chain.

Energy From Fission What happens to all the energy released by these fission reactions? If a nuclear chain reaction is not controlled, the released energy causes a huge explosion. The explosion of an atomic bomb is an uncontrolled nuclear fission reaction. A few kilograms of matter explode with more force than several thousand tons of dynamite. However, if the chain reaction is controlled, the energy is released as heat, which can be used to generate electricity.

Reading Checkpoint What happens if a nuclear chain reaction is not controlled?

Lab zone Skills Activity

Calculating
A pellet of U-235 produces as much energy as 615 liters of fuel oil. An average home uses 5,000 liters of oil a year. How many U-235 pellets would be needed to supply the same amount of energy?

Lab zone Skills Activity

Skills Focus Calculating

Materials calculator (optional)

Time 5 minutes

Tips If needed, help students determine how to calculate the answer (divide 5,000 by 615).

Expected Outcome About 8 pellets would be needed.

Extend Suggest that each student estimate how many homes are in his or her neighborhood and then calculate how many pellets would be needed to supply energy to all those homes for a year.
learning modality: logical/mathematical

Nuclear Fission

Teach Key Concepts [L2]
Energy From Fission

Focus Tell students that in a fission reaction, the nucleus of a large atom is split into smaller nuclei and the small amount of mass lost is converted into a great deal of energy.

Teach Tell students that an atom's nucleus splits when it is hit by a neutron. Ask: **When neutrons are released in a fission reaction, what happens to them?** *(They can strike other nuclei and cause additional fission reactions.)* **When does a nuclear chain reaction take place?** *(When there are enough nuclei nearby as neutrons and energy are released, increasing numbers of fission reactions occur.)*

Apply Ask: **How is it that nuclear chain reactions can generate electricity as well as cause atomic bombs to explode?** *(Electricity is generated in controlled nuclear chain reactions; nuclear bombs explode in uncontrolled nuclear chain reactions.)* **learning modality: logical/mathematical**

Independent Practice [L2]

All in One Teaching Resources
• Guided Reading and Study Worksheet: *Nuclear Energy*
• Transparency E52

Student Edition on Audio CD

Monitor Progress _____ [L2]
Answers
Figure 12 A neutron "bullet" strikes an atom.

Reading Checkpoint An uncontrolled nuclear chain reaction results in an explosion.

Nuclear Power Plants

Teach Key Concepts L2
How Fission Generates Electricity

Focus Remind students that a nuclear power plant functions like other power plants: a heat source—in this case, fission—changes water into steam that powers turbines.

Teach Have students review Figure 14. Ask: **What are the three main components involved in creating power from nuclear fission?** *(Reactor vessel, heat exchanger, and generator)* **What are the differences between fuel rods and control rods?** *(Fuel rods contain the uranium involved in fission reactions. Control rods are made of cadmium metal that absorbs neutrons released in fission. They are placed between fuel rods to control fission reactions.)*

Apply Ask: **Name two other energy sources that create steam to turn turbines that generate electricity at a power plant.** *(Any two: fossil fuels, especially coal; solar power; geothermal energy)* **learning modality: visual**

All in One Teaching Resources
• Transparency E53

Help Students Read

Relating Cause and Effect Help students understand the process of producing power from nuclear fusion by asking them to analyze the cause-and-effect relationships in the process. Have them create a flowchart beginning with nuclear fusion and ending with electric current going to power lines.

FIGURE 13
Nuclear Power
Nuclear power plants generate much of the world's electricity. The inset shows autunite, one of the ores of uranium. The uranium fuel for nuclear power plants is refined from uranium ores.

Nuclear Power Plants

Controlled nuclear fission reactions take place inside nuclear power plants. Nuclear power plants generate much of the world's electricity—about 20 percent in the United States and more than 70 percent in France. **In a nuclear power plant, the heat released from fission reactions is used to change water into steam. The steam then turns the blades of a turbine to generate electricity.** Look at the diagram of a nuclear power plant in Figure 14. In addition to the generator, it has two main parts: the reactor vessel and the heat exchanger.

Reactor Vessel The **reactor vessel** is the part of the nuclear reactor where nuclear fission occurs. The reactor contains rods of U-235, called **fuel rods.** When several fuel rods are placed close together, a series of fission reactions occurs.

If the reactor vessel gets too hot, control rods are used to slow down the chain reactions. **Control rods,** made of the metal cadmium, are inserted between the fuel rods. The cadmium absorbs neutrons released during fission and slows the speed of the chain reactions. The cadmium control rods can then be removed to speed up the chain reactions again.

Heat Exchanger Heat is removed from the reactor vessel by water or another fluid that is pumped through the reactor. This fluid passes through a heat exchanger. There, the fluid boils water to produce steam, which runs the electrical generator. The steam is condensed again and pumped back to the heat exchanger.

The Risks of Nuclear Power At first, people thought that nuclear fission would provide an almost unlimited source of clean, safe energy. But accidents at nuclear power plants have led to safety concerns. In 1986, the reactor vessel in a nuclear power plant in Chernobyl, Ukraine, overheated. The fuel rods generated so much heat that they started to melt, a condition called a **meltdown.** The excess heat caused a series of explosions, which injured or killed dozens of people. In addition, radioactive materials escaped into the environment.

Accidents can be avoided by careful planning and improved safety features. A more difficult problem is the disposal of the radioactive wastes. Radioactive wastes remain dangerous for many thousands of years. Scientists must find a way to store these wastes safely for a long period of time.

Reading Checkpoint What are two problems with using nuclear fission as an energy source?

Go Online
active art

For: Nuclear Power Plant activity
Visit: PHschool.com
Web Code: cep-5053

Go Online
active art

For: Nuclear power plant activity
Visit: PHSchool.com
Web Code: cep-5053

Students explore how a nuclear power plant works.

FIGURE 14
Power From Nuclear Fission
Nuclear fission provides the energy to generate electricity in a nuclear power plant. **Interpreting Diagrams** *In what part of the power plant does nuclear fission occur?*

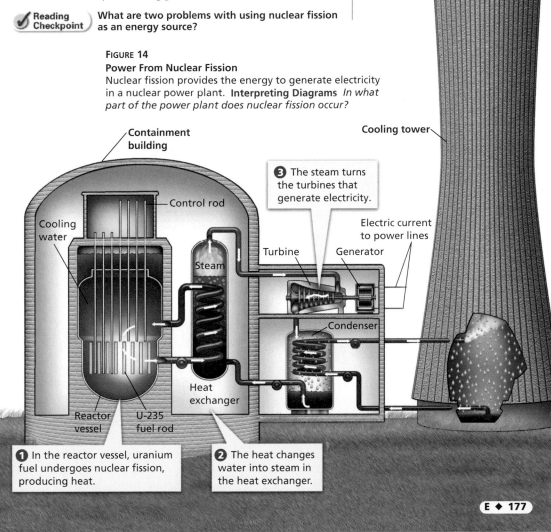

- Containment building
- Control rod
- Cooling water
- Steam
- Turbine
- Generator
- Electric current to power lines
- Condenser
- Cooling tower
- Heat exchanger
- Reactor vessel
- U-235 fuel rod

❶ In the reactor vessel, uranium fuel undergoes nuclear fission, producing heat.

❷ The heat changes water into steam in the heat exchanger.

❸ The steam turns the turbines that generate electricity.

E ◆ 177

Lab zone **Build Inquiry** ▣ L1

Nuclear Power Accidents

Materials large world map

Time 15 minutes

Focus Explain that radioactive fallout from the Chernobyl accident was spread by air currents.

Teach Display the map, and let volunteers locate Chernobyl (51° N, 30° about 130 km north of Kiev). Tell students that the force of the 1986 explosion carried radioactive materials high into the atmosphere, where they spread across the Northern Hemisphere and then settled back to Earth in what is called fallout. The heaviest fallout occurred in Ukraine, Belarus, Sweden, Norway, Denmark, France, and Switzerland. In addition, Finland, Lithuania, Germany, Poland, the Czech Republic, Slovakia, Austria, Hungary, Italy, and Great Britain suffered moderate fallout. Let students find all these countries on the map. Ask: **Which affected country was farthest from Chernobyl?** (*Great Britain*)

Apply Ask: **What does this tell you about the dangers of nuclear power plants?** (*An accident can affect a huge area.*) **learning modality: visual**

Differentiated Instruction

Gifted and Talented
Identifying Nuclear Accidents ▣ L3
Challenge students to use reference books or online sources to learn the typical temperatures reached in a nuclear power plant's reactor vessel and then find the temperatures reached in the Chernobyl accident. Ask students to investigate and report on the occurrence of other nuclear accidents, such as Three Mile Island.
learning modality: logical/mathematical

Monitor Progress _____ ▣ L2

Oral Presentation Call on students at random to each explain a step in the process of how a nuclear power plant converts nuclear energy to electricity.

Answers
Figure 14 The reactor vessel

Reading Checkpoint Potential problems include explosions and the spread of radioactive materials into the environment.

The Quest to Control Fusion

Teach Key Concepts `L2`

Nuclear Fusion

Focus Explain that fusion has great potential as an energy source, but we currently lack the technology to use it.

Teach Ask: **What are three advantages of fusion over fission?** *(Fusion's fuel source, water, is readily available; fusion would produce more energy per unit of atomic mass and less radioactive waste.)*

Apply Ask: **How are fission and fusion reactions alike?** *(Mass is lost, and energy is created.)* **learning modality: verbal**

All in One Teaching Resources
• Transparency E54

Monitor Progress `L2`

Answers
Figure 15 A neutron plus energy

Reading Checkpoint The high temperatures and pressures required cannot be reached.

Assess

Reviewing Key Concepts

1. a. the splitting of an atom's nucleus into two smaller nuclei **b.** A neutron strikes a U-235 nucleus, which splits into two smaller nuclei and releases two or more neutrons and energy. **c.** nonrenewable because it depends on nonrenewable uranium
2. a. controlled nuclear fission chain reaction **b.** Thermal energy released by a fission reaction is used to boil water, producing steam that turns the blades of a turbine to generate electricity. **c.** Excess heat could build up and cause a meltdown, leading to explosions and release of radioactive material.
3. a. Two hydrogen nuclei combine to create a helium nucleus. **b.** Lost mass converts to energy.

Reteach `L1`
Use Figures 12 and 15 to compare how nuclear fission and fusion produce energy.

All in One Teaching Resources
• Section Summary: *Nuclear Energy*
• Review and Reinforce: *Nuclear Energy*
• Enrich: *Nuclear Energy*

178 ● E

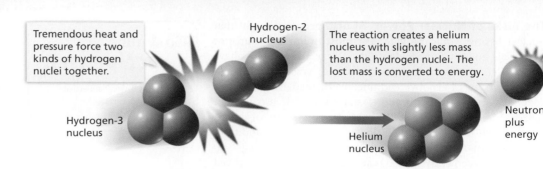

Tremendous heat and pressure force two kinds of hydrogen nuclei together.

Hydrogen-2 nucleus

The reaction creates a helium nucleus with slightly less mass than the hydrogen nuclei. The lost mass is converted to energy.

Hydrogen-3 nucleus

Helium nucleus

Neutron plus energy

FIGURE 15
Nuclear Fusion
In nuclear fusion, two hydrogen nuclei are forced together, forming a helium nucleus, a neutron, and energy.
Interpreting Diagrams *What is released during a fusion reaction?*

The Quest to Control Fusion

Nuclear fusion is the combining of two atomic nuclei to produce a single larger nucleus. **In nuclear fusion, two hydrogen nuclei combine to create a helium nucleus, which has slightly less mass than the two hydrogen nuclei. The lost mass is converted to energy.**

Nuclear fusion could produce much more energy per unit of atomic mass than nuclear fission. The fuel for a fusion reactor is readily available—water contains one kind of hydrogen needed for fusion. Nuclear fusion should also produce less radioactive waste than nuclear fission. Unfortunately, the pressure and temperature required for a reaction make the construction of a fusion reactor impractical at this time.

Reading Checkpoint What is preventing fusion energy from filling our current energy needs?

Section 3 Assessment

Target Reading Skill Comparing and Contrasting Use the information in your Venn diagram to answer Questions 1 and 3 below.

Reviewing Key Concepts
1. a. Defining What is nuclear fission?
   b. Sequencing Describe the steps that occur in a nuclear fission reaction.
   c. Classifying Is nuclear fission a renewable or nonrenewable energy source? Explain.
2. a. Identifying What type of nuclear reaction produces electricity in a nuclear power plant?
   b. Explaining Explain how electricity is produced in a nuclear power plant.
   c. Predicting What might happen in a nuclear power plant if too many control rods were removed?

3. a. Reviewing Define nuclear fusion.
   b. Relating Cause and Effect How is energy produced during a nuclear fusion reaction?

Lab zone At-Home Activity

Shoot the Nucleus With a family member, make a model of a nuclear fission reaction. Place a handful of marbles on the floor in a tight cluster, so that they touch one another. Step back about a half meter from the marbles. Shoot a marble at the cluster. Note what effect the moving marble has on the cluster. Then using a diagram, explain how this event models a nuclear fission reaction.

178 ◆ E

Lab zone Chapter Project

Keep Students on Track Encourage students to make their reports concise, focusing on the major points and, when appropriate, using visual displays, such as a neat copy of the data table. Also suggest that they explain how each recommendation would reduce energy use.

Lab zone At Home Activity

Shoot the Nucleus Before students present the activity at home, have them review Figure 12. Instruct them to determine what the marble being shot at the cluster represents. *(a neutron being shot at a nucleus)*

Reading Preview

Key Concept
• What are two ways to preserve our current energy sources?

Key Terms
• efficiency
• insulation
• energy conservation

Target Reading Skill
Using Prior Knowledge Before you read, write what you know about energy efficiency and conservation in a graphic organizer like the one below. As you read, write what you learn.

What You Know
1. I turn off lights to conserve energy. 2.

What You Learned
1. 2.

Lab zone Discover Activity

Which Bulb Is More Efficient?

1. Record the light output (listed in lumens) from the packages of a 60-watt incandescent light bulb and a 15-watt compact fluorescent bulb.
2. [icons] Place the fluorescent bulb in a lamp socket. **CAUTION:** *Make sure the lamp is unplugged.*
3. Plug in the lamp and turn it on. Hold the end of a thermometer about 8 centimeters from the bulb.
4. Record the temperature after five minutes.
5. Turn off and unplug the lamp. When the bulb is cool, remove it. Repeat Steps 2, 3, and 4 with the incandescent light bulb.

Think It Over
Inferring The 60-watt bulb uses four times as much energy as the 15-watt bulb. Does it also provide four times as much light output? If not, how can you account for the difference?

What would happen if the world ran out of fossil fuels today? The heating and cooling systems in most buildings would cease to function. Forests would disappear as people began to burn wood for heating and cooking. Cars, buses, and trains would be stranded wherever they ran out of fuel. About 80 percent of the electric power would disappear. Since televisions, computers, and telephones depend on electricity, communication would be greatly reduced. Lights, microwave ovens, and most other home appliances would no longer work.

Although fossil fuels won't run out immediately, they also won't last forever. Most people think that it makes sense to use fuels more wisely now to avoid fuel shortages in the future. **One way to preserve our current energy resources is to increase the efficiency of our energy use. Another way is to conserve energy whenever possible.**

Lab zone Discover Activity

Skills Focus Inferring

Materials light bulbs in packages (60-watt incandescent and 15-watt compact fluorescent), lamp, thermometer, clock or watch

Time 20 minutes

Tips Compact fluorescent bulbs, widely available in supermarkets and hardware stores, screw into a regular bulb socket.

Expected Outcome The fluorescent bulb will produce a lower temperature.

Think It Over Light output varies among bulbs. The fluorescent bulb is about 4 times more efficient (825 lumens/15 watt compared to 900 lumens/60 watt). The incandescent bulb is less efficient because it converts so much energy into heat.

Objectives
After completing the lesson, students will be able to

E.5.4.1 Name ways to ensure that there will be enough energy for the future.

E.5.4.2 Identify ways individuals can conserve energy.

Target Reading Skill ⊙

Using Prior Knowledge Explain that using prior knowledge helps students connect what they already know to what they are about to read.

Answers
Possible answers:

What You Know

1. I turn off lights to conserve energy.

2. I walk instead of ride in a car when possible.

What You Learned

1. One way to preserve our current energy resources is to increase efficiency.

2. One method of increasing efficiency of heating and cooling systems is to use insulation.

3. Compact fluorescent bulbs use about one fourth as much energy as incandescent light bulbs.

All in One Teaching Resources
• Transparency E55

Preteach

Build Background Knowledge ⬛L2

Identifying Wasteful Energy Use
Point out the section's title and ask: **What does the term *energy conservation* mean?** *(Accept all reasonable responses, such as "not wasting energy.")* **What are some examples of wasting energy?** *(Possible answers: Setting a thermostat too high; leaving lights on in an unoccupied room; running a dishwasher with only a small load)*

Instruct

Energy Efficiency

Teach Key Concepts   L2
Using Fuels Efficiently

Focus Remind students that when we say we are increasing the efficiency of a device that consumes energy, we mean that we are increasing the percentage of consumed energy the device uses to do work and decreasing the percentage of consumed energy that is lost to the surroundings.

Teach Explain to students that energy efficiency can be improved in many areas of our lives. Draw a chart on the board that will show types of energy use and ways to increase efficiency; fill it in as students discuss. Ask: **What are the main categories of energy use that can be affected by changes in energy efficiency?** *(Transportation, heating and cooling, lighting)* **What is the most common way to improve efficiency of heating and cooling?** *(Adding fiberglass insulation or a layer of air)* **Name ways that energy efficiency can be improved in transportation and lighting.** *(Transportation—better engines and tires, public transportation, carpooling; lighting— using compact fluorescent bulbs)*

Apply Ask: **How can you personally improve energy efficiency?** *(Take the bus or carpool, check on lighting and heating/ cooling at home)* **learning modality: visual**

Independent Practice   L2

All in One Teaching Resources

- Guided Reading and Study Worksheet: *Energy Conservation*

🔘 **Student Edition on Audio CD**

Energy Efficiency

One way to make energy resources last longer is to use fuels more efficiently. **Efficiency** is the percentage of energy that is actually used to perform work. The rest of the energy is "lost" to the surroundings, usually as heat. People have developed many ways to increase energy efficiency.

Heating and Cooling One method of increasing the efficiency of heating and cooling systems is insulation. **Insulation** is a layer of material that traps air to help block the transfer of heat between the air inside and outside a building. You have probably seen insulation made of fiberglass, which looks like pink cotton candy. A layer of fiberglass 15 centimeters thick insulates a room as well as a brick wall 2 meters thick!

Trapped air can act as insulation in windows, too. Many windows consist of two panes of glass with space between them. The air between the panes of glass acts as insulation.

• Tech & Design in History •

Energy-Efficient Products
Scientists and engineers have developed many technologies that improve energy efficiency and reduce energy use.

1958 Solar Cells
More than 150 years ago, scientists discovered that silicon can convert light into electricity. The first useful application of solar cells was to power the radio on a satellite. Now solar cells are even used on experimental cars like the one above.

1936 Fluorescent Lighting
Fluorescent bulbs were introduced to the public at the hundredth anniversary celebration of the United States Patent Office. Because these bulbs use less energy than incandescent bulbs, most offices and schools use fluorescent lights today.

1932 Fiberglass Insulation
Long strands of glass fibers trap air and keep buildings from losing heat. Less fuel is used for heating.

| 1930 | 1940 | 1950 | 1960 |

180 ◆ E

Lighting Much of the electricity used for home lighting is wasted. For example, less than 10 percent of the electricity that an incandescent light bulb uses is converted into light. The rest is given off as heat. In contrast, compact fluorescent bulbs use about one fourth as much energy to provide the same amount of light.

Transportation Engineers have improved the energy efficiency of cars by designing better engines and tires. Another way to save energy is to reduce the number of cars on the road. In many communities, public transit systems provide an alternative to driving. Other cities encourage carpooling. Many cities now set aside lanes for cars containing two or more people.

✓ **Reading Checkpoint** What are two examples of insulation?

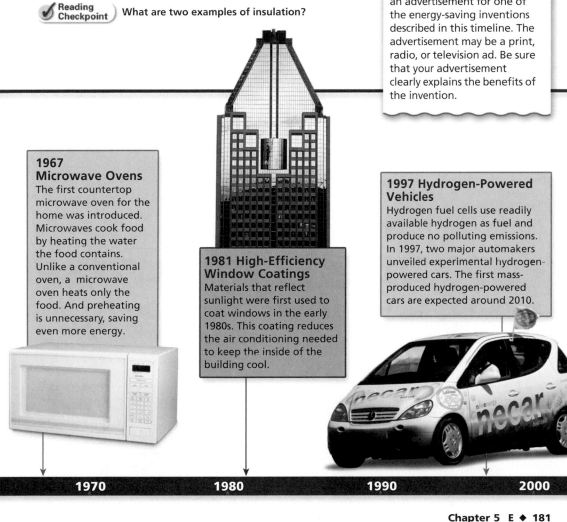

1967 Microwave Ovens
The first countertop microwave oven for the home was introduced. Microwaves cook food by heating the water the food contains. Unlike a conventional oven, a microwave oven heats only the food. And preheating is unnecessary, saving even more energy.

1981 High-Efficiency Window Coatings
Materials that reflect sunlight were first used to coat windows in the early 1980s. This coating reduces the air conditioning needed to keep the inside of the building cool.

1997 Hydrogen-Powered Vehicles
Hydrogen fuel cells use readily available hydrogen as fuel and produce no polluting emissions. In 1997, two major automakers unveiled experimental hydrogen-powered cars. The first mass-produced hydrogen-powered cars are expected around 2010.

1970   1980   1990   2000

Writing in Science

Research and Write Design an advertisement for one of the energy-saving inventions described in this timeline. The advertisement may be a print, radio, or television ad. Be sure that your advertisement clearly explains the benefits of the invention.

Help Students Read
Summarize Summarizing the information presented in the text will help students focus on main ideas and remember what they read. Have students read the paragraphs about energy efficiency and summarize them by restating the main idea in their own words.

• Tech & Design in History •

Focus Explain to students that new scientific discoveries and the development of new materials has helped produce many new energy-efficient products.

Teach Call on volunteers to read the entries on the time line. Ask students with personal experiences with the technologies to relate them to the class. Ask: **How could hydrogen-powered vehicles affect our lives?** (*Answers will vary. Sample answer: It could reduce environmental pollution and lessen political stress arising from dependence on fossil fuels.*)

Writing in Science

Writing Mode Research
Scoring Rubric
4 Includes clear explanations of several benefits; tone convincing
3 Includes clear explanations of a few benefits; tone convincing
2 Benefits named but explanations unclear; tone unconvincing
1 Number and explanation of invention's benefits inadequate

 Portfolio

Differentiated Instruction

Special Needs **L1**
Identifying Energy Efficiency Pair students having difficulty with those who have a clear concept of energy efficiency. Have each pair of students compile a list of ways to individually improve energy efficiency on a daily basis. Students can reinforce concepts with *Student Edition on Audio CD*. **learning modality: verbal**

Monitor Progress _____ **L2**

Drawing Have each student draw and label a diagram to explain how insulation conserves energy. Students can save their drawings in their portfolios.

Portfolio

Answer
✓ **Reading Checkpoint** Fiberglass, trapped air

Energy Conservation

Teach Key Concepts
Reducing Energy Use

Focus Tell students that the efforts any one person makes to conserve energy make a difference when many people make such an effort.

Teach Ask: **What are some ways to conserve energy?** (*Walk instead of riding in a car, recycle, use fans instead of air conditioners, turn off light and television when leaving a room*)

Apply Ask how many students practice these ideas. Then discuss other suggestions that students might have for conserving energy, such as using natural lighting instead of electric lights whenever possible, keeping the home cooler in winter and warmer in summer, and using public transportation.
learning modality: verbal

Monitor Progress —————— L2

✓ **Reading Checkpoint** Walking instead of riding in a car; recycle

---

Assess

Reviewing Key Concepts

1. a. increasing energy efficiency and reducing energy use **b.** Insulation reduces the amount of heat lost to the outside in cold weather and helps keep heat outside in warm weather, reducing the amount of fuel needed to heat and cool buildings. Carpooling results in fewer cars on the road and, therefore, a reduction in the amount of gas being used. **c.** The building with incandescent bulbs because they are far less efficient than fluorescent; most of the electrical energy they use is released as heat.

Reteach   L1

With students, list ways to improve energy efficiency and promote energy conservation.

Performance Assessment
Oral Presentation Have each student L2 describe one energy-saving idea that he or she will take responsibility for implementing at home.

All in One Teaching Resources
• Section Summary: *Energy Conservation*
• Review and Reinforce: *Energy Conservation*
• Enrich: *Energy Conservation*

Ways I can conserve energy:

✓ Walk or ride a bike for short trips

✓ Recycle

✓ Use fans instead of air conditioners when it's hot

✓ Turn off the lights and television when leaving a room

FIGURE 16
Energy Conservation
There are many ways you can conserve energy.

Energy Conservation

Another approach to making energy resources last longer is conservation. **Energy conservation** means reducing energy use.

You can reduce your personal energy use by changing your behavior in some simple ways. For example, if you walk to the store instead of getting a ride, you are conserving the gasoline it would take to drive to the store. You can also follow some of the suggestions in Figure 16.

While these suggestions seem like small things, multiplied by millions of people they add up to a lot of energy saved for the future.

✓ **Reading Checkpoint** What are two ways you can reduce your personal energy use?

Section 4 Assessment

⟳ **Target Reading Skill** Using Prior Knowledge Review your graphic organizer and revise it based on what you just learned in the section.

Reviewing Key Concepts

1. a. Identifying What are the two keys to preserving our current energy resources?
b. Applying Concepts How does insulating buildings help to preserve energy resources? How does carpooling preserve resources?
c. Predicting One office building contains only incandescent lights. The building next door contains only fluorescent lights. Predict which building has higher energy bills. Explain your answer.

Writing in Science

Energy Savings Brochure
Conduct an energy audit of your home. Look for places where energy is being lost, such as cracks around doors. Also look for ways to reduce energy use, such as running the dishwasher only when it is full. Then create a short, illustrated brochure of energy-saving suggestions. Keep the brochure where everyone can see it.

Writing in Science

Writing Mode Description
Scoring Rubric
4 Includes four or more suggestions with colorful illustrations; neat and organized
3 Includes two or three suggestions with colorful illustrations; neat and organized
2 Includes only one suggestion, well organized and illustrated, or more than one with poor illustrations or lack of organization
1 Includes only one suggestion, poor illustrations, lack of organization

Keeping Comfortable

Problem

How well do different materials prevent heat transfer?

Skills Focus

measuring, controlling variables

Materials

- watch or clock
- beakers
- ice water
- hot water
- thermometers or temperature probes
- containers and lids made of paper, glass, plastic, plastic foam, and metal

Procedure

1. Use a pencil to poke a hole in the lid of a paper cup. Fill the cup halfway with cold water.

2. Put the lid on the cup. Insert a thermometer into the water through the hole. (If you are using a temperature probe, see your teacher for instructions.) When the temperature stops dropping, place the cup in a beaker. Add hot water to the beaker until the water level is about 1 cm below the lid.

3. Record the water temperature once every minute until it has increased by 5°C. Use the time it takes for the temperature to increase 5°C as a measure of the effectiveness of the paper cup in preventing heat transfer.

4. Choose three other containers and their matching lids to test. Design an experiment to compare how well those materials prevent heat transfer. You can use a similar procedure to the one you used in Steps 1–3.

Analyze and Conclude

1. **Measuring** In Step 2, what was the starting temperature of the cold water? How long did it take for the temperature to increase by 5°C? In which direction did the heat flow? Explain.

2. **Making Models** If the materials in Steps 1–3 represented your home in very hot weather, which material would represent the rooms in your home? The outdoor weather? The building walls?

3. **Controlling Variables** In the experiment you conducted in Step 4, what were the manipulated and responding variables? What variables were kept constant?

4. **Drawing Conclusions** Which material was most effective at preventing the transfer of heat? Which was the least effective? Explain how your data support your conclusion.

5. **Communicating** Write a paragraph explaining why the results of your experiment could be useful to people building energy-efficient structures.

Design an Experiment

Design an experiment to compare how well the materials you tested would work if the hot water were inside the cup and the cold water were outside. With your teacher's permission, carry out your experiment.

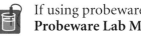

Go Online
PHSchool.com

For: Data sharing
Visit: PHschool.com
Web Code: ced-5054

Expected Outcome

Plastic foam is most effective for stopping heat transfer; metal is least effective.

Analyze and Conclude

1. Temperatures and times will vary. Heat flowed from the hot water to the cold water, as shown by the temperature changes.

2. *Rooms:* cold water; *outdoor weather:* hot water; *walls:* paper cup.

3. *Manipulated:* container material; *responding:* water temperature in cup; *constant:* initial temperature of water in beaker.

4. *Most effective:* plastic foam; *least effective:* metal. Cold water stayed close to its starting temperature for the longest time with plastic foam; temperature increased the fastest with metal.

5. Paragraph should discuss choices of building materials in terms of conserving energy used for heating and cooling.

Lab zone Consumer Lab

Keeping Comfortable

Prepare for Inquiry

Skills Objectives

After this lab, students will be able to

- measure temperature changes of water in a paper cup for use as a baseline
- control variables to compare how different materials slow heat transfer

Prep Time 20 minutes
Class Time 40 minutes

Advance Planning

Prepare hot and ice water ahead of time and keep them in insulated containers. **CAUTION:** *Do not use water hot enough to cause scalding.*

If using probeware, refer to the **Probeware Lab Manual.**

Safety

Students should use caution in handling the thermometers, hot water, and glass containers. Review the safety guidelines in Appendix A.

All in One Teaching Resources

- Lab Worksheet: *Keeping Comfortable*

Guide Inquiry

Invitation

Ask: **What experiences have you had with different materials stopping heat transfer?** *(Answers could include using a potholder versus a dishtowel, stirring hot liquid with a metal or plastic spoon, and so on.)*

Troubleshooting the Experiment

- Make sure students control all variables and record temperatures at regular intervals.

Extend the Inquiry

Design an Experiment Students' plans should follow an approach similar to that of Steps 1–4.

Go Online
PHSchool.com

For: Data sharing
Visit: PHSchool.com
Web Code: cep-5054

Students can share data online.

Technology and Society

The Hybrid Car

Key Concept
Hybrid cars can use both a gasoline engine and an electric motor to turn the transmission.

Build Background Knowledge

Recalling Effects of Fossil Fuel Use
Help students recall what they learned in this chapter that applies to the feature content. Ask: **What is a fossil fuel?** *(Energy-rich substance formed from the remains of organisms)* **What type of fossil fuel is used by most automobiles?** *(Gasoline)* **What are the problems associated with the use of fossil fuels?** *(Environmental pollution, limited supply)*

Introduce the Debate
Ask: **What are the main problems associated with the current way cars are fueled?** *(Possible answers: Gasoline contributes to air pollution; it is a limited resource; gasoline prices continue to rise.)* **What are some ways that individuals and governments have tried to solve some of the problems?** *(Students might suggest state and federal laws regarding emissions standards and fuel economy.)*

Facilitate the Debate
- Have students suppose that they are members of a consumer group studying the value of hybrid cars. Students can role-play different members of the group who have varying opinions about the value of hybrid cars.
- Students can find out if and how the body design of the hybrid cars differs from that of conventional cars, the problems associated with hybrid cars, and current research going on to improve them. Students should also consider where they can be bought, what to look for when buying one, and how their price compares with that of conventional cars.
- After the debate, students can write a consumer's report for a car magazine.

Technology and Society • Tech & Design •

The Hybrid Car

How do you get from here to there? Like most people, you probably rely on cars or buses. Engines that burn fossil fuels power most of these vehicles. To conserve fossil fuels, as well as to reduce air pollution, some car companies have begun to produce hybrid vehicles.

How Are Hybrid Cars Different?

The power source for most cars is a gasoline engine that powers the transmission. Unlike conventional cars, hybrid cars can use both a gasoline engine and an electric motor to turn the transmission. The generated power can be used by the transmission to turn the wheels. Or power can be converted into electricity for later use by the electric motor. Any extra electricity is stored in the car's battery. The gasoline engine in a hybrid car is smaller, more efficient, and less polluting than the engine in a conventional car.

Gasoline Engine The engine burns fuel to provide energy to the car.

Electric Motor and Generator In this model, the electric motor draws energy from the car's battery to help the car speed up. As the car slows down, the generator produces electricity to recharge the car's battery.

Transmission This device transmits power from the engine to the axle that turns the wheels.

Start The car uses power from its battery to start the gasoline engine.

Accelerate When the car accelerates, the electric motor and the gasoline engine work together to power the car.

Brake When the car brakes, the motor acts like a generator and stores electrical energy in the battery.

184 ◆ E

Are Hybrid Cars the Way to Go?

Hybrid cars consume less gas per mile and emit fewer pollutants than cars that run on gasoline alone. In spite of the benefits, there are some drawbacks to hybrid cars. In general, hybrid cars have less power for climbing steep hills and less acceleration than cars with larger engines. In addition, the large batteries could be an environmental hazard if they end up in a landfill. Drivers must make trade-offs in buying any car.

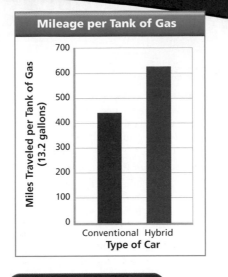

Mileage per Tank of Gas

Miles Traveled per Tank of Gas (13.2 gallons)

Conventional Hybrid
Type of Car

Fuel Tank Gasoline stored in the fuel tank flows to the engine where it's burned.

Battery The car's electric motor uses energy stored in the battery.

Stop
When the car stops or idles, the gasoline engine stops. It restarts when the driver steps on the gas pedal.

Weigh the Impact

1. Identify the Need
Why are some car companies developing hybrid cars?

2. Research
Research hybrid cars currently on the market. Use your findings to list the advantages and disadvantages of hybrid-car technology.

3. Write
Should your family's next car be a conventional or hybrid model? Use the information here and your research findings to write several paragraphs supporting your opinion.

For: More on hybrid cars
Visit: PHschool.com
Web Code: ceh-5050

Weigh the Impact

1. Students might cite new federal and state regulations regarding emission standards and fuel economy.
2. Information might include advantages such as fuel economy and environmental friendliness; disadvantages might include more complicated production process and reduced trunk capacity in some models.
3. Encourage students to consider all the information they have collected before they write their opinions. Remind them to support their opinions with facts.

Go Online
PHSchool.com

For: More on hybrid cars
Visit: PHSchool.com
Web Code: ceh-5050

Students can research this issue online.

Extend

Encourage students to search the Internet for diagrams of hybrid cars. Students can include a diagram in their written opinions to support their information.

Study Guide

• Complete student edition
• Section and chapter self-assessments
• Assessment reports for teacher

Help Students Read

Developing Vocabulary

Word Forms Ask students to use a dictionary to write in their own words definitions of *vessel* and *exchanger*. Then have students explain how these definitions relate to the terms *reactor vessel* and *heat exchanger*.

Words in Context Help students review the material in this chapter by looking again at the Key Terms. To figure out the meanings of unfamiliar words, have them look at the text surrounding the unfamiliar word. For example, for the Key Term *energy transformation*, have students look at Figure 1 and note the energy conversions in the production of electricity. Ask: **How does energy change form in the process of producing electricity in a power plant?** (*Chemical energy into thermal energy during burning of fuel, thermal energy into mechanical energy when steam is produced, mechanical energy into electrical energy when the turbine turns the shaft of the generator*) Then have students write a sentence for each Key Term, placing the term in a correct context.

Connecting Concepts

Concept Maps Help students develop one way to show how the information in this chapter is related: Energy resources can be renewable and nonrenewable. Have students brainstorm to identify the Key Concepts, Key Terms, details, and examples, and then write each one on a sticky note and attach it at random on chart paper or on the board.

Tell students that this concept map will be organized in hierarchical order and to begin at the top with the Key Concepts. Ask

① Fossil Fuels

Key Concepts

• When fuels are burned, the chemical energy that is released can be used to generate another form of energy, such as heat, light, motion, or electricity.

• The three major fossil fuels are coal, oil, and natural gas.

• Since fossil fuels take hundreds of millions of years to form, they are considered nonrenewable resources.

Key Terms

fuel
energy transformation
combustion
fossil fuel
hydrocarbon
petroleum
refinery
petrochemical

② Renewable Sources of Energy

Key Concepts

• The sun constantly gives off energy in the forms of light and heat.

• In addition to solar energy, renewable sources of energy include water, the wind, biomass fuels, geothermal energy, and hydrogen.

Key Terms

solar energy
hydroelectric power
biomass fuel
gasohol
geothermal energy

③ Nuclear Energy

Key Concepts

• During nuclear fission, when a neutron hits a U-235 nucleus, the nucleus splits apart into two smaller nuclei and two or more neutrons.

• In a nuclear power plant, the heat released from fission reactions is used to change water into steam. The steam then turns the blades of a turbine to generate electricity.

• In nuclear fusion, two hydrogen nuclei combine to create a helium nucleus, which has slightly less mass than the two hydrogen nuclei. The lost mass is converted to energy.

Key Terms

nucleus
nuclear fission
reactor vessel
fuel rod
control rod
meltdown
nuclear fusion

④ Energy Conservation

Key Concept

• One way to preserve our current energy resources to increase the efficiency of our energy use. Another way is to conserve energy whenever possible.

Key Terms

efficiency
insulation
energy conservation

students these questions to guide them to categorize the information on the stickies: **What are renewable resources? What are some nonrenewable resources? How can fossil fuels be used wisely? What is nuclear energy? How can energy be converted from one form to another?**

Prompt students by using connecting words or phrases, such as "produce" and "include." The phrases should form a sentence between or among a set of concepts.

All in One Teaching Resources

• Key Terms Review: *Energy Resources*
• Transparency E56

Organizing Information

Comparing and Contrasting Copy the graphic organizer about sources of energy onto a separate sheet of paper. Then complete it and add a title. (For more on Comparing and Contrasting, see the Skills Handbook.)

Energy Type	Advantage	Disadvantage
Coal	Easy to transport	a. ?
Oil	b. ?	Nonrenewable
Solar	c. ?	d. ?
Wind	e. ?	f. ?
Hydroelectric	No pollution	g. ?
Geothermal	h. ?	i. ?
Nuclear	j. ?	Radioactive waste

Reviewing Key Terms

Choose the letter of the best answer.

1. Which of the following is *not* a fossil fuel?
   a. coal
   b. wood
   c. oil
   d. natural gas

2. Wind and water energy are both indirect forms of
   a. nuclear energy.
   b. electrical energy.
   c. solar energy.
   d. geothermal energy.

3. Which of the following is *not* a biomass fuel?
   a. methane
   b. gasohol
   c. hydrogen
   d. sugar cane wastes

4. The particle used to start a nuclear fission reaction is a(n)
   a. neutron.
   b. nucleus.
   c. proton.
   d. atom.

5. A part of a nuclear power plant that undergoes a fission reaction is called a
   a. turbine.
   b. control rod.
   c. heat exchanger.
   d. fuel rod.

If the statement is true, write *true*. If it is false, change the underlined word or words to make the statement true.

6. The process of burning a fuel for energy is called <u>combustion</u>.

7. Most of the energy used today comes from <u>fossil fuels</u>.

8. Products made from petroleum are called <u>hydrocarbons</u>.

9. Geothermal energy is an example of a <u>nonrenewable</u> energy source.

10. <u>Insulation</u> means reducing energy use.

Writing in Science

Letter In a letter to a friend, predict how solar energy will change your life over the next 20 years. Include specific details in your description.

Discovery SCHOOL

Energy Resources
Video Preview
Video Field Trip
▶ Video Assessment

Review and Assessment

Organizing Information
Compare and Contrast Table
Coal: disadvantage—pollutes air; **Oil:** advantage—produces large amount of energy; **Solar:** advantages—renewable, does not pollute; disadvantage—requires sunshine; **Wind:** advantages—renewable, does not pollute; disadvantages—requires strong and steady winds, generators noisy; **Hydroelectric:** disadvantage—dams cause environmental harm; **Geothermal:** advantages—renewable, does not pollute; disadvantages—limited availability, deep drilling expensive; **Nuclear:** advantage—produces huge amount of energy

Reviewing Key Terms
1. b 2. c 3. c 4. a 5. d
6. true
7. true
8. false; petrochemicals
9. false; renewable
10. false; conservation

Writing in Science

Writing Mode Exposition
Scoring Rubric
4 Includes several effects of solar energy over the years, with complete details for each
3 Includes several effects; few details
2 Includes a few effects; details lacking
1 Includes minimal effects; inadequate details

Discovery SCHOOL Video Assessment

Energy Resources

Show the Video Assessment to review chapter content and as a prompt for the writing assignment. Discussion questions: **What is the difference between renewable and nonrenewable sources of energy?** (*Renewable resources will not run out, but nonrenewable sources are limited.*)

Go Online
PHSchool.com
For: Self-assessment
Visit: PHSchool.com
Web Code: cea-5050

Students can take a practice test online that is automatically scored.

Teaching Resources
- Transparency E57
- Chapter Test
- Performance Assessment Teacher Notes
- Performance Assessment Student Worksheet
- Performance Assessment Scoring Rubric

💿 **ExamView® Computer Test Bank CD-ROM**

Checking Concepts

11. As plants die and decay, their remains pile up and are buried by layers of sand, rock, and mud. Over time, heat and pressure change the decaying remains into coal.

12. Natural gas is a mixture of methane and other gases. It is transported by pipeline.

13. Possible answers include: overhangs to shade the windows in summer, large windows on south and west sides, solar cells on the roof to provide electricity, and a backup energy source.

14. The sun's energy is the driving force behind the water cycle, and it is the water cycle that leads to flowing water and the energy it can generate.

15. Wind can turn a turbine.

16. by placing control rods made of cadmium between the fuel rods to limit chain reactions

17. Energy efficiency is the percentage of energy actually used to perform work; *examples*: insulation, fluorescent light bulbs, window coatings, microwave ovens.

Thinking Critically

18. *Similarities:* All form from the remains of organisms, contain hydrocarbons, and produce a large amount of energy when burned. *Differences:* Coal forms from plant remains; oil and natural gas form from the remains of small animals, algae, and other organisms. Coal is solid, oil is liquid, and natural gas is a gas. Natural gas causes less air pollution than coal and oil.

19. Students should support their predictions with references to the local climate, including the frequency of sunny days and days with extreme temperatures.

20. Coal is nonrenewable because it takes so long to form. Solar power is renewable because its supply is unlimited. Methane is renewable because it is produced as wastes decompose. Hydrogen is renewable because it can be obtained from water, which is abundant on Earth.

21. Accept both "agree" and "disagree" responses. Students should support their views with explanations that cite the advantages and disadvantages of nuclear power as an energy source.

22. The nucleus will split, forming two smaller nuclei and releasing more neutrons and a great deal of energy.

Checking Concepts

11. Describe how coal forms.

12. What is natural gas? How is natural gas transported to where it is needed?

13. Describe three features of a solar home. (Your answer may include passive and active solar systems.)

14. Explain why solar energy is the indirect source of hydroelectric power.

15. Explain how wind can be used to generate electricity.

16. How is a nuclear fission reaction controlled in a nuclear reactor?

17. Define energy efficiency. Give three examples of inventions that increase energy efficiency.

Thinking Critically

18. Comparing and Contrasting Discuss how the three major fossil fuels are alike and how they are different.

19. Predicting Do you think you will ever live in a solar house? Support your prediction with details about the climate in your area.

20. Classifying State whether each of the following energy sources is renewable or nonrenewable: coal, solar power, natural gas, hydrogen. Give a reason for each answer.

21. Making Judgments Write a short paragraph explaining why you agree or disagree with the following statement: "The United States should build more nuclear power plants to prepare for the future shortage of fossil fuels."

22. Relating Cause and Effect In the nuclear reaction shown below, a neutron is about to strike a U-235 nucleus. What will happen next?

Neutron

Uranium-235 nucleus

188 ◆ E

Applying Skills

Use the information in the table to answer Questions 23–26.

The table below shows how the world's energy production changed between 1973 and today.

World Energy Production		
Energy Source	**Units Produced 1973**	**Units Produced Today**
Oil	2,861	3,574
Natural gas	1,226	2,586
Coal	2,238	3,833
Nuclear	203	2,592
Hydroelectric	1,300	2,705
Total	7,828	15,290

23. Interpreting Data How did the total energy production change between 1973 and today?

24. Calculating What percentage of the total world energy production did nuclear power provide in 1973? What percentage does it provide today?

25. Classifying Classify the different energy sources according to whether they are renewable or nonrenewable. How important is renewable energy to the world's energy production today?

26. Predicting How do you think the world's energy production will change over the next 40 years? Explain.

Lab zone Chapter **Project**

Performance Assessment Share your energy-audit report with another group. The group should review the report for clarity, organization, and detail. Make revisions based on feedback from the other group. As a class, discuss each group's findings. Then prepare a class proposal with the best suggestions for conserving energy in your school.

Lab zone Chapter **Project**

Project Wrap-Up Encourage groups to give each other specific suggestions for improving the reports and to avoid making overly general criticisms. In the whole-class discussion, give each group an opportunity to summarize its findings, then focus on the group's suggestions for reducing energy use. Ask students for their ideas about how the proposal should be organized and presented. You may want to have a group of volunteers compile the final proposal and present it to the entire class for further discussion.

Have students prepare a project log that describes which types of energy were hardest to measure, lists other information that would have helped with making recommendations, and records students' overall opinions of the school's energy efficiency.

Standardized Test Prep

Choose the letter of the best answer.

1. The interior of your car heats up on a sunny day because of
   A passive solar heating.
   B solar cells.
   C active solar heating.
   D indirect solar heating.

2. The main function of a dam in producing electricity is to
   F form a reservoir for recreation.
   G prevent flooding after a heavy rain.
   H provide a source of fast-moving water.
   J provide a source of wind.

Use the graph to answer Questions 3–4.

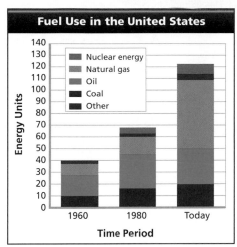

Fuel Use in the United States

3. According to the graph, most of the fuel sources used in the United States today are
   A renewable fuels.   B nuclear fuels.
   C fossil fuels.   D solar energy.

4. Which statement about fuel use in the United States is best supported by the graph?
   F Natural gas has become the most widely used fuel source.
   G Nuclear energy is not used today.
   H Coal is becoming the main source of fuel.
   J The amount of oil being used today has greatly decreased since 1980.

5. Which of the following is the first step in producing electricity in a nuclear reactor?
   A Steam turns the blades of a turbine.
   B Water boils to produce steam.
   C U-235 atoms are split by nuclear fission.
   D Heat is released.

Constructed Response

6. Explain what is meant by this statement: Electricity is *not* itself a source of energy. Then choose one energy source and explain how it can be used to produce electricity.

Applying Skills

23. It increased from 7,828 units to 15,290 units.

24. *1973:* 2.6% (3%); *today:* 16.9% (17%)

25. *Renewable:* hydroelectric; *nonrenewable:* coal, gas, nuclear, oil. Renewable energy (hydroelectric power) has grown a great deal in importance over the years, representing approximately 18% of the total energy units produced today.

26. Students' answer will vary, but should be supported with information from the chapter. Some students might suggest that the dependence on fossil fuels will decline as new technologies are developed for using other sources of energy.

Standardized Test Prep

1. A   **2.** H   **3.** C   **4.** F   **5.** B

6. Electricity is a form of energy. Solar energy can be used to boil water, creating steam. The steam can be used to generate electricity.

African Rain Forests

The interdisciplinary feature presents the central theme of rain forest diversity from four different curriculum perspectives: science, mathematics, social studies, and language arts. The four explorations are designed to capture students' interest and help them see how the content they are studying in science relates to other school subjects and real-world events. Share with others for a team-teaching experience.

All in One Teaching Resources

- Interdisciplinary Exploration: *Science*
- Interdisciplinary Exploration: *Mathematics*
- Interdisciplinary Exploration: *Social Studies*
- Interdisciplinary Exploration: *Language Arts*

Build Background Knowledge

Where are rain forests located?
Help students recall what they learned in the chapter *Ecosystems and Biomes*. Ask: **Where are Earth's tropical rain forests located?** *(South and Central America, Southeast Asia, Indonesia, and Africa)* **What other type of rain forest is there? Where is it located?** *(Temperate rain forests are found along the northwestern coast of the United States and Canada.)*

Introduce the Exploration

Have students examine the map on this page. Ask: **Where are rain forests in Africa located?** *(At or close to the equator)* **Describe the climate of a tropical rain forest.** *(Warm, humid, and rainy)* **Why do you think many nations in East Africa do not have tropical rain forests?** *(Much of East Africa's climate is not humid and rainy enough to support a rain forest.)*

African Rain Forests

What forest—
- **contains a frog that's 30 cm long?**
- **is home to gorillas, pottos, and pygmy hippos?**
- **is preserving diversity?**

It's an African rain forest. Thousands of plants and animals live here, from colorful orchids to fruit bats to elephants.

The rain forests of Africa grow near the equator. About 70 percent of the rain forests are in central Africa, in the vast basin of the great Congo River. Some parts of the central African rain forest are so dense and hard to reach that explorers have never visited them. East Africa, which is drier, has only scattered areas of rain forest.

African Rain Forests

[Map of Africa showing major areas of tropical rain forest, with labels: Mediterranean Sea, AFRICA, Niger, Guinea, Sierra Leone, Liberia, Côte d'Ivoire, Ghana, Togo, Benin, Nigeria, Cameroon, Equatorial Guinea, Central African Rep., Gabon, Congo, Rep. of the Congo, Dem. Rep. of the Congo, INDIAN OCEAN, ATLANTIC OCEAN, Madagascar. Scale: 0 500 1,000 mi / 0 500 1,000 km. Legend: Major areas of tropical rain forest. Coordinates: 20° N, 0° Equator, 20° S, 20° W, 0°, 20° E, 40° E]

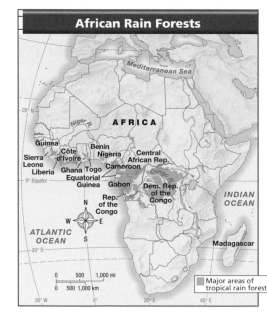

Golden Potto
This golden potto eats insects and fruits in the African rain forest.

Rain Forest Layers

The rain forest is really many forests in one—like different levels in an apartment building. Each layer varies in climate and is home to different plants and animals. The four layers are the emergent layer, the canopy, the understory, and the forest floor.

Over time, plants and animals have developed unusual adaptations to life at different layers of the rain forest. Some monkeys living in the canopy have long, muscular legs so they can run and leap through branches. Others have strong teeth and jaws that allow them to crunch fruits, nuts, and seeds. Some monkeys that live mainly on the forest floor have shorter tails but longer front legs.

Emergent Layer   40–70 Meters
This layer is formed by a few taller trees that poke through the canopy. The emergent layer captures the most rain, sunlight, heat, and wind. Colobus monkeys and vast numbers of birds live at this level.

Black and White Colobus Monkey

Canopy   10–40 Meters
The canopy is the dense "roof" of the rainforest. The crowns of trees capture sunlight to use in photosynthesis. Rain and sunlight filter through thick vegetation. Epiphytic orchids grow to the top of the canopy.

Epiphytic Orchid

Paradise Flycatcher

Understory   0–10 Meters
The understory has trees and plants that need little light. Pythons lurk in the vegetation. Some small animals such as squirrels glide from branch to branch.

Forest Floor   0 Meters
The forest floor is dark, humid, and still. Some animals, including frogs and insects, grow to gigantic sizes. Others are little, like the pygmy hippo.

Pygmy Hippo

E ◆ 191

Science Activity

Design a rain forest animal that is adapted to life at a certain level of the rain forest. Consider how your animal lives, how it travels, and what food it eats. Outline its characteristics and explain how each adaptation helps the animal survive. Draw a sketch of your design.

Background

Facts and Figures Taking up less space than the area of Texas, Madagascar is home to some 200,000 species of plants and animals, making it one of the most biologically diverse countries in the world. Separated from the African continent by plate tectonics, the island has been isolated for more than 100 million years. Most of the species that evolved on the island are found nowhere else on Earth. Ninety percent of the known species of lemurs, a type of primate, are found on Madagascar. People have lived on Madagascar for about 2,000 years, but during that time the island has lost about 80 percent of its rain forests and about 50 percent of its native species. Except for a few patches, the forests that once covered the island's eastern half have been cleared to create farms and housing for Madagascar's 17 million people.

Explore Science Concepts

Use Tables Challenge students to make tables to compare the features of the four layers of the rain forest. The headings for the table could include Layer, Height, Microclimate Conditions, and Sample Organisms. After students have completed their tables, ask: **Why is biodiversity in rain forests so high?** *(Students may answer that there are many different niches within the rain forest, there is high productivity in the rain forest, and that temperatures and rainfall amounts are stable year round.)*

Research Have students choose an animal or plant that lives in the rain forest, identify which layer it lives in, and describe the adaptations the organism has to help it survive and succeed in the rain forest. Students should create a one-page profile about the animal to display in the classroom.

Extend Ask students to research the impact that deforestation of tropical rain forests has on the plants and animals that inhabit this biome. Suggest they pay particular attention to efforts that are being made throughout the world to conserve rain forests.

Science Activity

Focus Encourage students to refer to their tables about each layer of the rain forest to determine what type of adaptations would be helpful in order to survive. Have students explain the different structures or behaviors the animal would have and what purpose each would serve toward the animal's survival.

Teach Have students work individually or in pairs. Students could create a bulletin board display with an enlarged version of the text's illustration in the center and each student's sketch posted next to the appropriate layer.

Scoring Rubric

4 Includes which layer of forest the animal will live in, a detailed description of structures and behaviors that will allow it to survive, and a sketch of the animal

3 Includes a description of structures and behaviors that will allow the animal to survive and a sketch of the animal

2 Includes a description of structures and behaviors that will allow the animal to survive

1 Includes a sketch of the animal with no details

Explore Mathematics Concepts

Teach Key Concepts Ask: **Why must trees in a rain forest grow tall and straight?** *(So they can reach sunlight at the top of the canopy)* **What might happen to older trees to give young trees a better chance of growing?** *(The older trees might fall and open up sunny clearings.)* **What are some products that can be made from African trees?** *(Student answers may include furniture, tools, boats, soaps, and candles.)*

Use Visuals Have students compare the tree heights listed in the table with the figure of forest layers on the previous page. Ask: **Which trees' tops are found in each forest layer?** *(Emergent: kapok, teak; canopy: African oil palm, African yellowwood, ebony, raffia palm; understory: cape fig)*

Math Activity

Focus Review how to make and label a bar graph.

Teach Have each student make his or her own graph. Some students may want to sequence the trees from shortest to tallest (or vice versa) on the horizontal axis.

Expected Outcome See Below

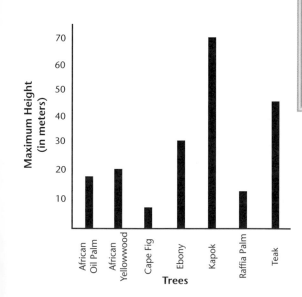

Reaching for Sunlight

Most rain forest trees are evergreens with broad leathery leaves. Some, like the African yellowwood, are conifers. Because the forest is so dense, trees must grow tall and straight to reach sunlight at the top of the canopy.

Along rivers, the floor and understory of the rain forest are a tangle of thick vegetation. But deep in the rain forest the floor is surprisingly bare. The canopy trees prevent sunlight from reaching plants below. Water drips from the leaves of the canopy high overhead. Young trees have the best chance to grow when older trees fall and open up sunny clearings.

West Africa's tropical forests contain many valuable trees. African mahogany and teak are used to make furniture, tools, and boats. Oil from the oil palm is used in soaps, candles, and some foods. Trees, such as ebony, that can tolerate shade grow slowly and develop dark, hard, long-lasting wood.

Rain Forest Tree
Rain forest trees like this kapok tree grow straight up toward the sun.

Trees of the Rain Forest	
Tree	**Maximum Height**
African oil palm	18 m
African yellowwood	20 m
Cape fig	7 m
Ebony	30 m
Kapok	70 m
Raffia palm	12 m
Teak	46 m

Math Activity

The table on this page gives the height of some of the trees in the rain forest. Use the information in the table to make a bar graph. Label the horizontal axis with the tree names. Use the vertical axis to show the heights of the trees.

- Which tree has the greatest maximum height? The least maximum height?
- What is the difference between the maximum heights of the tallest and the shortest trees?
- What is the average maximum height of all the trees shown in the graph?

192 ◆ E

Bark Cloth
Traditional Mbuti clothing is made of bark cloth.

Ituri Forest People

The native peoples of the African rain forest live as they have for thousands of years—by hunting and gathering. The forest supplies them with everything they need—food, water, firewood, building materials, and medicines.

One group of rain forest dwellers is the Mbuti people. The Mbuti live in the Ituri forest of the Democratic Republic of the Congo. Many of the Mbuti are quite small. The men hunt game, such as gazelle and antelope. The women gather wild fruits, nuts, and greens. Their traditional Mbuti clothing is made of tree bark and is wrapped around the waist. The bark is beaten to make it soft. Then it's decorated with geometric designs.

Most Mbuti live as nomads, with no settled home. Every few months they set up new hunting grounds. They build temporary dome-shaped huts of branches and leaves. Hunting groups of about 10 to 25 families live together.

Modern Africa has brought changes to the forest people, especially for those who live near the edges of the rain forest. For a few months of the year, some Mbuti work as laborers for farmers who live in villages at the edge of the forest. When their work is finished, the Mbuti return to the Ituri forest. Most forest people prefer not to cultivate their own land. Since the farmers don't hunt, they trade their goods for meat. In exchange for meat, the Mbuti receive goods such as iron tools, cooking pots, clothes, bananas, and other farm produce.

The Mbuti
The Mbuti hunt and fish along the Congo River.

Social Studies Activity

List the goods that forest people and farmers might have to trade. Assume that no modern conveniences, such as tractors and stoves, are available. In writing, explain how goods might be exchanged. Assign a value to the farmers' goods and the Mbuti goods, depending upon each group's needs. How would the trading process change if money were exchanged?

E ◆ 193

Explore Language Arts Concepts

Oral Presentation To enhance student comprehension of Durrell's memoirs, have volunteers take turns reading the selection aloud. Encourage students to read with drama by including appropriate vocal inflections, word emphasis, gestures, and facial expressions. Ask: **Why did Durrell use the word *magical* to describe his experience?** *(He had never seen the rain forest and its wildlife from that viewpoint before.)* Ask students if they have ever ridden in an airplane, been on a mountain, or been in a tall building where they could look down on things they usually only see from ground level. Encourage them to describe their experiences.

Language Arts Activity

Focus Have students work in pairs. To make the task manageable, limit the pamphlet size to four or six pages. Six pages can be created by folding a standard sheet of paper into thirds.

Teach Provide students with a variety of source materials to prompt their ideas. Use materials that are generously illustrated with color photographs of the rain forest and its wildlife. Allow students to photocopy or scan photographs and incorporate them into their pamphlets. If possible, allow students to use software programs to create their pamphlets. Have students share their pamphlets by posting them on a bulletin board.

Scoring Rubric

4 Includes at least four pages of photos, facts, and descriptive, persuasive information that would encourage people to travel to the rain forest

3 Includes at least four pages of photos, facts, and information that would encourage people to travel to the rain forests, does not include descriptive or persuasive phrasing

2 Less than four pages of photos, facts, and information that would encourage people to travel to the rain forest

1 Less than four pages of information with inaccurate facts or no photos

Climbing the Canopy

Much of the rain forest is still a mystery because it's so difficult for scientists to study the canopy. Native forest people sometimes climb these tall trees using strong, thick vines called lianas as support. But rain forest scientists have had to find different methods. Naturalist Gerald Durrell, working in the African rain forest, was lucky enough to find another way to observe the canopy. He describes it here.

Gerald Durrell
British conservationist Gerald Durrell wrote about his adventures with wildlife around the world. In this photo, Durrell holds an anteater.

While the canopy is one of the most richly inhabited regions of the forest it is also the one that causes the naturalist the greatest frustration. There he is, down in the gloom among the giant tree trunks, hearing the noises of animal life high above him and having half-eaten fruit, flowers, or seeds rained on him by legions of animals high in their sunlit domain—all of which he cannot see. Under these circumstances the naturalist develops a very bad temper and a permanent crick in the neck.

However, there was one occasion when I managed to transport myself into the forest canopy, and it was a magical experience. It happened in West Africa when I was camped on the thickly forested lower slopes of a mountain called N'da Ali. Walking through the forest one day I found I was walking along the edge of a great step cut out of the mountain. The cliff face, covered with creepers, dropped away for about 50 yards, so that although I was walking through forest, just next to me and slightly below was the canopy of the forest growing up from the base of the cliff. This cliff was over half a mile in length and provided me with a natural balcony from which I could observe the treetop life simply by lying on the cliff edge, concealed in the low undergrowth.

Over a period of about a week I spent hours up there and a whole pageant of wildlife passed by. The numbers of birds were incredible, ranging from minute glittering sunbirds in rainbow coloring, zooming like helicopters from blossom to blossom as they fed on the nectar, to the flocks of huge black hornbills with their monstrous yellow beaks who flew in such an ungainly manner and made such a noise over their choice of forest fruits.

From early morning to evening when it grew too dark to see, I watched this parade of creatures. Troops of monkeys swept past, followed by attendant flocks of birds who fed eagerly on the insects that the monkeys disturbed during their noisy crashing through the trees. Squirrels chased each other, or hotly pursued lizards, or simply lay spread-eagled on branches high up in the trees, enjoying the sun.

Background

Facts and Figures Gerald Durrell (1925–1995) first developed his love of animals and ambition to be a naturalist during childhood on the island of Corfu, off the west coast of Greece. Long hours spent observing wildlife led Durrell to collect many local animals as pets—to the consternation of his family.

Durrell's first job was as a student keeper at England's Whipsnade Zoo. After joining several collecting expeditions abroad, he began to organize them himself. In the 1950s, he founded the Jersey Wildlife Preservation and Zoological Garden to raise, study, and breed rare and threatened species. Durrell wrote the first of his many books, The Overloaded Ark, when he was only 22.

African Eagle

Language Arts Activity

Besides being an experienced naturalist and writer, Gerald Durrell was also a careful observer. In this selection, he describes in detail the "magical experience" of being in the canopy. Reread Durrell's description. Now work with a partner to write and design a pamphlet that will persuade visitors to come to an African rain forest. For your pamphlet, write strong, lively descriptions of what you might see, hear, and experience. Be persuasive.

Tie It All **Together**

Celebrate Diversity

Rain forests have the greatest biodiversity—variety of plant and animal life—of any ecosystem on Earth. Many species have yet to be discovered! Plan a display for your school to celebrate biodiversity in the rain forests. Include drawings, photos, and detailed captions.

- On a large map, locate and label Earth's tropical rain forests. Divide into groups to choose one rain forest region to research, such as Africa, Brazil, Costa Rica, Hawaii, or Borneo.

- With your group, study several animal and plant species in your chosen rain forest. You might choose monkeys, butterflies, birds, orchids, or medicinal plants.

- For each species, describe its appearance, where it occurs in the rain forest, its role in the ecosystem, and how it is useful to humans.

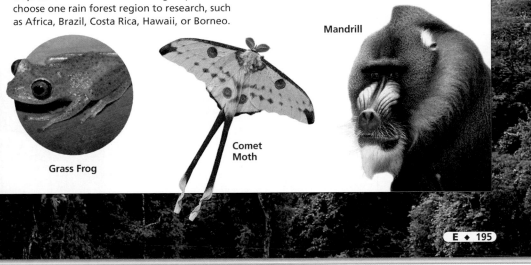

Grass Frog

Comet Moth

Mandrill

Time 4 class periods (2 for research, 2 for designing and creating the display)

Tips Have students work in groups of three or four.

- Monitor each group's choices of plant and animal species to make sure the group's research will be well-focused and not too wide-ranging.

- Arrange with your school office for a suitable display area, such as the school entryway, a heavily trafficked hallway, the library, or the cafeteria.

Extend After students have displayed their work in their own school, encourage them to ask permission to post the displays in areas accessible to the general public, such as the local library.

Think Like a Scientist

The Skills Handbook is designed as a reference for students to use whenever they need to review inquiry, reading, or math skills. You can use the activities in this part of the Skills Handbook to teach or reinforce inquiry skills.

Observing

Focus Remind students that an observation is what they can see, hear, smell, taste, or feel.

Teach Invite students to make observations of the classroom. List these observations on the board. Challenge students to identify the senses they used to make each observation. Then, ask: **Which senses will you use to make observations from the photograph on this page?** (*Sight is the only sense that can be used to make observations from the photograph.*)

Activity

Some observations that students might make include that the boy is skateboarding, wearing a white helmet, and flying in the air. Make sure that students' observations are confined to only things that they can actually see in the photograph.

Inferring

Focus Choose one or two of the classroom observations listed on the board, and challenge students to interpret them. Guide students by asking why something appears as it does.

Teach Encourage students to describe their thought processes in making their inferences. Point out where they used their knowledge and experience to interpret the observations. Then invite students to suggest other possible interpretations for the observations. Ask: **How can you find out whether an inference is correct?** (*By further investigation*)

Activity

One possible inference is that the boy just skated off a ramp at a skate park. Invite students to share their experiences that helped them make the inference.

Predicting

Focus Discuss the weather forecast for the next day. Point out that this prediction is an inference about what will happen in the

Think Like a Scientist

Although you may not know it, you think like a scientist every day. Whenever you ask a question and explore possible answers, you use many of the same skills that scientists do. Some of these skills are described on this page.

Observing

When you use one or more of your five senses to gather information about the world, you are **observing.** Hearing a dog bark, counting twelve green seeds, and smelling smoke are all observations. To increase the power of their senses, scientists sometimes use microscopes, telescopes, or other instruments that help them make more detailed observations.

An observation must be an accurate report of what your senses detect. It is important to keep careful records of your observations in science class by writing or drawing in a notebook. The information collected through observations is called evidence, or data.

Inferring

When you interpret an observation, you are **inferring,** or making an inference. For example, if you hear your dog barking, you may infer that someone is at your front door. To make this inference, you combine the evidence—the barking dog—and your experience or knowledge—you know that your dog barks when strangers approach—to reach a logical conclusion.

Notice that an inference is not a fact; it is only one of many possible interpretations for an observation. For example, your dog may be barking because it wants to go for a walk. An inference may turn out to be incorrect even if it is based on accurate observations and logical reasoning. The only way to find out if an inference is correct is to investigate further.

Predicting

When you listen to the weather forecast, you hear many predictions about the next day's weather—what the temperature will be, whether it will rain, and how windy it will be. Weather forecasters use observations and knowledge of weather patterns to predict the weather. The skill of **predicting** involves making an inference about a future event based on current evidence or past experience.

Because a prediction is an inference, it may prove to be false. In science class, you can test some of your predictions by doing experiments. For example, suppose you predict that larger paper airplanes can fly farther than smaller airplanes. How could you test your prediction?

Activity

Use the photograph to answer the questions below.

Observing Look closely at the photograph. List at least three observations.

Inferring Use your observations to make an inference about what has happened. What experience or knowledge did you use to make the inference?

Predicting Predict what will happen next. On what evidence or experience do you base your prediction?

future based on observations and experience.

Teach Help students differentiate between a prediction and an inference. You might organize the similarities and differences in a Venn diagram on the board. Both are interpretations of observations using experience and knowledge, and both can be incorrect. Inferences describe current or past events. Predictions describe future events.

Activity

Students might predict that the boy will land and skate to the other side. Others might predict that the boy will fall. Students should also describe the evidence or experience on which they based their predictions.

Classifying

Could you imagine searching for a book in the library if the books were shelved in no particular order? Your trip to the library would be an all-day event! Luckily, librarians group together books on similar topics or by the same author. Grouping together items that are alike in some way is called **classifying.** You can classify items in many ways: by size, by shape, by use, and by other important characteristics.

Like librarians, scientists use the skill of classifying to organize information and objects. When things are sorted into groups, the relationships among them become easier to understand.

Activity

Classify the objects in the photograph into two groups based on any characteristic you choose. Then use another characteristic to classify the objects into three groups.

Making Models

Have you ever drawn a picture to help someone understand what you were saying? Such a drawing is one type of model. A model is a picture, diagram, computer image, or other representation of a complex object or process. **Making models** helps people understand things that they cannot observe directly.

Scientists often use models to represent things that are either very large or very small, such as the planets in the solar system, or the parts of a cell. Such models are physical models—drawings or three-dimensional structures that look like the real thing. Other models are mental models—mathematical equations or words that describe how something works.

Activity

This student is using a model to demonstrate what causes day and night on Earth. What do the flashlight and the tennis ball in the model represent?

Communicating

Whenever you talk on the phone, write a letter, or listen to your teacher at school, you are communicating. **Communicating** is the process of sharing ideas and information with other people. Communicating effectively requires many skills, including writing, reading, speaking, listening, and making models.

Scientists communicate to share results, information, and opinions. Scientists often communicate about their work in journals, over the telephone, in letters, and on the Internet.

They also attend scientific meetings where they share their ideas with one another in person.

Activity

On a sheet of paper, write out clear, detailed directions for tying your shoe. Then exchange directions with a partner. Follow your partner's directions exactly. How successful were you at tying your shoe? How could your partner have communicated more clearly?

Skills Handbook ◆ 197

Classifying

Focus Encourage students to think of common things that are classified.

Teach Ask: **What things at home are classified?** (*Clothing might be classified in order to place it in the appropriate dresser drawer; glasses, plates, and silverware are grouped in different parts of the kitchen; screws, nuts, bolts, washers, and nails might be separated into small containers.*) **What are some things that scientists classify?** (*Scientists classify many things they study, including organisms, geological features and processes, and kinds of machines.*)

Activity

Some characteristics students might use include color, pattern of color, use of balls, and size. Students' criteria for classification should clearly divide the balls into two, and then three, distinct groups.

Making Models

Focus Ask: **What are some models you have used to study science?** (*Students might have used human anatomical models, solar system models, maps, or stream tables.*) **How have these models helped you?** (*Models can help you learn about things that are difficult to study because they are very large, very small, or highly complex.*)

Teach Be sure students understand that a model does not have to be three-dimensional. For example, a map is a model, as is a mathematical equation. Have students look at the photograph of the student modeling the causes of day and night on Earth. Ask: **What quality of each item makes this a good model?** (*The flashlight gives off light, and the ball is round and can be rotated by the student.*)

Activity

The flashlight represents the sun and the ball represents Earth.

Communicating

Focus Have students identify the methods of communication they have used today.

Teach Ask: **How is the way you communicate with a friend similar to and different from the way scientists communicate about their work to other scientists?** (*Both may communicate using various methods, but scientists must be very detailed and precise, whereas communication between friends may be less detailed and*

precise.) Encourage students to communicate like a scientist as they carry out the activity.

Activity

Students' answers will vary but should identify a step-by-step process for tying a shoe. Help students identify communication errors such as leaving out a step, putting steps in the wrong order, or disregarding the person's handedness.

Making Measurements

Students can refer to this part of the Skills Handbook whenever they need to review how to make measurements with SI units. You can use the activities here to teach or reinforce SI units.

Measuring in SI

Focus Review SI units with students. Begin by providing metric rulers, graduated cylinders, balances, and Celsius thermometers. Use these tools to reinforce that the meter is the unit of length, the liter is the unit of volume, the gram is the unit of mass, and the degree Celsius is the unit of temperature.

Teach Ask: **If you want to measure the length and the width of the classroom, which SI unit would you use?** *(Meter)* **Which unit would you use to measure the amount of mass in your textbook?** *(Gram)* **Which would you use to measure how much water a drinking glass holds?** *(Liter)* **When would you use the Celsius scale?** *(To measure the temperature of something)* Then use the measuring equipment to review SI prefixes. For example, ask: **What are the smallest units on the metric ruler?** *(Millimeters)* **How many millimeters are there in one centimeter?** *(10 millimeters)* **How many in 10 centimeters?** *(100 millimeters)* **How many centimeters are there in one meter?** *(100 centimeters)* **What does 1,000 meters equal?** *(One kilometer)*

> **Activity**
>
> **Length** The length of the shell is 7.8 centimeters, or 78 millimeters. If students need more practice measuring length, have them use meter sticks and metric rulers to measure various objects in the classroom.

> **Activity**
>
> **Liquid Volume** The volume of water in the graduated cylinder is 62 milliliters. If students need more practice, have them use a graduated cylinder to measure different volumes of water.

Making Measurements

When scientists make observations, it is not sufficient to say that something is "big" or "heavy." Instead, scientists use instruments to measure just how big or heavy an object is. By measuring, scientists can express their observations more precisely and communicate more information about what they observe.

Measuring in SI

The standard system of measurement used by scientists around the world is known as the International System of Units, which is abbreviated as SI (in French, **Système International d'Unités**). SI units are easy to use because they are based on multiples of 10. Each unit is ten times larger than the next smallest unit and one tenth the size of the next largest unit. The table lists the prefixes used to name the most common SI units.

Common SI Prefixes		
Prefix	**Symbol**	**Meaning**
kilo-	k	1,000
hecto-	h	100
deka-	da	10
deci-	d	0.1 (one tenth)
centi-	c	0.01 (one hundredth)
milli-	m	0.001 (one thousandth)

Length To measure length, or the distance between two points, the unit of measure is the **meter (m)**. The distance from the floor to a doorknob is approximately one meter. Long distances, such as the distance between two cities, are measured in kilometers (km). Small lengths are measured in centimeters (cm) or millimeters (mm). Scientists use metric rulers and meter sticks to measure length.

Common Conversions	
1 km	= 1,000 m
1 m	= 100 cm
1 m	= 1,000 mm
1 cm	= 10 mm

> **Activity**
>
> The larger lines on the metric ruler in the picture show centimeter divisions, while the smaller, unnumbered lines show millimeter divisions. How many centimeters long is the shell? How many millimeters long is it?

Liquid Volume To measure the volume of a liquid, or the amount of space it takes up, you will use a unit of measure known as the **liter (L).** One liter is the approximate volume of a medium-size carton of milk. Smaller volumes are measured in milliliters (mL). Scientists use graduated cylinders to measure liquid volume.

> **Activity**
>
> | Common Conversion |
> |---|
> | 1 L = 1,000 mL |
>
> The graduated cylinder in the picture is marked in milliliter divisions. Notice that the water in the cylinder has a curved surface. This curved surface is called the *meniscus*. To measure the volume, you must read the level at the lowest point of the meniscus. What is the volume of water in this graduated cylinder?

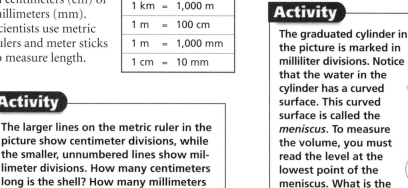

Mass To measure mass, or the amount of matter in an object, you will use a unit of measure known as the **gram (g).** One gram is approximately the mass of a paper clip. Larger masses are measured in kilograms (kg). Scientists use a balance to find the mass of an object.

Common Conversion

1 kg = 1,000 g

Activity

The mass of the potato in the picture is measured in kilograms. What is the mass of the potato? Suppose a recipe for potato salad called for one kilogram of potatoes. About how many potatoes would you need?

0.25 KG

Temperature To measure the temperature of a substance, you will use the **Celsius scale.** Temperature is measured in degrees Celsius (°C) using a Celsius thermometer. Water freezes at 0°C and boils at 100°C.

Time The unit scientists use to measure time is the **second (s).**

Activity

What is the temperature of the liquid in degrees Celsius?

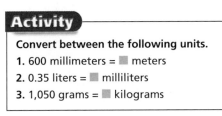

Converting SI Units

To use the SI system, you must know how to convert between units. Converting from one unit to another involves the skill of **calculating,** or using mathematical operations. Converting between SI units is similar to converting between dollars and dimes because both systems are based on multiples of ten.

Suppose you want to convert a length of 80 centimeters to meters. Follow these steps to convert between units.

1. Begin by writing down the measurement you want to convert—in this example, 80 centimeters.

2. Write a conversion factor that represents the relationship between the two units you are converting. In this example, the relationship is 1 meter = 100 centimeters. Write this conversion factor as a fraction, making sure to place the units you are converting from (centimeters, in this example) in the denominator.

3. Multiply the measurement you want to convert by the fraction. When you do this, the units in the first measurement will cancel out with the units in the denominator. Your answer will be in the units you are converting to (meters, in this example).

Example

80 centimeters = ■ meters

$$80 \text{ centimeters} \times \frac{1 \text{ meter}}{100 \text{ centimeters}} = \frac{80 \text{ meters}}{100}$$

$$= 0.8 \text{ meters}$$

Activity

Convert between the following units.
1. 600 millimeters = ■ meters
2. 0.35 liters = ■ milliliters
3. 1,050 grams = ■ kilograms

Activity

Mass The mass of the potato is 0.25 kilograms. You would need 4 potatoes to make one kilogram. If students need more practice, give them various objects, such as coins, paper clips, and books, to measure mass.

Activity

Temperature The temperature of the liquid is 35°C. Students who need more practice can measure the temperatures of various water samples.

Converting SI Units

Focus Review the steps for converting SI units, and work through the example with students.

Teach Ask: **How many millimeters are in 80 centimeters?** (*With the relationship 10 millimeters = 1 centimeter, students should follow the steps to calculate that 80 centimeters is equal to 800 millimeters.*) Have students do the conversion problems in the activity.

Activity

1. *600 millimeters = 0.6 meters*
2. *0.35 liters = 350 milliliters*
3. *1,050 grams = 1.05 kilograms*

If students need more practice converting SI units, have them make up conversion problems to trade with partners.

Conducting a Scientific Investigation

Students can refer to this part of the Skills Handbook whenever they need to review the steps of a scientific investigation. You can use the activities here to teach or reinforce these steps.

Posing Questions

Focus Ask: **What do you do when you want to learn about something?** *(Answers might include asking questions about it or looking for information in books or on the Internet.)* Explain that scientists go through the same process to learn about something.

Teach Tell students that the questions scientists ask may have no answers or many different answers. To answer their questions, scientists often conduct experiments. Ask: **Why is a scientific question important to a scientific investigation?** *(It helps the scientist decide if an experiment is necessary; the answer might already be known. It also helps focus the idea so that the scientist can form a hypothesis.)* **What is the scientific question in the activity on the next page?** *(Is a ball's bounce affected by the height from which it is dropped?)*

Developing a Hypothesis

Focus Emphasize that a hypothesis is one possible explanation for a set of observations. It is *not* a guess. It is often based on an inference.

Teach Ask: **On what information do scientists base their hypotheses?** *(Their observations and previous knowledge or experience)* Point out that a hypothesis does not always turn out to be correct. Ask: **When a hypothesis turns out to be incorrect, do you think the scientist wasted his or her time? Explain.** *(No. The scientist learned from the investigation and will develop another hypothesis that could prove to be correct.)*

Designing an Experiment

Focus Have a volunteer read the Experimental Procedure in the box. Invite students to identify the manipulated variable *(amount of salt)*, the variables kept constant *(amount and temperature of water, location of containers)*, the control *(Container 3)*, and the responding variable *(time required for the water to freeze)*.

Conducting a Scientific Investigation

In some ways, scientists are like detectives, piecing together clues to learn about a process or event. One way that scientists gather clues is by carrying out experiments. An experiment tests an idea in a careful, orderly manner. Although experiments do not all follow the same steps in the same order, many follow a pattern similar to the one described here.

Posing Questions

Experiments begin by asking a scientific question. A scientific question is one that can be answered by gathering evidence. For example, the question "Which freezes faster—fresh water or salt water?" is a scientific question because you can carry out an investigation and gather information to answer the question.

Developing a Hypothesis

The next step is to form a hypothesis. A **hypothesis** is a possible explanation for a set of observations or answer to a scientific question. In science, a hypothesis must be something that can be tested. A hypothesis can be worded as an *If . . . then . . .* statement. For example, a hypothesis might be *"If I add salt to fresh water, then the water will take longer to freeze."* A hypothesis worded this way serves as a rough outline of the experiment you should perform.

200 ♦ E

Teach Ask: **How might the experiment be affected if Container 1 had only 100 milliliters of water?** *(It wouldn't be an accurate comparison with the containers that have more water.)* Also make sure that students understand the importance of the control. Then, ask: **What operational definition is used in this experiment?** *("Frozen" means the time at which a wooden stick can no longer move in a container.)*

Designing an Experiment

Next you need to plan a way to test your hypothesis. Your plan should be written out as a step-by-step procedure and should describe the observations or measurements you will make.

Two important steps involved in designing an experiment are controlling variables and forming operational definitions.

Controlling Variables In a well-designed experiment, you need to keep all variables the same except for one. A **variable** is any factor that can change in an experiment. The factor that you change is called the manipulated variable. In this experiment, the **manipulated variable** is the amount of salt added to the water. Other factors, such as the amount of water or the starting temperature, are kept constant.

The factor that changes as a result of the manipulated variable is called the **responding variable.** The responding variable is what you measure or observe to obtain your results. In this experiment, the responding variable is how long the water takes to freeze.

An experiment in which all factors except one are kept constant is called a **controlled experiment.** Most controlled experiments include a test called the control. In this experiment, Container 3 is the control. Because no salt is added to Container 3, you can compare the results from the other containers to it. Any difference in results must be due to the addition of salt alone.

Forming Operational Definitions Another important aspect of a well-designed experiment is having clear operational definitions. An **operational definition** is a statement that describes how a particular variable is to be measured or how a term is to be defined. For example, in this experiment, how will you determine if the water has frozen? You might decide to insert a stick in each container at the start of the experiment. Your operational definition of "frozen" would be the time at which the stick can no longer move.

Experimental Procedure
1. Fill 3 containers with 300 millileters of cold tap water.
2. Add 10 grams of salt to Container 1; stir. Add 20 grams of salt to Container 2; stir. Add no salt to Container 3.
3. Place the 3 containers in a freezer.
4. Check the containers every 15 minutes. Record your observations.

Interpreting Data

The observations and measurements you make in an experiment are called **data.** At the end of an experiment, you need to analyze the data to look for any patterns or trends. Patterns often become clear if you organize your data in a data table or graph. Then think through what the data reveal. Do they support your hypothesis? Do they point out a flaw in your experiment? Do you need to collect more data?

Drawing Conclusions

A **conclusion** is a statement that sums up what you have learned from an experiment. When you draw a conclusion, you need to decide whether the data you collected support your hypothesis or not. You may need to repeat an experiment several times before you can draw any conclusions from it. Conclusions often lead you to pose new questions and plan new experiments to answer them.

Activity

Is a ball's bounce affected by the height from which it is dropped? Using the steps just described, plan a controlled experiment to investigate this problem.

Interpreting Data

Focus Ask: **What kind of data would you collect from the experiment with freezing salt water?** *(Time and state of the water)*

Teach Ask: **What if you forgot to record some data during an investigation?** *(You wouldn't be able to draw valid conclusions because some data are missing.)* Then, ask: **Why are data tables and graphs a good way to organize data?** *(They make it easier to record data accurately, as well as compare and analyze data.)* **What kind of data table and graph might you use for this experiment?** *(A table would have columns for each container with a row for each time interval in which the state of water is recorded. A bar graph would show the time elapsed until water froze for each container.)*

Drawing Conclusions

Focus Help students understand that a conclusion is not necessarily the end of a scientific investigation. A conclusion about one experiment may lead right into another experiment.

Teach Point out that in scientific investigations, a conclusion is a summary and explanation of the results of an experiment. For the Experimental Procedure described on this page, tell students to suppose that they obtained the following results: Container 1 froze in 45 minutes, Container 2 in 80 minutes, and Container 3 in 25 minutes. Ask: **What conclusions can you draw from this experiment?** *(Students might conclude that water takes longer to freeze as more salt is added to it. The hypothesis is supported, and the question of which freezes faster is answered—fresh water.)*

Activity

You might wish to have students work in pairs to plan the controlled experiment. Students should develop a hypothesis, such as, "If I increase the height from which a ball is dropped, then the height of its bounce will increase." They can test the hypothesis by dropping a ball from varying heights (the manipulated variable). All trials should be done with the same kind of ball and on the same surface (constants). For each trial, they should measure the height of the bounce (responding variable). After students have designed the experiment, provide rubber balls, and invite them to carry out the experiment so they can collect and interpret data and draw conclusions.

Technology Design Skills

Students can refer to this part of the Skills Handbook whenever they need to review the process of designing new technologies. You can use the activities here to teach or reinforce the steps in this process.

Identify a Need

Focus Solicit from students any situations in which they have thought that a tool, machine, or other object would be really helpful to them or others. Explain that this is the first step in the design of new products.

Teach Point out that identifying specific needs is very important to the design process. Ask: **If it was not specified that the toy boat be wind-powered, how might that affect the design?** (*The boat would likely be designed without sails.*)

Research the Problem

Focus Explain that research focuses the problem so that the design is more specific.

Teach Ask: **What might happen if you didn't research the problem before designing the solution?** (*Answers include developing a design that has already been found to fail, using materials that aren't the best, or designing a solution that already exists.*) **What would you research before designing your wind-powered toy boat?** (*Students might research designs and materials.*)

Design a Solution

Focus Emphasize the importance of a design team. Ask: **Why are brainstorming sessions important in product design?** (*A group will propose more new ideas than one person.*)

Teach Divide the class into teams to design the wind-powered toy boat. Instruct them to brainstorm design ideas. Then, ask: **Why do you think engineers evaluate constraints after brainstorming?** (*Evaluating constraints while brainstorming often stops the flow of new ideas.*) **What design constraints do you have for your wind-powered toy boat?** (*Materials must be lightweight, sturdy, and teacher-approved. The boat must be 10 centimeters or less in length and must float across a dishpan in 10 seconds or less.*)

Technology Design Skills

Engineers are people who use scientific and technological knowledge to solve practical problems and design new technologies. To design new products, engineers usually follow the process described here, even though they may not follow these steps in the exact order. As you read the steps, think about how you might apply them in technology labs.

Identify a Need

Before engineers begin designing a new product, they must first identify the need they are trying to meet. For example, suppose you are a member of a design team in a company that manufactures toys. Your team has identified a need: a toy boat that is powered by wind. The new toy needs to be inexpensive and easy to assemble.

Research the Problem

Engineers need to research the problem to gather information that will help them with their new design. This research may include finding articles in books, magazines, or on the Internet. It may also include talking to other designers who have developed similar technologies or solved similar problems. Engineers almost always perform experiments related to the product they want to design.

For your wind-powered toy boat, you could look at toys that are similar to the one you want to design. You might also do research on the Internet. You will probably want to test some materials to see how well they float and other materials to see whether they can function as sails.

Design a Solution

Research gives engineers information that lets them begin designing the product. When engineers design new products, they usually work in groups.

Generating Ideas Often design groups hold brainstorming meetings in which any group member can contribute ideas. Brainstorming is a creative process in which one group member's suggestions often spark ideas in other group members. Together, the creativity of different group members leads to proposed solutions.

202 ◆ E

Evaluating Constraints Chances are good that during brainstorming, a design group will come up with several possible designs. The group must then evaluate each proposal.

As part of their evaluation, engineers consider constraints, which are factors that place limitations or restrictions on a product design. Physical characteristics, such as the properties of the materials used to make products, are typical constraints. The materials in your proposed toy boat, for example, can't be too heavy, or the boat won't float. The sails need to be made of materials that are lightweight enough not to weigh down the boat. But they also need to be sturdy enough that the sails won't collapse in breezes.

Money and time are other typical constraints. If the materials in a product cost a lot, or if the product takes a long time to manufacture, the design may be impractical.

Making Trade-offs Design teams usually need to make trade-offs, in which they give up one benefit of a proposed design in order to obtain another. In designing your toy boat, you may have to make trade-offs when choosing materials. For example, suppose one material is lightweight but not fully waterproof. An alternative material is sturdy and more waterproof, but also heavier. You may decide to give up the benefit of low weight in order to obtain the benefits of sturdiness and waterproofing.

Build and Evaluate a Prototype

Once the team has chosen a design plan, the engineers build a prototype of the product. A prototype is a working version of the chosen design, made of the materials that have been proposed for the product. Engineers construct a prototype so that it can be tested and evaluated. They evaluate the product to see whether it works well, is easy to operate, is safe to use, and holds up to repeated use.

Think of your wind-powered boat. What would the prototype be like? Of what materials would it be made? How would you test it?

Troubleshoot and Redesign

Few prototypes work perfectly, which is why they need to be tested. Once a design team has tested a prototype, the members analyze the results and identify any problems. The team then tries to troubleshoot, or correct the problems. The design of the prototype is changed or adjusted to address any problems. For example, if your prototype toy boat leaks or wobbles, the boat should be resdesigned to eliminate those problems.

Communicate the Solution

Once a team has decided on a final design, the team needs to communicate the design to people who will manufacture and use the product. Teams often use a variety of methods, including sketches and word descriptions, to communicate the design of their product.

Activity

Now it's your turn. Design and build a toy boat that is powered by wind. Follow the steps in the technology design process.

Your boat must

- be made of materials approved by your teacher
- be no longer than 10 cm
- float the length of a rectangular dishpan in 10 seconds or less, powered by a breeze from an electric fan
- be built following the safety guidelines in Appendix A

Skills Handbook ◆ 203

Activity

The design possibilities are endless. Students might use small plastic containers, wood, foil, or plastic drinking cups for the boat. Mast materials may include toothpicks, straws, or small wooden dowels. Sails might be made of paper or fabric. The boats may be any shape, but must be no longer than 10 centimeters. The boats must also float across the dishpan in 10 seconds or less.

As student groups follow the steps in the design process, have them record their sources, brainstorming ideas, and prototype design in a logbook. Also give them time to troubleshoot and redesign their boats. When students turn in their boats, they should include assembly directions with a diagram, as well as instructions for use.

Build and Evaluate a Prototype

Focus Explain that building a prototype enables engineers to test design ideas.

Teach Relate building and testing a prototype to conducting an experiment. Explain that engineers set up controlled experiments to test the prototype. Ask: **Why do you think engineers set up controlled experiments?** *(From the data, they can determine which component of the design is working and which is failing.)* **How would you test your prototype of the wind-powered boat?** *(Students might float it across the dishpan using the breeze from an electric fan.)*

Troubleshoot and Redesign

Focus Make sure students know what it means to troubleshoot. If necessary, give an example. One example is a stapler that isn't working. In that case, you would check to see if it is out of staples or if the staples are jammed. Then you would fix the problem and try stapling again. If it still didn't work, you might check the position of staples and try again.

Teach Explain that engineers often are not surprised if the prototype doesn't work. Ask: **Why isn't it a failure if the prototype doesn't work?** *(Engineers learn from the problems and make changes to address the problems. This process makes the design better.)* Emphasize that prototypes are completely tested before the product is made in the factory.

Communicate the Solution

Focus Inquire whether students have ever read the instruction manual that comes with a new toy or electronic device.

Teach Emphasize the importance of good communication in the design process. Ask: **What might happen if engineers did not communicate their design ideas clearly?** *(The product might not be manufactured correctly or used properly.)*

Creating Data Tables and Graphs

Students can refer to this part of the Skills Handbook whenever they need to review the skills required to create data tables and graphs. You can use the activities provided here to teach or reinforce these skills.

Data Tables

Focus Emphasize the importance of organizing data. Ask: **What might happen if you didn't use a data table for an experiment?** (*Possible answers include that data might not be collected or they might be forgotten.*)

Teach Have students create a data table to show how much time they spend on different activities during one week. Suggest that students first list the main activities they do every week. Then they should determine the amount of time they spend on each activity each day. Remind students to give the data table a title. A sample data table is shown below.

Bar Graphs

Focus Have students compare and contrast the data table and the bar graph on this page. Ask: **Why would you make a bar graph if the data are already organized in a table?** (*The bar graph organizes the data in a visual way that makes them easier to interpret.*)

Teach Students can use the data from the data table they created to make a bar graph that shows the amount of time they spend on different activities during a week. The vertical axis should be divided into units of time, such as hours. Remind students to label both axes and give their graph a title. A sample bar graph is shown below.

Creating Data Tables and Graphs

How can you make sense of the data in a science experiment? The first step is to organize the data to help you understand them. Data tables and graphs are helpful tools for organizing data.

Data Tables

You have gathered your materials and set up your experiment. But before you start, you need to plan a way to record what happens during the experiment. By creating a data table, you can record your observations and measurements in an orderly way.

Suppose, for example, that a scientist conducted an experiment to find out how many Calories people of different body masses burn while doing various activities. The data table shows the results.

Notice in this data table that the manipulated variable (body mass) is the heading of one column. The responding variable (for

Calories Burned in 30 Minutes

Body Mass	Experiment 1: Bicycling	Experiment 2: Playing Basketball	Experiment 3: Watching Television
30 kg	60 Calories	120 Calories	21 Calories
40 kg	77 Calories	164 Calories	27 Calories
50 kg	95 Calories	206 Calories	33 Calories
60 kg	114 Calories	248 Calories	38 Calories

Experiment 1, the number of Calories burned while bicycling) is the heading of the next column. Additional columns were added for related experiments.

Bar Graphs

To compare how many Calories a person burns doing various activities, you could create a bar graph. A bar graph is used to display data in a number of separate, or distinct, categories. In this example, bicycling, playing basketball, and watching television are the three categories.

To create a bar graph, follow these steps.

1. On graph paper, draw a horizontal, or *x*-, axis and a vertical, or *y*-, axis.

2. Write the names of the categories to be graphed along the horizontal axis. Include an overall label for the axis as well.

3. Label the vertical axis with the name of the responding variable. Include units of measurement. Then create a scale along the axis by marking off equally spaced numbers that cover the range of the data collected.

4. For each category, draw a solid bar using the scale on the vertical axis to determine the height. Make all the bars the same width.

5. Add a title that describes the graph.

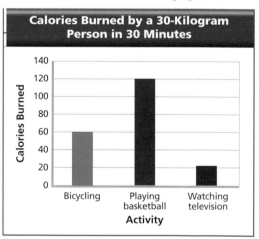

Calories Burned by a 30-Kilogram Person in 30 Minutes

Time Spent on Different Activities in a Week

	Going to Classes	Eating Meals	Playing Soccer	Watching Television
Monday	6	2	2	0.5
Tuesday	6	1.5	1.5	1.5
Wednesday	6	2	1	2
Thursday	6	2	2	1.5
Friday	6	2	2	0.5
Saturday	0	2.5	2.5	1
Sunday	0	3	1	2

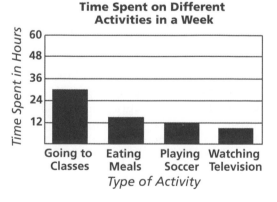

Time Spent on Different Activities in a Week

Line Graphs

To see whether a relationship exists between body mass and the number of Calories burned while bicycling, you could create a line graph. A line graph is used to display data that show how one variable (the responding variable) changes in response to another variable (the manipulated variable). You can use a line graph when your manipulated variable is **continuous,** that is, when there are other points between the ones that you tested. In this example, body mass is a continuous variable because there are other body masses between 30 and 40 kilograms (for example, 31 kilograms). Time is another example of a continuous variable.

Line graphs are powerful tools because they allow you to estimate values for conditions that you did not test in the experiment. For example, you can use the line graph to estimate that a 35-kilogram person would burn 68 Calories while bicycling.

To create a line graph, follow these steps.

1. On graph paper, draw a horizontal, or x-, axis and a vertical, or y-, axis.

2. Label the horizontal axis with the name of the manipulated variable. Label the vertical axis with the name of the responding variable. Include units of measurement.

3. Create a scale on each axis by marking off equally spaced numbers that cover the range of the data collected.

4. Plot a point on the graph for each piece of data. In the line graph above, the dotted lines show how to plot the first data point (30 kilograms and 60 Calories). Follow an imaginary vertical line extending up from the horizontal axis at the 30-kilogram mark. Then follow an imaginary horizontal line extending across from the vertical axis at the 60-Calorie mark. Plot the point where the two lines intersect.

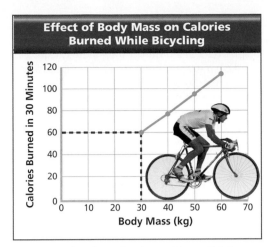

Effect of Body Mass on Calories Burned While Bicycling

5. Connect the plotted points with a solid line. (In some cases, it may be more appropriate to draw a line that shows the general trend of the plotted points. In those cases, some of the points may fall above or below the line. Also, not all graphs are linear. It may be more appropriate to draw a curve to connect the points.)

6. Add a title that identifies the variables or relationship in the graph.

Activity

Create line graphs to display the data from Experiment 2 and Experiment 3 in the data table.

Activity

You read in the newspaper that a total of 4 centimeters of rain fell in your area in June, 2.5 centimeters fell in July, and 1.5 centimeters fell in August. What type of graph would you use to display these data? Use graph paper to create the graph.

Skills Handbook ◆ 205

Line Graphs

Focus Ask: **Would a bar graph show the relationship between body mass and the number of calories burned in 30 minutes?** *(No. Bar graphs can only show data in distinct categories.)* Explain that line graphs are used to show how one variable changes in response to another variable.

Teach Walk students through the steps involved in creating a line graph using the example illustrated on the page. For example, ask: **What is the label on the horizontal axis? On the vertical axis?** *(Body Mass (kg); Calories Burned in 30 Minutes)* **What scale is used on each axis?** *(10 kg on the x-axis and 20 calories on the y-axis)* **What does the second data point represent?** *(77 calories burned for a body mass of 40 kg)* **What trend or pattern does the graph show?** *(The number of calories burned in 30 minutes of cycling increases with body mass.)*

Activity

Students should make a different graph for each experiment. Each graph should have a different x-axis scale that is appropriate for the data. See sample graphs below.

Activity

Students should conclude that a bar graph would be best for displaying the data. A sample bar graph for these data is shown below.

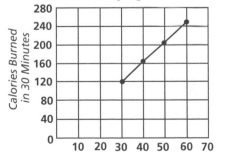

Effect of Body Mass on Calories Burned While Playing Basketball

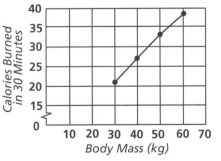

Effect of Body Mass on Calories Burned While Watching Television

E ● 205

Circle Graphs

Focus Emphasize that a circle graph must include 100 percent of the categories for the topic being graphed. For example, ask: **Could the data in the bar graph titled "Calories Burned by a 30-kilogram Person in Various Activities" (on the previous page) be shown in a circle graph? Why or why not?** *(No. It does not include all the possible ways a 30-kilogram person can burn calories.)*

Teach Walk students through the steps for making a circle graph. If necessary, help them with the compass and the protractor. Use the protractor to illustrate that a circle has 360 degrees. Make sure students understand the mathematical calculations involved in making a circle graph.

Activity

You might have students work in pairs to complete the activity. Students' circle graphs should look like the graph below.

Ways Students Get to School

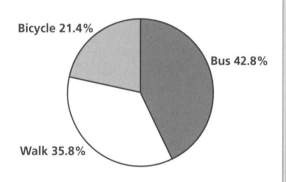

Bicycle 21.4%

Bus 42.8%

Walk 35.8%

Circle Graphs

Like bar graphs, circle graphs can be used to display data in a number of separate categories. Unlike bar graphs, however, circle graphs can only be used when you have data for *all* the categories that make up a given topic. A circle graph is sometimes called a pie chart. The pie represents the entire topic, while the slices represent the individual categories. The size of a slice indicates what percentage of the whole a particular category makes up.

The data table below shows the results of a survey in which 24 teenagers were asked to identify their favorite sport. The data were then used to create the circle graph at the right.

Favorite Sports

Sport	Students
Soccer	8
Basketball	6
Bicycling	6
Swimming	4

To create a circle graph, follow these steps.

1. Use a compass to draw a circle. Mark the center with a point. Then draw a line from the center point to the top of the circle.

2. Determine the size of each "slice" by setting up a proportion where x equals the number of degrees in a slice. (*Note:* A circle contains 360 degrees.) For example, to find the number of degrees in the "soccer" slice, set up the following proportion:

$$\frac{\text{Students who prefer soccer}}{\text{Total number of students}} = \frac{x}{\text{Total number of degrees in a circle}}$$

$$\frac{8}{24} = \frac{x}{360}$$

Cross-multiply and solve for x.

$$24x = 8 \times 360$$
$$x = 120$$

The "soccer" slice should contain 120 degrees.

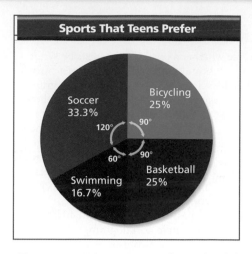

Sports That Teens Prefer

Soccer 33.3%

Bicycling 25%

120° 90°

60° 90°

Swimming 16.7%

Basketball 25%

3. Use a protractor to measure the angle of the first slice, using the line you drew to the top of the circle as the 0° line. Draw a line from the center of the circle to the edge for the angle you measured.

4. Continue around the circle by measuring the size of each slice with the protractor. Start measuring from the edge of the previous slice so the wedges do not overlap. When you are done, the entire circle should be filled in.

5. Determine the percentage of the whole circle that each slice represents. To do this, divide the number of degrees in a slice by the total number of degrees in a circle (360), and multiply by 100%. For the "soccer" slice, you can find the percentage as follows:

$$\frac{120}{360} \times 100\% = 33.3\%$$

6. Use a different color for each slice. Label each slice with the category and with the percentage of the whole it represents.

7. Add a title to the circle graph.

Activity

In a class of 28 students, 12 students take the bus to school, 10 students walk, and 6 students ride their bicycles. Create a circle graph to display these data.

Math Review

Math is a key tool in the study of science. Scientists use math to organize, analyze, and present data. This appendix will help you review some basic math skills.

Mean, Median, and Mode

When scientists analyze data, they may use the terms *mean*, *median*, and *mode*. The **mean** is the average, or the sum of the data divided by the number of data items. The **median** is the middle number in a set of ordered data. The **mode** is the number that appears most often in a set of data.

Example

A scientist counted the number of distinct songs sung by seven different male birds and collected the data shown below.

Male Bird Songs							
Bird	A	B	C	D	E	F	G
Number of Songs	36	29	40	35	28	36	27

To determine the mean number of songs, add the total number of songs and divide by the number of data items—in this case, the number of male birds.

$$\text{Mean} = \frac{231}{7} = 33 \text{ songs}$$

To find the median number of songs, arrange the data in numerical order and find the number in the middle of the series.

27 28 29 35 36 36 40

The number in the middle is 35, so the median number of songs is 35.

The mode is the value that appears most frequently. In the data, 36 appears twice, while each other item appears only once. Therefore, 36 songs is the mode.

Practice

Find out how many minutes it takes each student in your class to get to school. Then find the mean, median, and mode for the data.

Area

The **area** of a surface is the number of square units that cover it. The front cover of your textbook has an area of about 600 cm².

Area of a Rectangle and a Square To find the area of a rectangle, multiply its length times its width. The formula for the area of a rectangle is

$$A = \ell \times w, \text{ or } A = \ell w$$

Since all four sides of a square have the same length, the area of a square is the length of one side multiplied by itself, or squared.

$$A = s \times s, \text{ or } A = s^2$$

Example

A scientist is studying the plants in a field that measures 75 m × 45 m. What is the area of the field?

$$A = \ell \times w$$
$$A = 75 \text{ m} \times 45 \text{ m}$$
$$A = 3{,}375 \text{ m}^2$$

Area of a Circle The formula for the area of a circle is

$$A = \pi \times r \times r, \text{ or } A = \pi r^2$$

The length of the radius is represented by r, and the value of π is approximately $\frac{22}{7}$.

Math Review

Students can refer to this part of the Skills Handbook whenever they need to review some basic math skills. You can use the activities provided here to teach or reinforce these skills.

Mean, Median, and Mode

Focus Remind students that data from an experiment might consist of hundreds or thousands of numbers. Unless analyzed, the numbers likely will not be helpful.

Teach Work through the process of determining mean, median, and mode using the example in the book. Make sure students realize that these three numbers do not always equal each other. Point out that taken together, these three numbers give more information about the data than just one of the numbers alone.

Practice

Answers will vary based on class data. The mean should equal the total number of minutes divided by the number of students. The median should equal the number in the middle after arranging the data in numerical order. The mode should equal the number of minutes that is given most frequently.

Area

Focus Ask: **Who knows what area is?** *(Area is equal to the number of squares needed to cover a certain shape or object.)* On the board, write the formulas for the area of a rectangle and a circle.

Teach Give students various objects of different shapes. Have them measure each object and determine its area based on the measurements. Point out that the units of the answer are squared because they are multiplied together. If students are interested, you might also explain that π is equal to the ratio of the circumference of a circle to its diameter. For circles of all sizes, π is approximately equal to the number 3.14, or $\frac{22}{7}$.

Practice

The area of the circle is equal to 21 m × 21 m × $\frac{22}{7}$, or 1,386 m².

Circumference

Focus Draw a circle on the board. Then trace the outline with your finger and explain that this is the circumference of the circle, or the distance around it.

Teach Show students that the radius is equal to the distance from the center of the circle to any point on it. Point out that the diameter of a circle is equal to two times the radius. Give students paper circles of various sizes, and have them calculate the circumference of each.

Practice

The circumference is equal to $2 \times 28 \text{ m} \times \frac{22}{7}$, or 176 m.

Volume

Focus Fill a beaker with 100 milliliters of water. Ask: **What is the volume of water?** *(100 milliliters)* Explain that volume is the amount of space that something takes up. Then point out that one milliliter is equal to one cubic centimeter (cm^3).

Teach Write on the board the formulas for calculating the volumes of a rectangle and a cylinder. Point out that volume is equal to the area of an object multiplied by its height. Then measure the beaker to show students the relationship between liquid volume (100 milliliters) and the number of cubic units it contains (100 cubic centimeters).

Practice

The volume of the cylinder is equal to $\frac{22}{7} \times 7 \text{ m} \times 7 \text{ m} \times 5 \text{ m}$, or 770 m^3.

Fractions

Focus Draw a circle on the board, and divide it into eight equal sections. Shade in one of the sections, and explain that one out of eight, or one eighth, of the sections is shaded. Also use the circle to show that four eighths is the same as one half.

Teach Write the fraction $\frac{3}{4}$ on the board. Ask: **What is the numerator?** *(Three)* **What is the denominator?** *(Four)* Emphasize that when adding and subtracting fractions, the denominators of the two fractions must be the same. If necessary, review how to find the least common denominator. Remind students that when multiplying and dividing, the denominators do not have to be the same.

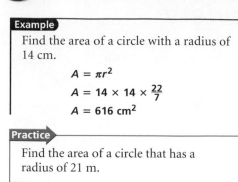

Example

Find the area of a circle with a radius of 14 cm.

$$A = \pi r^2$$
$$A = 14 \times 14 \times \frac{22}{7}$$
$$A = 616 \text{ cm}^2$$

Practice

Find the area of a circle that has a radius of 21 m.

Circumference

The distance around a circle is called the circumference. The formula for finding the circumference of a circle is

$$C = 2 \times \pi \times r, \text{ or } C = 2\pi r$$

Example

The radius of a circle is 35 cm. What is its circumference?

$$C = 2\pi r$$
$$C = 2 \times 35 \times \frac{22}{7}$$
$$C = 220 \text{ cm}$$

Practice

What is the circumference of a circle with a radius of 28 m?

Volume

The volume of an object is the number of cubic units it contains. The volume of a wastebasket, for example, might be about 26,000 cm^3.

Volume of a Rectangular Object To find the volume of a rectangular object, multiply the object's length times its width times its height.

$$V = \ell \times w \times h, \text{ or } V = \ell wh$$

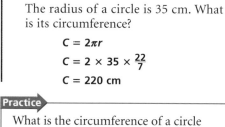

Practice

$$\frac{3}{7} \div \frac{4}{5} = \frac{3}{7} \times \frac{5}{4} = \frac{15}{28}$$

Example

Find the volume of a box with length 24 cm, width 12 cm, and height 9 cm.

$$V = \ell wh$$
$$V = 24 \text{ cm} \times 12 \text{ cm} \times 9 \text{ cm}$$
$$V = 2,592 \text{ cm}^3$$

Volume of a Cylinder To find the volume of a cylinder, multiply the area of its base times its height. Since the base of a cylinder is a circle, the formula for its area is $A = \pi r^2$. Therefore, the formula for the volume of a cylinder is

$$V = (\pi r^2)h$$

Example

Find the volume of a coffee can with radius 5 cm and height 14 cm.

$$V = (\pi r^2)h$$
$$V = \frac{22}{7} \times 5 \text{ cm} \times 5 \text{ cm} \times 14 \text{ cm}$$
$$V = 1,100 \text{ cm}^3$$

Practice

What is the volume of a cylinder with height 5 m and base radius of 7 m?

Fractions

A **fraction** is a way to express a part of a whole. For example, a baseball team has nine players. The three outfielders make up three parts of the nine-part team. This can be expressed as $\frac{3}{9}$ of the team. In the fraction $\frac{3}{9}$, 3 is the numerator and 9 is the denominator.

Adding and Subtracting Fractions To add or subtract two or more fractions that have a common denominator, first add or subtract the numerators. Then write the sum or difference over the common denominator.

Example

$$\frac{2}{7} + \frac{3}{7} = \frac{2 + 3}{7} = \frac{5}{7}$$

To find the sum or difference of fractions with different denominators, first find the least common multiple of the denominators. This is known as the least common denominator. Then convert each fraction to equivalent fractions with the least common denominator. Add or subtract the numerators. Then write the sum or difference over the common denominator.

Example

$$\frac{5}{6} - \frac{3}{4} = \frac{10}{12} - \frac{9}{12} = \frac{10-9}{12} = \frac{1}{12}$$

Multiplying Fractions To multiply two fractions, first multiply the two numerators to find the product's numerator. Then multiply the two denominators to find the product's denominator.

Example

$$\frac{5}{6} \times \frac{2}{3} = \frac{5 \times 2}{6 \times 3} = \frac{10}{18} = \frac{5}{9}$$

Dividing Fractions Dividing by a fraction is the same as multiplying by its reciprocal. Reciprocals are numbers whose numerators and denominators have been switched. To divide one fraction by another, first invert the fraction you are dividing by—in other words, turn it upside down. Then multiply the two fractions.

Example

$$\frac{2}{5} \div \frac{7}{8} = \frac{2}{5} \times \frac{8}{7} = \frac{2 \times 8}{5 \times 7} = \frac{16}{35}$$

Practice

Solve the following: $\frac{3}{7} \div \frac{4}{5}$.

Decimals

Fractions whose denominators are 10, 100, or some other power of 10 are often expressed as decimals. For example, the fraction $\frac{9}{10}$ can be expressed as the decimal 0.9, and the fraction $\frac{7}{100}$ can be written as 0.07.

Adding and Subtracting With Decimals
To add or subtract decimals, line up the decimal points before you carry out the operation.

Example

```
   27.4          278.635
 + 6.19        - 191.4
 ------        --------
  33.59          87.235
```

Multiplying With Decimals When you multiply two numbers with decimals, the number of decimal places in the product is equal to the total number of decimal places in each number being multiplied.

Example

```
     46.2   (one decimal place)
   × 2.37   (two decimal places)
 --------
 109.494   (three decimal places)
```

Dividing With Decimals To divide a decimal by a whole number, put the decimal point in the quotient above the decimal point in the dividend.

Example

$$15.5 \div 5$$

```
      3.1
   5)15.5
```

To divide a decimal by a decimal, you need to rewrite the divisor as a whole number. Do this by multiplying both the divisor and dividend by the same multiple of 10.

Example

$$1.68 \div 4.2 = 16.8 \div 42$$

```
      0.4
  42)16.8
```

Practice

Multiply 6.21 by 8.5.

Converting Fractions to Decimals
To convert a fraction to a decimal, divide the numerator by the denominator.

Example

$$\frac{5}{8} = \begin{array}{r} 0.625 \\ 8)\overline{5} \end{array}$$

Decimals

Focus Write the number *129.835* on the board. Ask: **What number is in the ones position?** *(9)* **The tenths position?** *(8)* **The hundredths position?** *(3)* Make sure students know that 0.8 is equal to $\frac{8}{10}$ and 0.03 is equal to $\frac{3}{100}$.

Teach Use the examples in the book to review addition, subtraction, multiplication, and division with decimals. Make up a worksheet of similar problems to give students additional practice. Also show students how a fraction is converted to a decimal by dividing the numerator by the denominator. For example, $\frac{1}{2}$ is equal to 0.5.

Practice

$6.21 \times 8.5 = 52.785$

Ratio and Proportion

Focus Differentiate a ratio from a fraction. Remind students that a fraction tells how many parts of the whole. In contrast, a ratio compares two different numbers. For example, $\frac{12}{22}$, or $\frac{6}{11}$, of a class are girls. But the ratio of boys to girls in the class is 10 to 12, or $\frac{5}{6}$.

Teach Use the example in the book to explain how to use a proportion to find an unknown quantity. Provide students with additional practice problems, if needed.

Practice

$6 \times 49 = 7x$
$294 = 7x$
$294 \div 7 = x$
$x = 42$

Percentage

Focus On the board, write $50\% = \frac{50}{100}$. Explain that a percentage is a ratio that compares a number to 100.

Teach Point out that when calculating percentages, you are usually using numbers other than 100. In this case, you set up a proportion. Go over the example in the book. Emphasize that the number representing the total goes on the bottom of the ratio, as does the 100%.

Practice

Students should set up the proportion
$\frac{24 \text{ beans}}{80 \text{ beans}} = \frac{x\%}{100\%}$
$24 \times 100 = 80x$
$2400 = 80x$
$2400 \div 80 = 30\%$

Precision and Significant Digits

Focus Measure the length of a paper clip using two different rulers. Use one ruler that is less precise than the other. Compare the two measurements. Ask: **Which measurement is more precise?** *(The ruler with the smallest units will give the more precise measurement.)*

Teach Give students the opportunity to take measurements of an object using tools with different precision. Encourage students to add and subtract their measurements, making sure that they round the answers to reflect the precision of the instruments. Go over the example for significant digits. Check

Ratio and Proportion

A **ratio** compares two numbers by division. For example, suppose a scientist counts 800 wolves and 1,200 moose on an island. The ratio of wolves to moose can be written as a fraction, $\frac{800}{1,200}$, which can be reduced to $\frac{2}{3}$. The same ratio can also be expressed as 2 to 3 or 2 : 3.

A **proportion** is a mathematical sentence saying that two ratios are equivalent. For example, a proportion could state that $\frac{800 \text{ wolves}}{1,200 \text{ moose}} = \frac{2 \text{ wolves}}{3 \text{ moose}}$. You can sometimes set up a proportion to determine or estimate an unknown quantity. For example, suppose a scientist counts 25 beetles in an area of 10 square meters. The scientist wants to estimate the number of beetles in 100 square meters.

Example

1. Express the relationship between beetles and area as a ratio: $\frac{25}{10}$, simplified to $\frac{5}{2}$.
2. Set up a proportion, with x representing the number of beetles. The proportion can be stated as $\frac{5}{2} = \frac{x}{100}$.
3. Begin by cross-multiplying. In other words, multiply each fraction's numerator by the other fraction's denominator.

   $5 \times 100 = 2 \times x$, or $500 = 2x$

4. To find the value of x, divide both sides by 2. The result is 250, or 250 beetles in 100 square meters.

Practice

Find the value of x in the following proportion: $\frac{6}{7} = \frac{x}{49}$.

Percentage

A **percentage** is a ratio that compares a number to 100. For example, there are 37 granite rocks in a collection that consists of 100 rocks. The ratio $\frac{37}{100}$ can be written as 37%. Granite rocks make up 37% of the rock collection.

You can calculate percentages of numbers other than 100 by setting up a proportion.

Example

Rain falls on 9 days out of 30 in June. What percentage of the days in June were rainy?

$$\frac{9 \text{ days}}{30 \text{ days}} = \frac{d\%}{100\%}$$

To find the value of d, begin by cross-multiplying, as for any proportion:

$9 \times 100 = 30 \times d$ $\quad d = \frac{900}{30}$ $\quad d = 30$

Practice

There are 80 beans in a jar, and 24 of those beans are red. What percentage of the beans are red?

Precision and Significant Digits

The **precision** of a measurement depends on the instrument you use to take the measurement. For example, suppose you measure a box with a ruler. If the smallest unit on the ruler is millimeters, then the most precise measurement you can make will be in millimeters.

The sum or difference of measurements can only be as precise as the least precise measurement being added or subtracted. Round your answer so that it has the same number of digits after the decimal as the least precise measurement. Round up if the last digit is 5 or more, and round down if the last digit is 4 or less.

Example

Subtract a temperature of 5.2°C from the temperature 75.47°C.

$$75.46 - 5.2 = 70.26$$

5.2 has the fewest digits after the decimal, so it is the least precise measurement. Since the last digit of the answer is 6, round up to 3. The most precise difference between the measurements is 70.3°C.

for understanding by asking: **How many significant digits are in the number 324,000?** *(Three)* **In the number 5, 901?** *(Four)* **In the number 0.706?** *(Three)* If students need additional practice, create a worksheet with problems in multiplying and dividing numbers with various significant digits.

Practice

$26.4 \text{ m} + 8.37 \text{ m} = 34.77 \text{ m}$
This answer should be rounded to 34.8 m because the least precise measurement has only one digit after the decimal. This number is rounded up to 8 because the last digit is more than 5.

Practice

$306 \text{ L} \div 2.5 \text{ L} = 122.4 \text{ L}$
Because 2.5 has only two significant digits, the answer is rounded to 120 L.

Practice

Add 26.4 m to 8.37 m. Round your answer according to the precision of the measurements.

Significant digits are the number of nonzero digits in a measurement. Zeroes between nonzero digits are also significant. For example, the measurements 12,500 L, 0.125 cm, and 2.05 kg all have three significant digits. When you multiply and divide measurements, the one with the fewest significant digits determines the number of significant digits in your answer.

Example

Multiply 110 g by 5.75 g.

$$110 \times 5.75 = 632.5$$

Because 110 has only two significant digits, round the answer to 630 g.

Practice

Divide 306 L by 2.5 L.

Scientific Notation

A **factor** is a number that divides into another number with no remainder. In the example, the number 3 is used as a factor four times.

Example

$$3 \times 3 \times 3 \times 3 = 81$$

An **exponent** tells how many times a number is used as a factor. For example, $3 \times 3 \times 3 \times 3$ can be written as 3^4. The exponent 4 indicates that the number 3 is used as a factor four times. Another way of expressing this is to say that 81 is equal to 3 to the fourth power.

Scientific notation uses exponents and powers of ten to write very large or very small numbers in shorter form. When you write a number in scientific notation, you write the number as two factors. The first factor is any number between 1 and 10. The second factor is a power of 10, such as 10^3 or 10^6.

Example

The average distance between the planet Mercury and the sun is 58,000,000 km. To write the first factor in scientific notation, insert a decimal point in the original number so that you have a number between 1 and 10. In the case of 58,000,000, the number is 5.8.

To determine the power of 10, count the number of places that the decimal point moved. In this case, it moved 7 places.

$$58{,}000{,}000 \text{ km} = 5.8 \times 10^7 \text{ km}$$

Practice

Express 6,590,000 in scientific notation.

Probability

Probability is the chance that an event will occur. Probability can be expressed as a ratio, a fraction, or a percentage. For example, when you flip a coin, the probability that the coin will land heads up is 1 in 2, or $\frac{1}{2}$, or 50 percent.

The probability that an event will happen can be expressed in the following formula.

$$P(\text{event}) = \frac{\text{Number of times the event can occur}}{\text{Total number of possible events}}$$

Example

A paper bag contains 25 blue marbles, 5 green marbles, 5 orange marbles, and 15 yellow marbles. If you close your eyes and pick a marble from the bag, what is the probability that it will be yellow?

$$P(\text{yellow marbles}) = \frac{15 \text{ yellow marbles}}{50 \text{ marbles total}}$$

$$P = \frac{15}{50}, \text{ or } \frac{3}{10}, \text{ or } 30\%$$

Practice

Each side of a cube has a letter on it. Two sides have *A*, three sides have *B*, and one side has *C*. If you roll the cube, what is the probability that *A* will land on top?

Scientific Notation

Focus Write a very large number on the board, such as 100 million, using all the zeros. Then, write the number using scientific notation. Ask: **Why do you think scientists prefer to write very large numbers using scientific notation?** *(Possible answers include that it is easier to do calculations, convert units, and make comparisons with other numbers.)*

Teach Go over the examples, and ask: **In the second example, which numbers are the factors?** *(5.8 and 10^7)* **Which number is the exponent?** *(7)* Explain that very small numbers have a negative exponent because the decimal point is moved to the right to produce the first factor. For example, 0.00000628 is equal to 6.28×10^{-6}.

Practice

$$6{,}590{,}000 = 6.59 \times 10^6$$

Probability

Focus Show students a coin and ask: **What is the chance that I will get tails when I flip the coin?** *(Some students might know that there is a 1 in 2, or 50 percent, chance of getting tails.)*

Teach Set up a bag of marbles like the one in the example. Allow students to practice determining the probabilities of picking marbles of different colors. Then, encourage them to actually pick marbles and compare their actual results with those results predicted by probability.

Practice

$$P(A) = 2 \text{ sides with } \frac{A}{6} \text{ sides total}$$
$$P = \frac{2}{6}, \text{ or } \frac{1}{3}, \text{ or } 33\%$$

Reading Skills

Students can refer to this part of the Skills Handbook whenever they need to review a reading skill. You can use the activities provided here to teach or reinforce these skills.

Introduction: Learning From Science Textbooks

Reading in a content area presents challenges different from those encountered when reading fiction. Science texts often have more new vocabulary and more unfamiliar concepts that place greater emphasis on inferential reasoning. Students who can apply reading skills and information-organizing strategies will be more successful in reading and understanding a science textbook.

Activity

Turn with students to the first page of any section. Walk through the Reading Preview with students, showing them the Key Concepts that provide a guiding set of questions that students can answer from the text. Next, point out the Key Terms list, which highlights the science vocabulary. Last, have students find the Target Reading Skill emphasized with the sample graphic organizer. Make the connection for students to the additional help found in this Skills Handbook.

All in One Teaching Resources

• Reading Skills Handbook

Building Vocabulary

Focus Explain to students that knowing the definitions of key concept words can help them understand what they read.

Teach List on the board various strategies to learn the definitions of new terms. Also solicit from students strategies that work for them. Other strategies include drawing a picture for the term, acting it out, or using it in conversation. Challenge students to choose a new strategy to learn the Key Terms in your next section.

Using Prior Knowledge

Focus Explain to students that using prior knowledge helps connect what they already know to what they are about to read.

Teach Point out that students should consider carefully what they remember. Their prior knowledge might not be accurate because memories have faded or

---

Reading Skills

Your textbook is an important source of science information. As you read your science textbook, you will find that the book has been written to assist you in understanding the science concepts.

Introduction: Learning From Science Textbooks

As you study science in school, you will learn science concepts in a variety of ways. Sometimes you will do interesting activities and experiments to explore science ideas. To fully understand what you observe in experiments and activities, you will need to read your science textbook. To help you read, some of the important ideas are highlighted so that you can easily recognize what they are. In addition, a target reading skill in each section will help you understand what you read.

By using the target reading skills, you will become a strategic reader—that is, one who can easily apply the appropriate reading skills. As you learn science, you will build knowledge that will help you understand even more of what you read. This knowledge will help you learn about all the topics presented in this textbook.

And—guess what?—these reading skills can be useful whenever you are reading. Reading to learn is important for your entire life. You have an opportunity to begin that process now.

The target reading skills that will make you a strategic reader are described below.

Building Vocabulary

To understand the science concepts taught in this textbook, you need to remember the meanings of the Key Terms. One strategy consists of writing the definitions of these terms in your own words. You can also practice using the terms in sentences and make lists of words or phrases you associate with each term.

Using Prior Knowledge

Your prior knowledge is what you already know before you begin to read about a topic. Building on what you already know gives you a head start on learning new information. Before you begin a new assignment, think about what you know. You might page through your reading assignment, looking at the headings and the visuals to spark your memory. You can list what you know in the graphic organizer provided in the section opener. Then, as you read, consider questions like the ones below to connect what you learn to what you already know.

• How does what you learn relate to what you know?
• How did something you already know help you learn something new?
• Did your original ideas agree with what you have just learned? If not, how would you revise your original ideas?

Asking Questions

Asking yourself questions is an excellent way to focus on and remember new information in your textbook. You can learn how to ask good questions.

One way is to turn the text headings into questions. Then your questions can guide you to identify and remember the important information as you read. Look at these examples:

Heading: Using Seismographic Data
Question: How are seismographic data used?
Heading: Kinds of Faults
Question: What are the kinds of faults?

---

their perspective was different. Encourage students to ask questions to resolve discrepancies between their prior knowledge and what they have learned

Asking Questions

Focus Demonstrate to students how to change a text heading into a question to help them anticipate the concepts, facts, and events they will read about.

Teach Encourage students to use this reading skill for the next section they read. Instruct them to turn the text headings into questions. Also challenge students to write at least four *what, how, why, who, when,* or *where* questions. Then, have students evaluate the skill. Ask: **Did asking questions about the text help you focus on the reading and remember what you read?** (*Answers will vary, but encourage honesty.*) If this reading skill didn't help, challenge them to assess why not.

You do not have to limit your questions to the text headings. Ask questions about anything that you need to clarify or that will help you understand the content. *What* and *how* are probably the most common question words, but you may also ask *why, who, when,* or *where* questions. Here is an example:

Properties of Waves

Question	Answer
What is amplitude?	Amplitude is . . .

Previewing Visuals

Visuals are photographs, graphs, tables, diagrams, and illustrations. Visuals, such as this diagram of a normal fault, contain important information. Look at visuals and their captions before you read. This will help you prepare for what you will be reading about.

Often you will be asked what you want to learn about a visual. For example, after you look at the normal fault diagram, you might ask: What is the movement along a normal fault? Questions about visuals give you a purpose for reading—to answer your questions. Previewing visuals also helps you see what you already know.

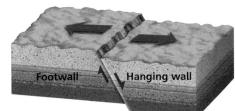

Footwall   Hanging wall

Normal Fault

Outlining

An outline shows the relationship between main ideas and supporting ideas. An outline has a formal structure. You write the main ideas, called topics, next to Roman numerals. The supporting ideas, sometimes called subtopics, are written under the main ideas and labeled A, B, C, and so on. An outline looks like this:

Technology and Society

I. Technology through history
II. The impact of technology on society
   A.
   B.

When you have completed an outline like this, you can see at a glance the structure of the section. You can use this outline as a study tool.

Identifying Main Ideas

When you are reading, it is important to try to understand the ideas and concepts that are in a passage. As you read science material, you will recognize that each paragraph has a lot of information and detail. Good readers try to identify the most important—or biggest—idea in every paragraph or section. That's the main idea. The other information in the paragraph supports or further explains the main idea.

Sometimes main ideas are stated directly. In this book, some main ideas are identified for you as key concepts. These are printed in boldface type. However, you must identify other main ideas yourself. In order to do this, you must identify all the ideas within a paragraph or section. Then ask yourself which idea is big enough to include all the other ideas.

Previewing Visuals

Focus Explain to students that looking at the visuals before reading will help them activate prior knowledge and predict what they are about to read.

Teach Assign a section for students to preview the visuals. First, instruct them to write a sentence describing what the section will be about. Then, encourage them to write one or two questions for each visual to give purpose to their reading. Also have them list any prior knowledge about the subject.

Outlining

Focus Explain that using an outline format helps organize information by main topic, subtopic, and details.

Teach Choose a section in the book, and demonstrate how to make an outline for it. Make sure students understand the structure of the outline by asking: **Is this a topic or a subtopic? Where does this information go in the outline? Would I write this heading next to a Roman numeral or a capital letter?** *(Answers depend on the section being outlined.)* Also show them how to indent and add details to the outline using numerals and lowercase letters.

Identifying Main Ideas

Focus Explain that identifying main ideas and details helps sort the facts from the information into groups. Each group can have a main topic, subtopics, and details.

Teach Tell students that paragraphs are often written so that the main idea is in the first or second sentence, or in the last sentence. Assign students a page in the book. Instruct them to write the main idea for each paragraph on that page. If students have difficulty finding the main idea, suggest that they list all of the ideas given in the paragraph, and then choose the idea that is big enough to include all the others.

Comparing and Contrasting

Focus Explain that comparing and contrasting information shows how concepts, facts, and events are similar or different. The results of the comparison can have importance.

Teach Point out that Venn diagrams work best when comparing two things. To compare more than two things, students should use a compare/contrast table. Have students make a Venn diagram or compare/contrast table using two or more different sports or other activities, such as playing musical instruments. Emphasize that students should select characteristics that highlight the similarities and differences in the activities.

Sequencing

Focus Tell students that organizing information from beginning to end will help them understand a step-by-step process.

Teach Encourage students to create a flowchart to show the things they did this morning to get ready for school. Remind students that a flowchart should show the correct order in which events occur. *(A typical flowchart might include: got up ➤ took a shower ➤ got dressed ➤ ate breakfast ➤ brushed teeth ➤ gathered books and homework ➤ put on jacket.)* Then explain that a cycle diagram shows a sequence of events that is continuous. Challenge students to create a cycle diagram that shows how the weather changes with the seasons where they live. *(Most cycle diagrams will include four steps, one for each season.)*

Comparing and Contrasting

When you compare and contrast, you examine the similarities and differences between things. You can compare and contrast in a Venn diagram or in a table. Your completed diagram or table shows you how the items are alike and how they are different.

Venn Diagram A Venn diagram consists of two overlapping circles. In the space where the circles overlap, you write the characteristics that the two items have in common. In one of the circles outside the area of overlap, you write the differing features or characteristics of one of the items. In the other circle outside the area of overlap, you write the differing characteristics of the other item.

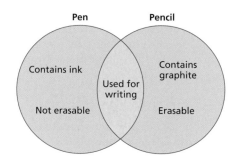

Table In a compare/contrast table, you list the items to be compared across the top of the table. Then list the characteristics or features to be compared in the left column. Complete the table by filling in information about each characteristic or feature.

	Loop One	Loop Two
Side of heart		
Blood flows to		
Blood returns from		

Sequencing

A sequence is the order in which a series of events occurs. Recognizing and remembering the sequence of events is important to understanding many processes in science. Sometimes the text uses words like *first, next, during,* and *after* to signal a sequence. A flowchart or a cycle diagram can help you visualize a sequence.

Flowchart To make a flowchart, write a brief description of each step or event in a box. Place the boxes in order, with the first event at the top of the page. Then draw an arrow to connect each step or event to the next.

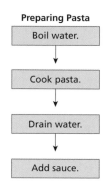

Cycle Diagram A cycle diagram shows a sequence that is continuous, or cyclical. A continuous sequence does not have an end because when the final event is over, the first event begins again. To create a cycle diagram, write the starting event in a box placed at the top of a page in the center. Then, moving in a clockwise direction around an imaginary circle, write each event in a box in its proper sequence. Draw arrows that connect each event to the one that occurs next, forming a continuous circle.

Identifying Supporting Evidence

A hypothesis is a possible explanation for observations made by scientists or an answer to a scientific question. A hypothesis is tested over and over again. The tests may produce evidence that supports the hypothesis. When enough supporting evidence is collected, a hypothesis may become a theory.

Identifying the supporting evidence for a hypothesis or theory can help you understand the hypothesis or theory. Evidence consists of facts—information whose accuracy can be confirmed by testing or observation.

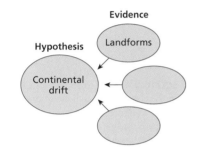

Relating Cause and Effect

Identifying causes and effects helps you understand relationships among events. A cause makes something happen. An effect is what happens. When you recognize that one event causes another, you are relating cause and effect. Words like *cause, because, effect, affect,* and *result* often signal a cause or an effect.

Sometimes an effect can have more than one cause, or a cause can produce several effects. For example, car exhaust and smoke from industrial plants are two causes of air pollution. Some effects of air pollution include breathing difficulties for some people, death of plants along some highways, and damage to some building surfaces.

Science involves many cause-and-effect relationships. Seeing and understanding these relationships helps you understand science processes.

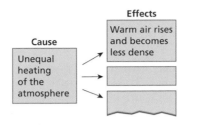

Concept Mapping

Concept maps are useful tools for organizing information on any topic. A concept map begins with a main idea or core concept and shows how the idea can be subdivided into related subconcepts or smaller ideas. In this way, relationships between concepts become clearer and easier to understand.

You construct a concept map by placing concepts (usually nouns) in ovals and connecting them with linking words. The biggest concept or idea is placed in an oval at the top of the map. Related concepts are arranged in ovals below the big idea. The linking words are often verbs and verb phrases and are written on the lines that connect the ovals.

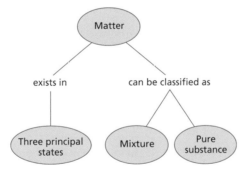

Identifying Supporting Evidence

Focus Explain to students that identifying the supporting evidence will help them to understand the relationship between the facts and the hypothesis.

Teach Remind students that a hypothesis is neither right nor wrong, but it is either supported or not supported by the evidence from testing or observation. If evidence is found that does not support a hypothesis, the hypothesis can be changed to accommodate the new evidence, or it can be dropped.

Relating Cause and Effect

Focus Explain to students that cause is the reason for what happens. The effect is what happens in response to the cause. Relating cause and effect helps students relate the reason for what happens to what happens as a result.

Teach Emphasize that not all events that occur together have a cause-and-effect relationship. For example, tell students that you went to the grocery store and your car stalled. Ask: **Is there a cause-and-effect relationship in this situation? Explain.** (*No. Going to the grocery store could not cause a car to stall. There must be another cause to make the car stall.*)

Concept Mapping

Focus Elicit from students how a map shows the relationship of one geographic area to another. Connect this idea to how a concept map shows the relationship between terms and concepts.

Teach Challenge students to make a concept map with at least three levels of concepts to organize information about types of transportation. All students should start with the phrase *Types of transportation* at the top of the concept map. After that point, their concepts may vary. (*For example, some students might place* private transportation *and* public transportation *at the next level, while other students might choose* human-powered *and* gas-powered.) Make sure students connect the concepts with linking words.

- Complete student edition
- Video and audio
- Simulations and activities
- Section and chapter activities

Appendix A Laboratory Safety

Laboratory Safety

Laboratory safety is an essential element of a successful science class. Students need to understand exactly what is safe and unsafe behavior and what the rationale is behind each safety rule.

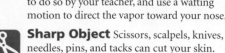 **Teaching Resources**

- Laboratory Safety Teacher Notes
- Laboratory Safety Rules
- Laboratory Safety Symbols
- Laboratory Safety Contract

General Precautions

- Post safety rules in the classroom, and review them regularly with students before beginning every science activity.
- Familiarize yourself with the safety procedures for each activity before introducing it to your students.
- For open-ended activities like Chapter Projects, have students submit their procedures or design plans in writing and check them for safety considerations.
- Always act as an exemplary role model by displaying safe behavior.
- Know how to use safety equipment, such as fire extinguishers and fire blankets, and always have it accessible.
- Have students practice leaving the classroom quickly and orderly to prepare them for emergencies.
- Explain to students how to use the intercom or other available means of communication to get help during an emergency.
- Never leave students unattended while they are engaged in science activities.
- Provide enough space for students to safely carry out science activities.
- Instruct students to report all accidents and injuries to you immediately.

Safety Symbols

These symbols warn of possible dangers in the laboratory and remind you to work carefully.

 Safety Goggles Wear safety goggles to protect your eyes in any activity involving chemicals, flames or heating, or glassware.

 Lab Apron Wear a laboratory apron to protect your skin and clothing from damage.

 Breakage Handle breakable materials, such as glassware, with care. Do not touch broken glassware.

 Heat-Resistant Gloves Use an oven mitt or other hand protection when handling hot materials such as hot plates or hot glassware.

 Plastic Gloves Wear disposable plastic gloves when working with harmful chemicals and organisms. Keep your hands away from your face, and dispose of the gloves according to your teacher's instructions.

 Heating Use a clamp or tongs to pick up hot glassware. Do not touch hot objects with your bare hands.

 Flames Before you work with flames, tie back loose hair and clothing. Follow instructions from your teacher about lighting and extinguishing flames.

 No Flames When using flammable materials, make sure there are no flames, sparks, or other exposed heat sources present.

 Corrosive Chemical Avoid getting acid or other corrosive chemicals on your skin or clothing or in your eyes. Do not inhale the vapors. Wash your hands after the activity.

 Poison Do not let any poisonous chemical come into contact with your skin, and do not inhale its vapors. Wash your hands when you are finished with the activity.

 Fumes Work in a ventilated area when harmful vapors may be involved. Avoid inhaling vapors directly. Only test an odor when directed to do so by your teacher, and use a wafting motion to direct the vapor toward your nose.

 Sharp Object Scissors, scalpels, knives, needles, pins, and tacks can cut your skin. Always direct a sharp edge or point away from yourself and others.

 Animal Safety Treat live or preserved animals or animal parts with care to avoid harming the animals or yourself. Wash your hands when you are finished with the activity.

 Plant Safety Handle plants only as directed by your teacher. If you are allergic to certain plants, tell your teacher; do not do an activity involving those plants. Avoid touching harmful plants such as poison ivy. Wash your hands when you are finished with the activity.

 Electric Shock To avoid electric shock, never use electrical equipment around water, or when the equipment is wet or your hands are wet. Be sure cords are untangled and cannot trip anyone. Unplug equipment not in use.

 Physical Safety When an experiment involves physical activity, avoid injuring yourself or others. Alert your teacher if there is any reason you should not participate.

 Disposal Dispose of chemicals and other laboratory materials safely. Follow the instructions from your teacher.

Hand Washing Wash your hands thoroughly when finished with the activity. Use antibacterial soap and warm water. Rinse well.

General Safety Awareness When this symbol appears, follow the instructions provided. When you are asked to develop your own procedure in a lab, have your teacher approve your plan before you go further.

End-of-Experiment Rules

- Always have students use warm water and soap for washing their hands.

Heating and Fire Safety

- No flammable substances should be in use around hot plates, light bulbs, or open flames.
- Test tubes should be heated only in water baths.
- Students should be permitted to strike matches to light candles or burners *only* with strict supervision. When possible, you should light the flames, especially when working with younger students.
- Be sure to have proper ventilation when fumes are produced during a procedure.
- All electrical equipment used in the lab should have GFI switches.

Science Safety Rules

General Precautions

Follow all instructions. Never perform activities without the approval and supervision of your teacher. Do not engage in horseplay. Never eat or drink in the laboratory. Keep work areas clean and uncluttered.

Dress Code

Wear safety goggles whenever you work with chemicals, glassware, heat sources such as burners, or any substance that might get into your eyes. If you wear contact lenses, notify your teacher.

Wear a lab apron or coat whenever you work with corrosive chemicals or substances that can stain. Tie back long hair. Remove or tie back any article of clothing or jewelry that can hang down and touch chemicals, flames, or equipment. Roll up long sleeves. Never wear open shoes or sandals.

First Aid

Report all accidents, injuries, or fires to your teacher, no matter how minor. Be aware of the location of the first-aid kit, emergency equipment such as the fire extinguisher and fire blanket, and the nearest telephone. Know whom to contact in an emergency.

Heating and Fire Safety

Keep all combustible materials away from flames. When heating a substance in a test tube, make sure that the mouth of the tube is not pointed at you or anyone else. Never heat a liquid in a closed container. Use an oven mitt to pick up a container that has been heated.

Using Chemicals Safely

Never put your face near the mouth of a container that holds chemicals. Never touch, taste, or smell a chemical unless your teacher tells you to.

Use only those chemicals needed in the activity. Keep all containers closed when chemicals are not being used. Pour all chemicals over the sink or a container, not over your work surface. Dispose of excess chemicals as instructed by your teacher.

Be extra careful when working with acids or bases. When mixing an acid and water, always pour the water into the container first and then add the acid to the water. Never pour water into an acid. Wash chemical spills and splashes immediately with plenty of water.

Using Glassware Safely

If glassware is broken or chipped, notify your teacher immediately. Never handle broken or chipped glass with your bare hands.

Never force glass tubing or thermometers into a rubber stopper or rubber tubing. Have your teacher insert the glass tubing or thermometer if required for an activity.

Using Sharp Instruments

Handle sharp instruments with extreme care. Never cut material toward you; cut away from you.

Animal and Plant Safety

Never perform experiments that cause pain, discomfort, or harm to animals. Only handle animals if absolutely necessary. If you know that you are allergic to certain plants, molds, or animals, tell your teacher before doing an activity in which these are used. Wash your hands thoroughly after any activity involving animals, animal parts, plants, plant parts, or soil.

During field work, wear long pants, long sleeves, socks, and closed shoes. Avoid poisonous plants and fungi as well as plants with thorns.

End-of-Experiment Rules

Unplug all electrical equipment. Clean up your work area. Dispose of waste materials as instructed by your teacher. Wash your hands after every experiment.

Handling Organisms Safely

- In an activity where students are directed to taste something, be sure to store the material in clean, *nonscience* containers. Distribute the material to students in *new* plastic or paper dispensables, which should be discarded after the tasting. Tasting or eating should never be done in a lab classroom.

- When growing bacterial cultures, use only disposable petri dishes. After streaking, the dishes should be sealed and not opened again by students. After the lab, students should return the unopened dishes to you.

- Two methods are recommended for the safe disposal of bacterial cultures. *First method:* Autoclave the petri dishes and discard without opening. *Second method:* If no autoclave is available, carefully open the dishes (never have a student do this) and pour full-strength bleach into the dishes and let stand for a day. Then pour the bleach from the petri dishes down a drain, and flush the drain with lots of water. Tape the petri dishes back together, and place in a sealed plastic bag. Wrap the plastic bag with a brown paper bag or newspaper, and tape securely. Throw the sealed package in the trash. Thoroughly disinfect the work area with bleach.

- To grow mold, use a new, sealable plastic bag that is two to three times larger than the material to be placed inside. Seal the bag and tape it shut. After the bag is sealed, students should not open it. To dispose of the bag and mold culture, make a small cut near an edge of the bag, and cook in a microwave oven on high setting for at least one minute. Discard the bag according to local ordinance, usually in the trash.

- Students should wear disposable nitrile, latex, or food-handling gloves when handling live animals or nonliving specimens.

Using Glassware Safely

- Use plastic containers, graduated cylinders, and beakers whenever possible. If using glass, students should wear safety goggles.
- Use only nonmercury thermometers with anti-roll protectors.

Using Chemicals Safely

- When students use both chemicals and microscopes in one activity, microscopes should be in a separate part of the room from the chemicals so that when students remove their goggles to use the microscopes, their eyes are not at risk.

English and Spanish Glossary

A

abiotic factor A nonliving part of an organism's habitat. (p. 8)
factor abiótico La parte no viva del hábitat de un organismo.

acid rain Precipitation that is more acidic than normal because of air pollution. (p. 140)
lluvia ácida Precipitación que es más ácida de lo normal debido a la contaminación del aire.

adaptation A behavior or physical characteristic that allows an organism to live successfully in its environment. (p. 25)
adaptación Comportamiento o característica física que permite a un organismo vivir en su medio ambiente.

aquaculture The practice of raising fish and other water-dwelling organisms for food. (p. 93)
acuicultura Técnica del cultivo de peces y otros organismos acuáticos para consumo humano.

B

bedrock Rock that makes up Earth's crust. (p. 118)
lecho rocoso Roca que forma la corteza de la Tierra.

biodegradable Capable of being broken down by bacteria and other decomposers. (p. 125)
biodegradable Sustancia que las bacterias y otros descomponedores pueden descomponer.

biodiversity The number of different species in an area. (p. 95)
biodiversidad Número de diferentes especies en un área.

biogeography The study of where organisms live. (p. 54)
biogeografía Estudio del lugar donde viven los organismos.

biomass fuel Fuel made from living things. (p. 169)
combustible de biomasa Combustible formado a partir de seres vivos.

biome A group of land ecosystems with similar climates and organisms. (p. 58)
bioma Grupo de ecosistemas terrestres con climas y organismos similares.

biotic factor A living part of an organism's habitat. (p. 7)
factor biótico La parte viva del hábitat de un organismo.

birth rate

birth rate The number of births in a population in a certain amount of time. (p. 16)
tasa de natalidad Número de nacimientos en una población en un período determinado.

C

canopy A leafy roof formed by tall trees in a forest. (p. 60)
bóveda arborea Cubierta densa formada por las cimas hojeadas de los árboles altos de un bosque.

captive breeding The mating of animals in zoos or wildlife preserves. (p. 104)
reproducción en cautiverio Apareamiento de animales en zoológicos y reservas naturales.

carnivore A consumer that eats only animals. (p. 43)
carnívoro Consumidor que come sólo animales.

carrying capacity The largest population that an area can support. (p. 19)
capacidad de carga La mayor población que puede sustentar un área.

chlorofluorocarbons Human-made gases containing chlorine and fluorine (also called CFCs). (p. 148)
clorofluorocarbonos Gases producidos por el ser humano que contienen cloro y flúor (también llamados CFC).

clear-cutting The process of cutting down all the trees in an area at once. (p. 90)
tala total Proceso de cortar simultáneamente todos los árboles de un área.

climate The typical weather pattern in an area over a long period of time. (p. 57)
clima Patrón típico del tiempo en un área durante un largo período.

combustion The process of burning a fuel. (p. 159)
combustión Proceso en el que se quema un combustible.

commensalism A relationship between two species in which one species benefits and the other is neither helped nor harmed. (p. 30)
comensalismo Relación entre dos especies donde una se beneficia y la otra no obtiene ni beneficio ni perjuicio.

community All the different populations that live together in an area. (p. 9)
comunidad Todas las diferentes poblaciones que viven juntas en un área.

competition The struggle between organisms to survive as they attempt to use the same limited resource. (p. 26)
competencia Lucha entre organismos por sobrevivir a medida que usan los recursos limitados en un mismo hábitat.

composting The process of helping biodegradable wastes to decompose naturally. (p. 127)
hacer abono orgánico Proceso de ayudar a que los desechos biodegradables se descompongan de manera natural.

condensation The process by which a gas changes to a liquid. (p. 49)
condensación Proceso por el cual un gas se convierte en líquido.

coniferous tree A tree that produces its seeds in cones and that has needle-shaped leaves. (p. 64)
árbol conífero Árbol que produce sus semillas en conos y sus hojas tienen forma de aguja.

consumer An organism that obtains energy by feeding on other organisms. (p. 43)
consumidor Organismo que obtiene energía alimentándose de otros organismos.

continental drift The very slow motion of the continents. (p. 55)
deriva continental Movimiento muy lento de los continentes.

control rod A cadmium rod used in a nuclear reactor to absorb neutrons from fission reactions. (p. 176)
varilla de control Varilla de cadmio que se usa en un reactor nuclear para absorber los neutrones emitidos por las reacciones de la fisión.

D

death rate The number of deaths in a population in a certain amount of time. (p. 16)
tasa de mortalidad Número de muertes en una población en un período determinado.

deciduous tree A tree that sheds its leaves and grows new ones each year. (p. 63)
árbol caducifolio Árbol cuyas hojas caen anualmente, pero vuelven a crecer.

decomposer An organism that breaks down wastes and dead organisms. (p. 43)
descomponedor Organismo que descompone desechos y organismos muertos.

desert An area that receives less than 25 centimeters of precipitation per year. (p. 61)
desierto Área que recibe menos de 25 centímetros de precipitación al año.

desertification The advance of desert-like conditions into areas that previously were fertile. (p. 120)
desertificación Avance de condiciones similares a las del desierto a áreas que anteriormente eran fértiles.

development The construction of buildings, roads, bridges, dams, and other structures. (p. 117)
desarrollo Construcción de edificios, carreteras, puentes, presas y otras estructuras.

dispersal The movement of organisms from one place to another. (p. 55)
dispersión Movimiento de los organismos de un lugar a otro.

drought A period of less rain than normal. (p. 120)
sequía Período de menor lluvia que lo normal.

E

ecology The study of how living things interact with each other and their environment. (p. 10)
ecología Estudio de cómo interactúan los seres vivos entre sí y con su medio ambiente.

ecosystem The community of organisms that live in a particular area, along with their nonliving surroundings. (p. 10)
ecosistema Comunidad de organismos que viven en un área determinada, junto con su medio ambiente no vivo.

efficiency The percentage of energy that is used to perform work. (p. 180)
eficiencia Porcentaje de energía usada para realizar trabajo.

emigration Leaving a population. (p. 16)
emigración Abandono de una población.

emissions Pollutants that are released into the air. (p. 138)
gases contaminantes Contaminantes liberados al aire.

endangered species A species in danger of becoming extinct in the near future. (p. 101)
especie en peligro de extinción Especie que corre el riesgo de desaparecer en el futuro próximo.

English and Spanish Glossary

energy conservation The practice of reducing energy use. (p. 182)
conservación de la energía Práctica de reducción del uso de energía.

energy pyramid A diagram that shows the amount of energy that moves from one feeding level to another in a food web. (p. 46)
pirámide de la energía Diagrama que muestra la cantidad de energía que pasa de un nivel de alimentación a otro en una red alimentaria.

energy transformation A change from one form of energy to another; also called an energy conversion. (p. 158)
transformación de la energía Cambio de una forma de energía a otra; también se le llama conversión de energía.

environmental science The study of the natural processes that occur in the environment and how humans can affect them. (p. 86)
ciencias del medio ambiente Estudio de los procesos naturales que ocurren en el medio ambiente y cómo los seres humanos pueden afectarlos.

erosion The process by which water, wind, or ice moves particles of rock or soil. (p. 119)
erosión Proceso por el cual el agua, el viento o el hielo mueven partículas de roca o suelo.

estimate An approximation of a number, based on reasonable assumptions. (p. 14)
estimación Cálculo aproximado de un número, basándose en supuestos razonables.

estuary A habitat in which the fresh water of a river meets the salt water of the ocean. (p. 72)
estuario Hábitat en el cual el agua dulce de un río se encuentra con el agua salada del mar.

evaporation The process by which molecules of a liquid absorb energy and change to a gas. (p. 49)
evaporación Proceso por el cual las moléculas de un líquido absorben energía y pasan al estado gaseoso.

exotic species Species that are carried to a new location by people. (p. 56)
especies exóticas Especies que lleva la gente a un nuevo lugar.

extinction The disappearance of all members of a species from Earth. (p. 100)
extinción Desaparición de la Tierra de todos los miembros de una especie.

F

fertilizer A substance that provides nutrients to help crops grow better. (p. 119)
fertilizante Sustancia que proporciona nutriente para ayudar a que crezcan mejor los cultivos.

fishery An area with a large population of valuable ocean organisms. (p. 92)
pesquería Área con una gran población de organismos marinos aprovechables.

food chain A series of events in which one organism eats another and obtains energy. (p. 44)
cadena alimentaria Serie de sucesos en los que un organismo se come a otro y obtiene energía.

food web The pattern of overlapping food chains in an ecosystem. (p. 44)
red alimentaria Patrón de cadenas alimentarias sobrepuestas en un ecosistema.

fossil fuel An energy-rich substance (such as coal, oil, or natural gas) formed from the remains of organisms. (p. 160)
combustible fósil Sustancia rica en energía (como carbón mineral, petróleo o gas natural) que se forma a partir de los restos de organismos.

fuel A substance that provides energy as the result of a chemical change. (p. 158)
combustible Sustancia que libera energía como resultado de un cambio químico.

fuel rod A uranium rod that undergoes fission in a nuclear reactor. (p. 176)
varilla de combustible Varilla de uranio que se somete a la fisión en un reactor nuclear.

G

gasohol A mixture of gasoline and alcohol. (p. 169)
gasohol Mezcla de gasolina y alcohol.

gene A structure in an organism's cells that carries its hereditary information. (p. 99)
gen Estructura en las células de un organismo que contiene la información hereditaria.

geothermal energy Heat from Earth's interior. (p. 170)
energía geotérmica Calor del interior de la Tierra.

global warming The theory that increasing carbon dioxide in the atmosphere will raise Earth's average temperature. (p. 155)
calentamiento global Teoría que dice que al aumentar el dióxido de carbono en la atmósfera, aumentará la temperatura promedio de la Tierra.

grassland An area populated by grasses and other nonwoody plants. Most grasslands get 25 to 75 centimeters of rain each year. (p. 62)
pradera Área poblada de pastos y de otras plantas no leñosas. La mayoría de las praderas recibe de 25 a 75 centímetros de lluvia al ãno.

greenhouse effect The trapping of heat near Earth's surface by certain gases in the atmosphere. (p. 150)
efecto invernadero Calor atrapado cerca de la superficie de la Tierra por ciertos gases de la atmósfera.

groundwater Water stored in underground layers of soil and rock. (p. 132)
agua freática Agua acumulada en capas subterráneas de suelo y roca.

H

habitat An environment that provides the things an organism needs to live, grow, and reproduce. (p. 7)
hábitat Ambiente que proporciona las cosas que un organismo necesita para vivir, crecer y reproducirse.

habitat destruction The loss of a natural habitat. (p. 102)
destrucción del hábitat Pérdida de un hábitat natural.

habitat fragmentation The breaking of a habitat into smaller, isolated pieces. (p. 102)
fragmentación del hábitat Desintegración de un hábitat en porciones aisladas más pequeñas.

hazardous waste A material that can be harmful if it is not properly disposed of. (p. 128)
desecho peligroso Material que puede ser dañino si no se elimina adecuadamente.

herbivore A consumer that eats only plants. (p. 43)
herbívoro Consumidor que come sólo plantas.

host The organism that a parasite lives in or on in a parasitism interaction. (p. 31)
huésped Organismo dentro o fuera del cual vive un parásito en una interacción de parasitismo.

hydrocarbon An energy-rich chemical compound that contains carbon and hydrogen atoms. (p. 160)
hidrocarburo Compuesto químico rico en energía que contiene átomos de carbono e hidrógeno.

hydroelectric power Electricity produced using the energy of flowing water. (p. 168)
energía hidroeléctrica Electricidad que se produce usando la energía de una corriente de agua.

I

immigration Moving into a population. (p. 16)
inmigración Ingreso a una población.

incineration The burning of solid waste. (p. 123)
incineración Quema de desechos sólidos.

insulation Material that blocks heat transfer between the air inside and outside a building. (p. 180)
aislante Material que impide la transferencia de calor entre el interior y el exterior de un edificio.

intertidal zone The area between the highest high-tide line and lowest low-tide line. (p. 72)
zona intermareal Área entre la línea más alta de la marea alta y la línea más baja de la marea baja.

K

keystone species A species that influences the survival of many others in an ecosystem. (p. 97)
especie clave Especie que influye en la supervivencia de muchas otras en un ecosistema.

L

land reclamation The process of restoring land to a more natural state. (p. 121)
recuperación de la tierra Proceso de restitución de la tierra a un estado más natural.

leachate Polluted liquid produced by water passing through buried wastes in a landfill. (p. 124)
lixiviado Líquido contaminado que se produce por el paso del agua a través de los desechos enterrados en un relleno sanitario.

limiting factor An environmental factor that causes a population to decrease. (p. 18)
factor limitante Factor ambiental que impide el crecimiento de una población.

litter The layer of dead leaves and grass on top of the soil. (p. 118)
mantillo Capa suelta de hierbas y hojas secas sobre el suelo.

M

meltdown A dangerous condition in which fuel rods inside a nuclear reactor melt. (p. 177)
fusión (del núcleo de un reactor) Condición peligrosa en la cual las varillas de combustible dentro del reactor nuclear se derriten.

municipal solid waste Waste produced in homes, businesses, and schools. (p. 123)
desechos sólidos urbanos Desechos producidos en hogares, oficinas y escuelas.

mutualism A relationship between two species in which both species benefit. (p. 30)
mutualismo Relación entre dos especies de la cual ambas se benefician.

N

natural resource Anything in the environment that is used by people. (p. 83)
recurso natural Cualquier cosa del medio ambiente que usa la gente.

natural selection A process by which characteristics that make an individual better suited to its environment become more common in a species. (p. 25)
selección natural Proceso por el cual las características que permiten a un individuo adaptarse mejor a su medio ambiente se hacen más comunes en una especie.

neritic zone The region of shallow ocean water over the continental shelf. (p. 72)
zona nerítica Región sobre la placa continental donde el agua del océano es poco profunda.

niche An organism's particular role in an ecosystem, or how it makes its living. (p. 25)
nicho Función particular de un organismo en un ecosistema, o cómo sobrevive.

nitrogen fixation The process of changing free nitrogen gas into a usable form. (p. 52)
fijación del nitrógeno Proceso de conversión del gas nitrógeno libre en una forma aprovechable.

nonrenewable resource A natural resource that is not replaced in a useful time frame. (p. 83)
recurso no renovable Recurso natural que no se restaura una vez usado, en un período relativamente corto.

nuclear fission The splitting of an atom's nucleus into two smaller nuclei and neutrons. (p. 175)
fisión nuclear División del núcleo de un átomo en dos núcleos más pequeños y neutrones.

nuclear fusion The combining of two atomic nuclei to produce a single larger nucleus and much energy. (p. 178)
fusión nuclear Unión de dos núcleos atómicos para producir un núcleo único más grande y liberar energía.

nucleus The central core of an atom that contains the protons and neutrons. (p. 174)
núcleo Parte central de un átomo que contiene protones y neutrones.

nutrient depletion The situation that arises when more soil nutrients are used than the decomposers can supply. (p. 119)
agotamiento de nutrientes Situación que se produce cuando se usan más nutrientes del suelo de lo que los descomponedores pueden proporcionar.

O

omnivore A consumer that eats both plants and animals. (p. 43)
omnívoro Consumidor que come tanto plantas como animales.

organism A living thing. (p. 7)
organismo Un ser viviente.

ozone A toxic form of oxygen. (p. 139)
ozono Forma tóxica del oxígeno.

ozone layer The layer of the atmosphere that contains a higher concentration of ozone than the rest of the atmosphere. (p. 147)
capa de ozono Capa atmosférica que contiene una mayor concentración de ozono que el resto de la atmósfera.

P

parasite The organism that benefits by living on or in a host in a parasitism interaction. (p. 31)
parásito Organismo que se beneficia de vivir en la superficie o en el interior de un huésped en una interacción de parasitismo.

parasitism A relationship in which one organism lives on or in a host and harms it. (p. 31)
parasitismo Relación en la cual un organismo vive en la superficie o en el interior de otro y lo perjudica.

permafrost Soil that is frozen all year. (p. 65)
permagélido Suelo que está congelado todo el año.

pesticide A chemical that kills crop-destroying organisms. (p. 134)
pesticida Sustancia química que mata los organismos que dañan los cultivos.

petrochemical A compound made from oil. (p. 162)
petroquímico Compuesto que se obtiene del petróleo.

petroleum Liquid fossil fuel; oil. (p. 162)
petróleo Combustible fósil líquido.

photochemical smog A thick, brownish haze formed when certain gases react with sunlight. (p. 139)
neblina tóxica fotoquímica Densa bruma parduzca que se forma cuando ciertos gases reaccionan con la luz solar.

photosynthesis The process in which organisms use water along with sunlight and carbon dioxide to make their own food. (p. 8)
fotosíntesis Proceso por el cual los organismos usan el agua junto con la luz solar y el dióxido de carbono para producir su alimento.

pioneer species The first species to populate an area. (p. 33)
especies pioneras Primeras especies en poblar una región.

poaching Illegal killing or removal of wildlife from their habitats. (p. 102)
caza ilegal Matanza o eliminación de la fauna silvestre de su hábitat.

pollutant A substance that causes pollution. (p. 133)
contaminante Sustancia que provoca contaminación.

pollution Contamination of land, water, or air. (p. 84)
polución Contaminación del suelo, agua o aire.

population All the members of one species in a particular area. (p. 9)
población Todos los miembros de una especie en un área particular.

population density The number of individuals in a specific area. (p. 18)
densidad de población Número de individuos en un área específica.

precipitation Rain, snow, sleet, or hail. (p. 49)
precipitación Lluvia, nieve, aguanieve o granizo.

predation An interaction in which one organism kills another for food. (p. 27)
depredación Interacción en la cual un organismo mata y se come a otro.

predator The organism that does the killing in a predation interaction. (p. 27)
depredador Organismo que mata en la depredación.

prey An organism that is killed and eaten by another organism. (p. 27)
presa Organismo que otro organismo mata y come.

primary succession The series of changes that occur in an area where no soil or organisms exist. (p. 33)
sucesión primaria Serie de cambios que ocurren en un área en donde no existe suelo ni organismos.

producer An organism that can make its own food. (p. 43)
productor Organismo que puede elaborar su propio alimento.

R

radon A colorless, odorless, radioactive gas. (p. 141)
radón Gas radioactivo que no tiene color ni olor.

reactor vessel The part of a nuclear reactor where nuclear fission occurs. (p. 176)
cuba de reactor Parte de un reactor nuclear donde ocurre la fisión nuclear.

recycling The process of reclaiming and reusing raw materials. (p. 125)
reciclaje Proceso de recuperar y volver a usar materias primas.

refinery A factory in which crude oil is heated and separated into fuels and other products. (p. 162)
refinería Planta en la que el petróleo crudo se calienta y fracciona en combustibles y otros productos.

renewable resource A resource that is either always available or is naturally replaced in a relatively short time. (p. 83)
recurso renovable Recurso que está siempre disponible o que es restituido de manera natural en un período relativamente corto.

S

sanitary landfill A landfill that holds nonhazardous waste such as municipal solid waste and construction debris. (p. 124)
relleno sanitario Relleno que contiene desechos no peligrosos, como desechos sólidos urbanos y escombros de la construcción.

savanna A grassland close to the equator that receives as much as 120 centimeters of rain per year. (p. 62)
sabana Tierra de pastos próxima al ecuador que recibe hasta 120 centímetros de lluvia al año.

scavenger A carnivore that feeds on the bodies of dead organisms. (p. 43)
carroñero Carnívoro que se alimenta de los cuerpos de animales muertos.

secondary succession The series of changes that occur in an area where the ecosystem has been disturbed, but where soil and organisms still exist. (p. 34)
sucesión secundaria Serie de cambios que ocurren en un área después de la perturbación de un ecosistema, pero donde todavía hay suelo y organismos.

sediments Particles of rock and sand. (p. 134)
sedimentos Partículas de roca y arena.

selective cutting The process of cutting down only some trees in an area. (p. 90)
tala selectiva Proceso de cortar sólo algunos árboles de un área.

sewage The water and human wastes that are washed down sinks, toilets, and showers. (p. 134)
aguas residuales Agua y desechos humanos que son desechados por lavamanos, servicios sanitarios y duchas.

solar energy Energy from the sun. (p. 166)
energía solar Energía del Sol.

species A group of organisms that are physically similar and can mate with each other and produce offspring that can also mate and reproduce. (p. 9)
especie Grupo de organismos que son físicamente semejantes, se pueden cruzar y producen crías que también se pueden cruzar y reproducir.

subsoil The layer of soil below topsoil that has less plant and animal matter than topsoil. (p. 118)
subsuelo Capa de suelo bajo el suelo superior que tiene menos material vegetal y animal que el suelo superior.

succession The series of predictable changes that occur in a community over time. (p. 32)
sucesión Serie de cambios predecibles que ocurren en una comunidad a través del tiempo.

sustainable yield An amount of a renewable resource that can be harvested regularly without reducing the future supply. (p. 91)
rendimiento sostenible Cantidad de un recurso renovable que puede ser recolectado constantemente sin reducir el abastecimiento futuro.

symbiosis A close relationship between two species that benefits at least one of the species. (p. 30)
simbiosis Relación estrecha entre dos especies de la que se beneficia al menos una de ellas.

 T

taxol A chemical in Pacific yew tree bark that has cancer-fighting properties. (p. 108)
taxol Sustancia química en la corteza del tejo del Pacífico con propiedades curativas contra el cáncer.

temperature inversion A condition in which a layer of warm air traps polluted air close to Earth's surface. (p. 139)
inversión térmica Condición en la que una capa de aire caliente atrapa aire contaminado cerca de la superficie de la Tierra.

threatened species A species that could become endangered in the near future. (p. 101)
especie amenazada Especie que puede llegar a estar en peligro de extinción en el futuro próximo.

topsoil An upper layer of soil consisting of rock fragments, nutrients, water, air, and decaying plant and animal matter. (p. 118)
suelo superior Capa superior de suelo formada por fragmentos de roca, nutrientes, agua, aire y materia animal y vegetal en descomposición.

tundra An extremely cold, dry biome. (p. 65)
tundra Bioma extremadamente frío y seco.

 U

understory A layer of shorter plants that grow in the shade of a forest canopy. (p. 60)
sotobosque Estrato de plantas pequeñas que crecen a la sombra de la bóveda arborea.

W

water cycle The continuous process by which water moves from Earth's surface to the atmosphere and back. (p. 48)
ciclo del agua Proceso continuo a través del cual el agua pasa de la superficie de la Tierra a la atmósfera y viceversa.

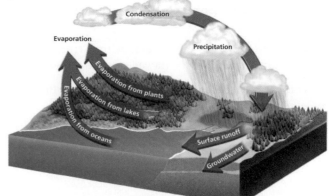

Page numbers for key terms are printed in **boldface** type.
Page numbers for illustrations, maps, and charts are printed in *italics*.

Index

Index

Page numbers for key terms are printed in **boldface** type.
Page numbers for illustrations, maps, and charts are printed in *italics*.

Index

Page numbers for key terms are printed in **boldface** type.
Page numbers for illustrations, maps, and charts are printed in *italics*.

Index

Page numbers for key terms are pinted in **boldface** type.
Page numbers for illustrations, maps, and charts are printed in *italics*.

Acknowledgments

Acknowledgment for page 194: Excerpt from *The Amateur Naturalist* by Gerald Durrell, copyright © 1982 by Gerald Durrell. Used by permission of Alfred A. Knopf, a division of Random House, Inc.

Staff Credits

Diane Alimena, Michele Angelucci, Scott Andrews, Jennifer Angel, Carolyn Belanger, Barbara A. Bertell, Suzanne Biron, Peggy Bliss, Stephanie Bradley, James Brady, Anne M. Bray, Sarah M. Carroll, Kerry Cashman, Jonathan Cheney, Joshua D. Clapper, Lisa J. Clark, Bob Craton, Patricia Cully, Patricia M. Dambry, Kathy Dempsey, Leanne Esterly, Emily Ellen, Thomas Ferreira, Jonathan Fisher, Patricia Fromkin, Paul Gagnon, Kathy Gavilanes, Joel Gendler, Holly Gordon, Robert Graham, Ellen Granter, Diane Grossman, Barbara Hollingdale, Linda Johnson, Anne Jones, John Judge, Kevin Keane, Kelly Kelliher, Toby Klang, Sue Langan, Russ Lappa, Carolyn Lock, Rebecca Loveys, Constance J. McCarty, Carolyn B. McGuire, Ranida Touranont McKneally, Anne McLaughlin, Eve Melnechuk, Natania Mlawer, Janet Morris, Karyl Murray, Francine Neumann, Baljit Nijjar, Marie Opera, Jill Ort, Kim Ortell, Joan Paley, Dorothy Preston, Maureen Raymond, Laura Ross, Rashid Ross, Siri Schwartzman, Melissa Shustyk, Laurel Smith, Emily Soltanoff, Jennifer A. Teece, Elizabeth Torjussen, Amanda M. Watters, Merce Wilczek, Amy Winchester, Char Lyn Yeakley. **Additional Credits** Allen Gold, Andrea Golden, Etta Jacobs, Meg Montgomery, Kim Schmidt, Adam Teller, Joan Tobin.

Illustration

Morgan Cain & Associates: 147, 154, 162, 175, 178, 183, 186r, 188; **Kerry Cashman:** 14–15, 55, 59–66; **John Ceballos:** 141; **John Edwards and Associates:** 124, 142, 150, 159, 161, 170, 177, 186l; **Biruta Hansen:** 24–25; **Robert Hynes:** 11; **Kevin Jones Associates:** 18t, 33, 34–35, 49, 51–52, 167; **Karen Minot:** 90, 97; **Pond and Giles:** 38, 93; **J/B Woolsey Associates:** 12, 74, 155; **XNR Productions:** 86–87, 120. **All charts and graphs by Matt Mayerchak.**

Photography

Photo Research John Judge
Cover image top, Muench Photography Inc.; **bottom,** J. David Andrews/Masterfile.

Page vi, Tony Craddock/Getty Images, Inc.; **vii,** Richard Haynes; **viii,** Richard Haynes; **x,** Christopher G. Knight; **1,** H. Bruce Rinker; **1,** Stephen Dalton/Photo Researchers, Inc.; **2bl,** Meg Lowman; **2br,** Meg Lowman/Australian Journals of Scientific Research; **2t,** Raphael Gaillarde/Gamma Press Images; **3,** Christopher G. Knight.

Chapter 1
Pages 4–5, Getty Images, Inc.; **5 inset,** Richard Haynes; **6t,** Tom Lazar/Animals Animals/Earth Scenes; **6b,** C.K. Lorenz/Photo Researchers, Inc.; **7,** C.W. Schwartz/Animals Animals/Earth Scenes; **8t,** Konrad Wothe/Minden Pictures; **8m,** Christoph Burki/Getty Images, Inc.; **8b,** John Cancalosi/Tom Stack & Associates; **9,** Breck P. Kent/Animals Animals/Earth Scenes; **13,** Frans Lanting/Minden Pictures; **14l,** Fred Bruemmer/Peter Arnold, Inc.; **14r,** C. Allan Morgan/DRK Photo; **15l,** Thomas Mangelsen/Minden Pictures; **15r,** Wallace J. Nichols; **17t,** Alan D. Carey/Photo Researchers, Inc.; **17b,** Leonard Lee Rue III/Photo Researchers, Inc.; **18,** Kenneth W. Fink/Photo Researchers, Inc.; **19t,** Anthony Bannister/Animals Animals/Earth Scenes; **19b,** Tony Craddock/Getty Images, Inc.; **20,** Tom & Pat Leeson/Photo Researchers, Inc.; **21,** Dave King/Dorling Kindersley; **22–23t,** Gary Griffen/Animals Animals/Earth Scenes; **22b,** Raymond Gehman/Corbis; **26tl,** Ron Willocks/Animals Animals/Earth Scenes; **26ml,** Patti Murray/Animals Animals/Earth Scenes; **26bl,** Rob Simpson/Visuals Unlimited; **26r,** Wally Eberhart/Visuals Unlimited; **27,** F. Stuart Westmorland/Photo Researchers, Inc.; **28,** S. Dalton/OSF/Animals Animals/Earth Scenes; **29tl,** Leroy Simon/Visuals Unlimited; **29tr,** Dante Fenolio/Photo Researchers, Inc.; **29mr,** Nigel J. Dennis/Photo Researchers. Inc.; **29bl,** Art Wolfe; **29br,** Brian Rogers/Visuals Unlimited; **30,** Daryl Balfour/Getty Images, Inc.; **31t,** Volker Steiger/SPL/Photo Researchers, Inc.; **31b,** Richard Haynes; **32 both,** Tom & Pat Leeson/Photo Researchers, Inc.

Chapter 2
Pages 40–41, Daniel J. Cox/Getty Images, Inc.; **41 inset,** Richard Haynes; **42–43,** Kent Foster/Photo Researchers, Inc.; **43t inset,** David Northcott/DRK Photo; **43m inset,** Adam Jones/Photo Researchers, Inc.; **43b inset,** S. Nielsen/DRK Photo; **46t,** Frank Greenaway/Dorling Kindersley; **46tm,** Kim Taylor & Jane Burton/Dorling Kindersley; **46bm,** Dorling Kindersley; **46bm,** Frank Greenaway/Dorling Kindersley Media Library; **46b,** Kim Taylor & Jane Burton/Dorling Kindersley; **47,** Andy Rouse/DRK Photo; **48,** Richard Haynes; **50,** Asa C. Thoresen/Photo Researchers, Inc.; **53,** E. R. Degginger/Photo Researchers, Inc.; **54t,** Richard Haynes; **54b,** Penny Tweedie/Getty Images, Inc.; **56l,** Gregory K. Scott/Photo Researchers, Inc.; **56m,** Kenneth H. Thomas/Photo Researchers, Inc.; **56r,** Runk/Schoenberger/Grant Heilman, Inc.; **59,** Jim Zipp/Photo Researchers, Inc.; **59l inset,** David Young Wolff/PhotoEdit; **59r inset,** Jack Clark/Animals Animals/Earth Scenes; **60l,** Frans Lanting/Minden Pictures; **60m,** Renee Lynn/Getty Images, Inc.; **60r,** Michael & Patricia Fogden/Minden Pictures; **61,** Barbara Gerlach/DRK Photo; **61 inset,** Maslowski/Photo Researchers, Inc.; **62,** Art Wolfe/Getty Images, Inc.; **62 inset,** Gerry Ellis/Minden Pictures; **63,** Carr Clifton/Minden Pictures; **63t inset,** Nick Bergkessel/Photo Researchers, Inc.; **63b inset,** Stephen J. Krasemann/DRK Photo;

64l, Stephen J. Krasemann/DRK Photo; **64r,** Jeff Lepore/Photo Researchers, Inc.; **65,** Michio Hoshino/Minden Pictures; **65 inset,** Yva Momotiuk/John Eastcott /Minden Pictures; **66,** Douglas E. Walker/Masterfile Corporation; **66 inset,** Frans Lanting/Minden Pictures; **69,** Richard Haynes; **70t,** Tom & Pat Leeson/Photo Researchers, Inc.; **70b,** Bill Kamin/Visuals Unlimited; **70b inset,** Kim Heacox/DRK Photo; **71,** David Weintraub/Photo Researchers, Inc.; **71 inset,** Steven David Miller/Animals Animals/Earth Scenes; **72,** Michele Burgess/Corbis; **75,** Russ Lappa; **76t,** Andy Rouse/DRK Photo; **76b,** Kim Heacox/DRK Photo.

Chapter 3
Pages 80–81, Animals Animals/Earth Scenes; **81 inset,** Russ Lappa; **82–83,** Key Sanders/Getty Images, Inc.; **84l,** Corbis; **84m,** Corbis; **84r,** UPI/Corbis-Bettmann; **85l,** Erich Hartmann/Magnum Photos; **85m,** Kevin Fleming/Corbis; **85r,** William Campbell/Peter Arnold, Inc.; **86t,** Corbis; **86b,** Warren Morgan/Corbis; **87t,** Ariel Skelley/Corbis; **87b,** Marc Epstein/DRK Photo; **88–89,** Richard Haynes; **91,** Inga Spence/Visuals Unlimited; **92,** G.R. Robinson/Visuals Unlimited; **93,** Greg Vaughn/Tom Stack & Associates; **94,** Russ Lappa; **95,** Richard Haynes; **96t,** C Squared Studios /Getty Images, Inc.; **96b,** Frans Lanting/Minden Pictures; **97t,** David Wrobel/Visuals Unlimited; **97b,** Stephen J. Krasemann/DRK Photo; **98t,** Wayne Lynch/DRK Photo; **98b,** Fred Bavendam/Minden Pictures; **99,** D. Cavagnaro/DRK Photo; **100tl,** David Sieren/Visuals Unlimited; **100tr,** David Dennis/Animals Animals/Earth Scenes; **100b,** Jeff Lepore/Photo Researchers, Inc.; **101t,** Stephen J. Krasemann/DRK Photo; **101bl,** David Liebman; **101bm,** Marilyn Kazmers/Peter Arnold, Inc.; **101br,** Ken Lucas/Visuals Unlimited; **102,** Kent Gilbert/AP/Wide World Photos; **103,** James H. Robinson/Animals Animals/Earth Scenes; **104t,** Roy Toft/Tom Stack & Associates; **104b,** Tom Uhlman/AP/Wide World Photos; **105,** James H. Robinson/Animals Animals/Earth Scenes; **106,** Doug Perrine/DRK Photo; **107l,** Walter H. Hodge/Peter Arnold, Inc.; **107m,** Doug Perrine/DRK Photo; **107r,** Ed Reschke/Peter Arnold, Inc.; **108t,** Greg Vaughn/Tom Stack & Associates; **108b,** Bill Greenblatt/Getty Images, Inc.; **109,** G. Payne/Liaison/Getty Images, Inc.; **110t,** David Dennis/Animals Animals/Earth Scenes; **110bl,** Greg Vaughn/Tom Stack & Associates; **110br,** Walter H. Hodge/Peter Arnold, Inc.

Chapter 4
Pages 114–115, Jim Wark/Airphoto; **115 inset,** Richard Haynes, **116t,** Richard Haynes; **116b,** Corbis; **117,** David Zalubowski/AP/Wide World Photos; **118l,** Peter Griffiths/Dorling Kindersley Media Library; **118t inset,** Michael Habicht/Animals Animals; **118m inset,** S.L. Rose/Visuals Unlimited; **118b inset,** Gilbert S. Grant/Photo Researchers, Inc.; **119l,** Martin Benjamin/The Image Works; **119r,** Iom Bean 1994/DRK Photo; **120l,** Peter Johnson/Corbis; **120r,** Walt Anderson/Visuals Unlimited; **121 both,** Department of Environmental Protection, Commonwealth of Pennsylvania/Mineral Information Institute; **122–123,** Nick Vedros, Vedros & Assoc./Getty Images, Inc.; **125,** David Joel/Getty Images, Inc.; **126l,** Richard Haynes; **126r,** Randy Faris/Corbis; **127t,** Larry Lefever/Grant Heilman Photography, Inc.; **127b,** Rosemary Mayer/Holt Studios/Photo Researchers, Inc.; **128 all,** Russ Lappa; **129 all,** Russ Lappa; **130,** Russ Lappa; **131,** Russ Lappa; **132–133,** Richard Berenholtz/Corbis; **133t,** Richard Hutchings/Photo Researchers, Inc.; **133b,** Michael S. Yamashita/Corbis; **135,** Dorling Kindersley; **136,** Norman McGrath; **137,** Armando Franca/AP/Wide World Photos; **138t,** Russ Lappa; **138b,** Derek Trask/Corbis; **139,** P. Baeza/Publiphoto/Photo Researchers, Inc.; **140,** Richard Megna/Fundamental Photographs; **142,** Eric Pearle/Getty Images, Inc.; **143,** Ed Pritchard/Getty Images, Inc.; **145,** Richard Haynes; **146 both,** Richard Haynes; **148,** NASA/Goddard Space Flight Center Scientific Visualization Studio; **149 all,** NASA/Goddard Space Flight Center Scientific Visualization Studio; **151,** NASA Goddard Space Flight Center.

Chapter 5
Pages 156–157, Didier Dorval/Masterfile Corporation; **157 inset,** Visuals Unlimited; **158t,** E.R. Degginger; **158b,** Toby Talbot/AP/Wide World Photos; **161t,** Colin Keates/Dorling Kindersley; **161m,** Andreas Einsiedel/Dorling Kindersley; **161b,** Andreas Einsiedel /Dorling Kindersley; **162,** Bill Ross/Corbis; **163,** Roger Ball/Corbis; **164,** Owen Franken/Corbis; **165,** Lawrence Migdale/Photo Researchers, Inc.; **166,** Nadia MacKenzie/Getty Images, Inc.; **168t,** Tom Bean/DRK Photo; **168b,** Doug Sokell/Tom Stack & Associates; **169t,** Daniel Putterman/Stock Boston, Inc./PictureQuest; **169b,** Brian Branch-Price/AP/Wide World Photos; **171,** NASA; **172,** Richard Haynes; **173,** Richard Haynes; **174t,** Russ Lappa; **174b,** Bettmann-Corbis; **176t,** Joseph Sohm/ChromoSohm, Inc./Corbis; **176b,** E.R. Degginger; **179,** Richard Haynes; **180l,** Mitch Kezar/Getty Images, Inc.; **180m,** Tony Freeman/PhotoEdit; **180r,** Scott Olson/Getty Images, Inc.; **181l,** Anthony Meshkinyar/Getty Images, Inc.; **181m,** Yves Marcoux/Getty Images, Inc.; **181r,** Mike Fiala/Getty Images, Inc.; **182l,** Michael Newman/Photo Edit; **182r,** David Young-Wolff/Photo Edit.

190, Devez/CNRS/Photo Researchers, Inc.; **191b,** Tom Brakefield/DRK Photo; **191ml,** Mc Donald Wildlife Photography/Animals Animals/Earth Scenes; **191mr,** Peter Steyn/Ardea London, Ltd.; **191t,** M.C. Chamberlain/DRK Photo; **192–193,** Chinch Gryniewicz/Ecoscene/Corbis; **193b,** Jose Anzel/Aurora Photos; **193t,** Christie's Images; **194t,** Corbis-Bettmann; **194–195,** M. Harvey/DRK Photo; **195bl,** Wolfgang Kaehler/Corbis; **195bm,** Frans Lanting/Minden Pictures; **195br,** Tim Davis/Photo Researchers, Inc.; **195t,** Neil Lucas/Nature Picture Library; **196,** Tony Freeman/PhotoEdit; **197b,** Russ Lappa; **197m,** Richard Haynes; **197t,** Russ Lappa; **198,** Richard Haynes; **200,** Richard Haynes; **202,** Morton Beebe/Corbis; **203,** Catherine Karnow/Corbis; **205b,** Richard Haynes; **205t,** Dorling Kindersley.